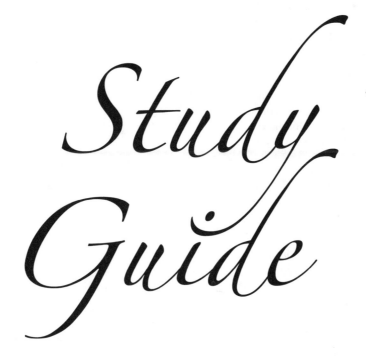

Study Guide

Darrel Hess

City College of San Francisco

Ninth Edition

Physical Geography

A Landscape Appreciation

Tom L. McKnight • Darrel Hess

PEARSON
Prentice
Hall

Upper Saddle River, NJ 07458

Editor-in-Chief, Science: Nicole Folchetti
Publisher: Dan Kaveney
Associate Editor: Amanda Brown
Senior Managing Editor, Science: Kathleen Schiaparelli
Assistant Managing Editor, Science: Gina M. Cheselka
Project Manager, Production: Ashley Booth
Supplement Cover Manager: Paul Gourhan
Supplement Cover Designer: Victoria Colotta
Senior Operations Specialist: Alan Fischer
Director of Operations: Barbara Kittle
Photo Credit: Tim Fitzharris / Minden Pictures

© 2008 Pearson Education, Inc.
Pearson Prentice Hall
Pearson Education, Inc.
Upper Saddle River, NJ 07458

Printed in the United States of America

10 9 8 7 6 5 4 3 2 1

ISBN 13: 978-0-13-230323-1

ISBN 10:   0-13-230323-X

Pearson Education Ltd., *London*
Pearson Education Australia Pty. Ltd., *Sydney*
Pearson Education Singapore, Pte. Ltd.
Pearson Education North Asia Ltd., *Hong Kong*
Pearson Education Canada, Inc., *Toronto*
Pearson Educación de Mexico, S.A. de C.V.
Pearson Education—Japan, *Tokyo*
Pearson Education Malaysia, Pte. Ltd.

Contents

Using This Study Guide

This Study Guide is designed to be used with the textbook *Physical Geography: A Landscape Appreciation*, ninth edition, by Tom L. McKnight and Darrel Hess. The 20 chapters of the Study Guide correspond to the equivalent chapters in the textbook. Each chapter of the Study Guide contains the following six sections:

OVERVIEW

Read the *Overview* in the Study Guide before you begin to study a text chapter. The *Overview* provides a general summary of the chapter and describes sections deserving special attention.

KEY CONCEPTS

The *Key Concepts* section is designed to summarize the principal points in selected sections of the textbook chapter. These are sections that contain concepts or terms that may pose difficulties to the reader, sections where additional clarification may help tie together important relationships, or sections with important diagrams or photographs. Each *Key Concepts* section provides page numbers for quick reference to the textbook. *Key Concepts* are best studied after reading the corresponding section in the textbook.

Although this Study Guide contains some diagrams, it is important that you have a copy of the textbook at hand when you are studying the *Key Concepts* material. The *Key Concepts* sections contain many references to diagrams, maps, and photographs that appear in the textbook, as well as animations that are on the **Student Animations CD** that accompanies the book. You will want to refer to these illustrations and animations when using the Study Guide—it is just as important to study the photographs, maps, diagrams, and animations as it is to read the text material itself.

PROGRESSIVE CONTENT REVIEW

This is a systematic test of key terms and factual information found in the textbook. It should be attempted after you have finished studying the chapter. The *Progressive Content Review* consists of a series of sentences with missing words or phrases. The correct answers are found along the right hand margin of the page, and a textbook page reference is provided for each item. Before you read a statement, cover the correct answers and try to complete each item. Check your answers before proceeding to the next statement.

Take advantage of the list of **Key Terms** provided at the end of each textbook chapter. A page reference is provided for each term. The definitions of these terms can also be found in the alphabetical **Glossary** in the back of the textbook (beginning on page G-1).

SELF-TEST

This collection of multiple choice questions is designed to test your comprehension of the chapter. Attempt the *Self-Test* after studying the chapter and completing the *Progressive Content Review*. In each case, circle the best answer from the list of possible answers. The correct answers to the *Self-Test* are provided. Review any incorrect answers before moving on to the next chapter.

HINTS FOR TEXTBOOK STUDY QUESTIONS

A series of **Study Questions for Key Concepts** is found in the **Learning Review** at the end of each chapter in the textbook. The hints presented here in the Study Guide will assist you in answering these questions or will direct you to helpful diagrams or textbook sections.

ADDITIONAL STUDY QUESTIONS

Additional Study Questions are presented to offer a final test of your comprehension of the material. Hints are provided for each question.

Acknowledgments:

I want to again express my gratitude to Dr. Norman Meek of California State University, San Bernardino, for his valuable advice on the original edition of this Study Guide. Thanks also to all at Prentice Hall, especially Associate Editor Amanda Brown, Copy Editor Marcia Youngman and Publisher for Geosciences, Dan Kaveney. I would especially like to thank my students for their help and suggestions on improving this Study Guide.

If students or instructors have any comments, please address them to:

Darrel Hess
Earth Sciences Department
City College of San Francisco
50 Phelan Avenue
San Francisco, CA 94112
dhess@ccsf.edu

CHAPTER 1

Introduction to Earth

OVERVIEW

Chapter 1 introduces the planet as a whole—discussing Earth's relation to the solar system, the general size and shape of Earth, the geographic grid of latitude and longitude, Earth–Sun relations, and telling time around the world.

This chapter covers a number of fundamental concepts and vocabulary terms that will be used throughout the remainder of the text. There are two especially important sections in this chapter. First, you should become familiar with latitude and longitude—the geographic grid system used for describing location on Earth. Second, give careful attention to the sections entitled "Earth–Sun Relations" and "The Annual March of the Seasons," which explain the changing relationship of Earth to the Sun throughout the year. Both of these topics—the geographic grid and Earth–Sun relations—must be understood before moving on to subsequent chapters, since this material forms the foundation for understanding a variety of other topics.

KEY CONCEPTS

THE SOLAR SYSTEM (p. 6):

View the animation **Solar System Formation** for a description of the early development and evolution of our solar system.

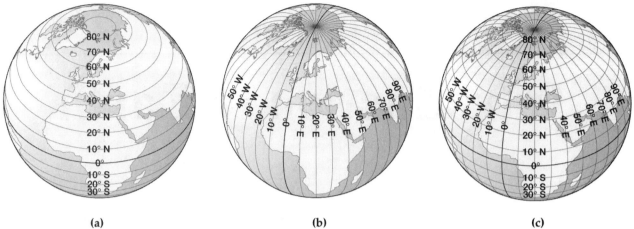

Figure 1-18: (a) Parallels of latitude. (b) Meridians of longitude. (c) Complete grid system.

THE SIZE AND SHAPE OF EARTH (p. 9):

Earth is about 12,700 kilometers (7900 miles) in diameter and is almost perfectly spherical in shape (it actually has a slightly flattened *oblate spheroid* shape). Note that, relative to its large size, the height or depth of Earth's surface features, such as mountains and ocean trenches, are quite small, and as we'll see in Chapter 3 the atmosphere is not very deep.

THE GEOGRAPHIC GRID (p. 10):

Locations on Earth are described with a grid system known as *latitude* and *longitude* (see **Figure 1-18**, shown above). Earth rotates on an imaginary axis running from the *North Pole* to the *South Pole*. The *equator* is a line traced out by an imaginary plane passing halfway between the North and South Poles, perpendicular to this axis (Figure 1-10, p. 11).

The equator is known as a *great circle* since it slices Earth into two equal halves or hemispheres. A great circle is the largest diameter circle that can be inscribed on a sphere (Figure 1-11, p. 11). There are other great circles mentioned in this chapter, such as the *circle of illumination* that divides Earth into equal halves of daylight and night.

Latitude (p. 11): Latitude is a measure of location north or south of the equator (see Figure 1-18a above). Note that latitude is actually the measure of an angle (Figure 1-12, p. 12). Latitude ranges from 0° at the equator, to 90° north latitude at the North Pole and 90° south latitude at the South Pole. Lines of latitude are also known as *parallels* since they are all parallel to each other.

Figure 1-13 (p. 12) shows seven important parallels you need to know. These parallels (the equator, the *Tropic of Cancer* and *Tropic of Capricorn*, the *Arctic Circle* and *Antarctic Circle*, and the North and South Poles) are key reference points in the discussion of Earth–Sun relations that follows.

Longitude (p. 13): Longitude is a measure of location east and west (see Figure 1-18b above). Longitude is also an angular measure. When traced out on a map or globe, lines of longitude (called *meridians*) run from the North Pole to the South Pole.

There is no natural starting point for measuring longitude, so an artificial starting point was established by international agreement. This *prime meridian* runs through Greenwich, England (near London) and has a longitude of 0°. Longitude is measured in degrees west or east of the prime meridian (Figure 1-16, p. 14). The maximum longitude is along the 180° meridian, on the opposite side of Earth from the prime meridian.

EARTH–SUN RELATIONS (p. 15):

This is an important section. It sets the stage for understanding patterns of weather and climate. It may be helpful for you to use a globe while studying this section.

Earth's Rotation on Its Axis (p. 15): Earth spins around on its axis, completing one *rotation* every 24 hours. The most important consequence of this rotation is the daily pattern of day and night. As we will see, the number of hours of daylight received at a particular location varies during the year (except at the equator).

Earth's Revolution Around the Sun (p. 17): Earth completes one *revolution* or orbit around the Sun every 365.25 days. The orbit of Earth around the Sun is not a perfect circle. Earth is on average about 150 million kilometers (93 million miles) from the Sun, but at its closest point Earth is 3.3 percent closer to the Sun than at its farthest point. Earth is closest to the Sun on about January 3rd (this is called *perihelion*), and farthest from the Sun on about July 4th (*aphelion*). Since Earth is closest to the Sun during the Northern Hemisphere winter, it is clear that variation in the distance to the Sun is not the cause of the changing seasons.

Inclination of Earth's Axis (p. 17): In addition to the rotation of Earth and its revolution around the Sun, two other factors account for the changing seasons. First, Earth's axis is tilted relative to its orbital path (known as the *plane of the ecliptic*). This characteristic is called the *inclination of the axis*. Earth's axis is tilted 23.5° from the vertical, and maintains this same inclination throughout the year (Figure 1-21, p. 17).

Polarity of Earth's Axis (p. 17): The fourth and final factor accounting for the change of the seasons is what is called *polarity* (or *parallelism*) of the axis. This means that Earth's axis is always pointing in the same direction, toward the star Polaris (see **Figure 1-23**, shown below). Because of this, in June the North Pole is leaning most directly toward the Sun, while in December it is leaning most directly away from the Sun.

As a consequence of rotation, revolution, inclination, and polarity, the amount of solar energy received at different latitudes on Earth varies throughout the year. At latitudes where sunlight strikes Earth most directly, the intensity of *insolation* (*in*coming *sol*ar radi*ation*) is greater than at latitudes where sunlight strikes Earth at a lesser angle.

THE ANNUAL MARCH OF THE SEASONS (p. 18):

At this point, you need to recall the seven important parallels shown in Figure 1-13 (p. 12). These seven parallels are key reference points in Earth-Sun relations.

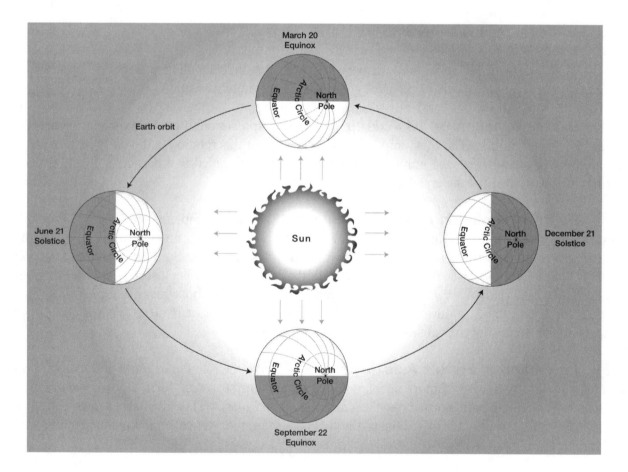

Figure 1-23: A "top view" of the march of the seasons. Earth's rotational axis maintains polarity (points in the same direction) throughout the year.

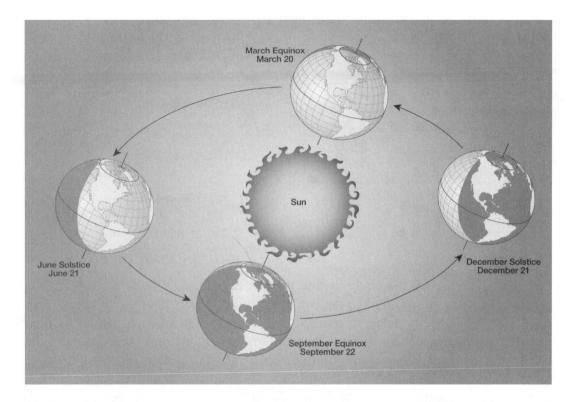

Figure 1-24: The position of Earth in its orbit around the Sun on the equinoxes and solstices.

To illustrate the changes in Earth-Sun relations throughout the year, the text highlights the situation on four important days: the June and December *solstices*, and the March and September *equinoxes*. Refer to **Figure 1-24** (shown above) to see the relative positions of Earth on these days.

On the June solstice, about June 21st, Earth is at the position in its orbit where the North Pole is leaning most directly toward the Sun (see **Figure 1-25**, shown on the following page). On this day the *perpendicular* (*vertical* or "direct") *rays* of the Sun are striking at the Tropic of Cancer (23.5° N). This means that on this day, at the Tropic of Cancer, the noon Sun would appear directly overhead in the sky. On this same day the *tangent rays* (rays that are just skimming past Earth) are striking at the Arctic Circle (at the far side of the North Pole), and at the Antarctic Circle (at the near side of the South Pole). This means that at the Antarctic Circle on this day, at noon, the Sun would appear to climb no higher in the sky than the horizon. The June solstice is associated with the Northern Hemisphere summer and the Southern Hemisphere winter.

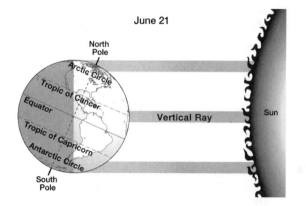

Figure 1-25: Earth–Sun relations on the June solstice.

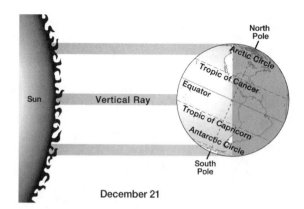

Figure 1-27: Earth–Sun relations on the December solstice.

In Figure 1-25, notice the circle of illumination dividing day from night. The equator is bisected by the circle of illumination, so the equator receives 12 hours of daylight and 12 hours of darkness. As we move north of the equator, a greater proportion of each parallel is in daylight. Because of this, the length of day increases steadily as we travel from the equator to the Arctic Circle. North of the Arctic Circle no portion of any parallel is in darkness, and so all locations between the Arctic Circle and the North Pole receive 24 hours of daylight. As we move through latitudes south of the equator, the length of day steadily decreases until we reach the Antarctic Circle. All locations between the Antarctic Circle and the South Pole receive 24 hours of darkness.

Six months later, on the December solstice, on about December 21st, Earth is at the position in its orbit where the North Pole is leaning most directly away from the Sun (see **Figure 1-27**, above). On this day the vertical rays of the Sun are striking the Tropic of Capricorn (23.5° S). This is the Southern Hemisphere summer (and the Northern Hemisphere winter). The tangent rays are again striking the Arctic and Antarctic Circles, but in this case, locations north of the Arctic Circle experience 24 hours of darkness, and locations south of the Antarctic Circle experience 24 hours of daylight. The equator is again bisected by the circle of illumination and receives 12 hours of daylight and 12 hours of darkness.

Note that the equator, and only the equator, has equal lengths of day and night on every day of the year. (To be perfectly precise, the length of day at the equator is not exactly 12 hours every day of the year—day length varies by a few minutes, due primarily to the elliptical nature of the Earth's orbit.)

Three months after a solstice, on about March 20th and September 22nd, an equinox occurs. On the equinoxes, the vertical rays of the Sun strike the equator (Figure 1-26, p. 20), and the tangent rays of the Sun strike the North and South Poles. Notice that the circle of illumination bisects all of the parallels, so on these two days of the year only, all places on Earth receive 12 hours of daylight and 12 hours of darkness.

It is sometimes difficult to visualize how the vertical rays of the Sun can strike the equator on the equinoxes (as in Figure 1-26, p. 20) even though the axis of Earth is always inclined by 23.5°. **Figure 1-23** (shown on page 4 of the Study Guide), a "top view" of Earth orbiting around the Sun, helps illustrate why this is true: Notice that the axis of Earth is always tilted the same amount and in the same direction. On the June solstice the North Pole is leaning most directly toward the Sun, on the December solstice the North Pole is leaning most directly away from the Sun, and on the equinoxes the tilt of Earth's axis is perpendicular to the incoming rays of the Sun—so the vertical rays strike the equator.

Seasonal Transitions (p. 21): When studying Earth–Sun relations, there is a tendency to memorize only the circumstances on the equinoxes and the solstices. However, you need to keep in mind what happens on the days in between.

For example, the vertical rays of the Sun strike the Tropic of Cancer on about June 21, and then migrate south to the equator by September 22; the vertical rays continue to migrate south until the December solstice when they strike the Tropic of Capricorn, at which point they begin to migrate north back to the equator.

After the December solstice, the days are growing longer in all locations north of the equator, reaching the longest day of the year six months later on the June Solstice. The actual number of hours of daylight at a given location depends on the latitude. Moving north from the equator, the days grow progressively longer with increasing latitude, reaching 24 hours of daylight at the Arctic Circle on the June solstice (Table 1-7, p. 22).

Be sure to view the animation *Earth–Sun Relations* when you are studying patterns of seasonal change—this animation is especially helpful in showing the changing patterns of daylight in the polar regions.

TELLING TIME (p. 23):

The "local Sun time" for a particular location is based on *solar noon*, when the Sun appears highest in the sky. However, locations east or west of this will have different local Sun times. For example, when the Sun is high in the sky at noon in New York, the Sun is still low in the morning sky at Denver to the west.

Standard Time (p. 23): By international agreement, 24 standard *time zones* have been established around the world. Each time zone is a band of longitude, within which it is the same hour. Each standard time zone is 15° of longitude wide, since Earth rotates through 360° of longitude in 24 hours (360° ÷ 24 = 15°).

Notice in Figure 1-29 (p. 24) and **Figure 1-30** (shown below) that while the time zone boundaries closely follow lines of longitude over the oceans, they often deviate significantly over land. In order to avoid splitting cities or small countries into different time zones, most time zone boundaries have been manipulated near political boundaries.

When moving from one time zone to another, reset your watch by one hour. Moving in the direction from San Francisco to New York (west to east) the time becomes later. Moving in the direction from San Francisco to Honolulu (east to west) the time becomes earlier.

You can visualize why this is true by using a globe. The direction of Earth's rotation is toward the east (looking down at the North Pole, Earth is spinning in a counterclockwise direction; Figure 1-19, p. 15). Look at the globe from the side. Imagine your eyes are the Sun—what you see is in daylight, and what you can't see is in darkness. As you spin the globe, you first see New York. At this moment it is "morning" in New York. By the time San Francisco appears, the Sun will be high overhead in New York.

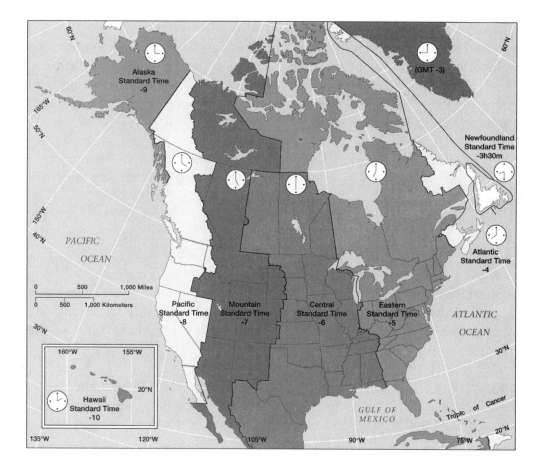

Figure 1-30: Time zones for Canada and the United States.

The International Date Line (p. 24): As Earth rotates and time changes around the world, the date changes when it becomes midnight in a time zone. The date also changes when crossing (either traveling across or phoning across) the *International Date Line*. The International Date Line generally follows the 180° meridian down the middle of the Pacific Ocean (Figure 1-32, p. 26). When crossing the International Date Line going from Japan toward Hawaii (from west to east) the date changes to the previous day. When crossing the International Date Line going from Hawaii toward Japan (from east to west) the date changes to the next day.

Note that the International Date Line runs down the middle of a time zone. When crossing the International Date Line, only the date changes, not the hour. The hour will change only after you reach the boundary of this time zone.

PROGRESSIVE CONTENT REVIEW

1. The lithosphere refers to the _____, inorganic portion of Earth and is comprised mainly of _____. (p. 5)

    solid
    rocks

2. The _____ refers to the waters of Earth. (p. 5)

    hydrosphere

3. Earth is one of _____ planets in the solar system. (p. 6)

    8

4. The four outer planets are much _____ in size than the four inner planets such as Earth. (p. 8)

    larger

5. Earth has a radius of about _____ kilometers (miles). Its highest point is about _____ meters (feet) above sea level, and the deepest spot in the oceans is about _____ meters (feet) below sea level. (p. 9)

    6400 km (4000 mi.)
    8850 m (29,035′)
    11,033 m (36,198′)

6. Earth is not a perfect sphere, but bulges slightly around the _____ (equator/poles). (p. 9)

    equator

7. The plane of the _____ is an imaginary plane that passes through Earth halfway between the _____, perpendicular to the axis of rotation. (p. 10)

    equator
    poles

8.   A "great circle" is the _____ diameter circle that can be drawn on a sphere. Examples of great circles include the _____ and the _____ of _____. (pp. 10–11)

largest

equator;
 circle of illumination

9.   Latitude is the measure of an _____ north or south of the _____. Each degree of latitude can be further divided into _____ minutes, and each minute further divided into _____ seconds. (p. 11)

angle
equator
60; 60

10.   Lines of latitude are called _____ since they never cross or meet. (p. 11)

parallels

11.   The latitude of the equator is _____ degrees. The latitude of the Tropic of Cancer is _____. (p. 12)

0
23.5° north

12.   66.5° north latitude is called the _____ Circle and 66.5° south latitude is called the _____ Circle. (p. 12)

Arctic
Antarctic

13.   Longitude is an angular measure of location east or west of the _____ _____, which runs through the Royal Observatory at Greenwich, near the city of _____, England. (p. 13)

prime meridian
London

14.   The maximum longitude is _____ degrees. (p. 14)

180

15.   Earth reaches its greatest distance from the Sun on _____. This position is called _____. (p. 17)

July 4th
aphelion

16.   The plane that Earth defines in its orbit around the Sun is called the plane of the _____. (p. 17)

ecliptic

17.   Earth's axis is tilted _____ degrees from the perpendicular. (p. 17)

23.5

18.   At all positions in its orbit, Earth's axis is pointing in the same direction. This is called _____ or _____. (pp. 17–18)

polarity; parallelism

19.   On the June solstice, about June _____, the rays of the Sun at noon are striking perpendicularly at _____ latitude. (p. 18)

21st
23.5° north

20.   On the September equinox, all latitudes receive approximately _____ hours of daylight. (p. 19)

12

21. On December 21st, areas north of the Arctic Circle, at _____ latitude, experience _____ hours of darkness. (p. 19)

66.5° north
24

22. During the March _____, on about March 20th, the perpendicular rays of the Sun are striking _____ latitude. (p. 21)

equinox
0°

23. The perpendicular rays of the Sun can never be experienced south of _____ or north of _____ latitude. (pp. 21–22)

23.5° S; 23.5° N

24. In the Northern Hemisphere winter, the number of hours of daylight _____ (increase/decrease) as you move toward the North Pole from the equator. (p. 22)

decrease

25. When the Sun's rays strike Earth _____ (perpendicularly/ obliquely), solar energy is concentrated in a small area. When they strike _____, the same energy is spread out over a larger area. (pp. 22–23)

perpendicularly

obliquely

26. There are _____ standard time zones around the world. Over the oceans, each time zone is _____ degrees of longitude wide. (p. 23)

24
15

27. Moving through time zones from east to west (from New York toward Denver), the time becomes _____ (later/earlier). (p. 25)

earlier

28. The date changes when the hour becomes _____ in a time zone, or when crossing the _____ _____ _____. (pp. 24–25)

midnight
International Date
Line

SELF-TEST

1. Which of the following parallels is a great circle?
   (a) equator
   (b) Tropic of Cancer
   (c) Arctic Circle
   (d) Antarctic Circle

2.   The latitude of the Tropic of Capricorn is:
        (a)   23.5° S   (b)   23.5° N
        (c)   66.5° S   (d)   66.5° N

3.   Lines of longitude (meridians):
        (a)   are always parallel.
        (b)   converge at the poles.
        (c)   indicate location in the north-south direction.
        (d)   represent an angular location measured from the equator.

4.   Earth is closest to the Sun on:
        (a)   January 3rd   (b)   March 20th
        (c)   June 21st   (d)   July 4th

5.   Earth is farthest from the Sun on:
        (a)   January 3rd   (b)   March 20th
        (c)   June 21st   (d)   July 4th

6.   On March 20th, the noon Sun is directly overhead at the:
        (a)   Tropic of Capricorn   (b)   equator
        (c)   Tropic of Cancer   (d)   Arctic Circle

7.   Approximately how many hours of daylight does the equator receive on March 20th?
        (a)   6 hours   (b)   12 hours
        (c)   8 hours   (d)   24 hours

8.   Approximately how many hours of daylight does 45° north latitude receive on September 22nd?
        (a)   6 hours   (b)   12 hours
        (c)   8 hours   (d)   24 hours

9.   On June 21st, the noon Sun is directly overhead at the:
        (a)   Tropic of Capricorn   (b)   equator
        (c)   Tropic of Cancer   (d)   Arctic Circle

10.   How many hours of daylight does 75° south latitude receive on June 21st?
        (a)   24 hours   (b)   12 hours
        (c)   6 hours   (d)   None

11.   How many hours of daylight does 75° north latitude receive on June 21st?
        (a)   24 hours   (b)   12 hours
        (c)   6 hours   (d)   None

12.   Between June 21st and September 22nd:
      (a)   the length of daylight is getting shorter in the midlatitudes of the Northern Hemisphere.
      (b)   the length of daylight is getting longer in the midlatitudes of the Northern Hemisphere.
      (c)   the Southern Hemisphere is experiencing its summer.
      (d)   the South Pole receives 24 hours of daylight.

13.   Between December 21st and June 21st, the latitude of the vertical (direct) rays of the Sun migrates from:
      (a)   23.5° south to 23.5° north.
      (b)   23.5° south to the equator.
      (c)   the equator to 23.5° north.
      (d)   66.5° south to 66.5° north.

14.   Which latitude always receives 24 hours of daylight?
      (a)   The equator
      (b)   66.5° N
      (c)   The North Pole
      (d)   No latitude always receives 24 hours of daylight.

15.   If it is 9:00 A.M. in Los Angeles, California, calculate the time in New York City using the time zone map (Figure 1-30, p. 8 of the Study Guide).
      (a)   10 A.M.   (b)   8 A.M.
      (c)   12 noon   (d)   6 A.M.

16.   If it is 4:00 P.M. at 105° east longitude, what time is it at 60° east longitude?
      (a)   3:00 P.M.   (b)   5:00 P.M.
      (c)   7:00 P.M.   (d)   1:00 P.M.

17.   If you are traveling west toward Hong Kong from Hawaii, when you cross the International Date Line at noon:
      (a)   it becomes the next day.
      (b)   it becomes the previous day.
      (c)   the day remains the same.
      (d)   it becomes midnight.

Answers to Self-Test:

1.	a	6.	b	11.	a	16.	d
2.	a	7.	b	12.	a	17.	a
3.	b	8.	b	13.	a		
4.	a	9.	c	14.	d		
5.	d	10.	d	15.	c		

HINTS FOR TEXTBOOK STUDY QUESTIONS

1.   See "Geography as a Field of Learning" (p. 1).

2.   This is discussed in the section, "The Environmental Spheres" (p. 5).

3.   Consider such factors as size and density.

4.   See Figure 1-7 (p. 9).

5.   Review the section "The Size and Shape of Earth" (p. 9) for a description of this deviation.

6.   Review the Key Terms in the section "The Geographic Grid" (pp. 10–13). Consider what each kind of line shows, as well as their patterns on the globe.

7.   See Figure 1-11 (p. 11).

8.   See "The Geographic Grid" (pp. 10–13).

9.   If you use a world map or atlas to answer this question, be sure to look for both of these cities on a globe as well.

10.   Figure 1-24 (on p. 5 of the Study Guide) may help you visualize some of these factors.

11.   Figure 1-21 (p. 17) illustrates this difference.

12.   These days are shown in Figure 1-20 (p. 16).

13. As a reminder of the maximum latitudes north and south, see Figures 1-25 and 1-27 (on p. 6 of the Study Guide).

14. Table 1-6 (p. 21) and Figures 1-26 (p. 20), 1-25, and 1-27 (on p. 6 of the Study Guide) describe and illustrate these conditions.

15. Table 1-6 (p. 21) and Figures 1-26 (p. 20), 1-25, and 1-27 (on p. 6 of the Study Guide) describe and illustrate these conditions.

16. Table 1-6 (p. 21) and Figures 1-26 (p. 20), 1-25, and 1-27 (on p. 6 of the Study Guide) describe and illustrate these conditions.

17. Table 1-6 (p. 21) and Figures 1-26 (p. 20), 1-25, and 1-27 (on p. 6 of the Study Guide) will remind you of the significance of these latitudes.

18. See the section "Day Length" on page 22.

19. See Study Question #17 above and consider the relationship of the inclination of Earth's axis to those special parallels.

20. Figure 1-30 (on p. 8 of the Study Guide) may help you determine this.

21. See Figure 1-32 (p. 26).

22. See Figure 1-30 (p. 25).

23. When using Figure 1-29 (p. 24) to determine the time difference be sure to take into account whether or not the time zone where it is midnight falls between the two cities.

ADDITIONAL STUDY QUESTIONS

1. If you travel north or south through one degree of latitude, you will cover a distance of about 111 kilometers (69 miles). Why can't we generalize about the distance you will cover if you travel east or west through one degree of longitude?

2. Explain why the North Pole, but *not* the Arctic Circle, has 24 hours of daylight in May.

3.   How would the pattern of Earth–Sun relations be different if Earth were inclined 30° rather than 23.5°?

4.   How would the pattern of seasons be different if the North Pole was always leaning away from the Sun?

Hints for Additional Study Questions:

1.   Use a globe to compare the distance between meridians at different latitudes.

2.   Estimate the latitude of the tangent rays of the Sun between the March equinox and the June solstice.

3.   What is the relationship between the inclination of Earth's axis and the latitudes of the Tropic of Cancer and the Tropic of Capricorn?

4.   Note the importance of polarity to the pattern of seasonal change.

CHAPTER 2

Portraying Earth

OVERVIEW

Maps are important tools in the study of physical geography. This chapter introduces how Earth is portrayed with maps, aerial photographs, and satellite images. The chapter discusses the nature of maps, essential map features, map scale, the control of distortions with different kinds of map projections, and the use of remote sensing for gathering and conveying information about Earth.

In this chapter you will learn to interpret maps with greater accuracy. These are skills you will use throughout the remaining chapters of the text. Several topics are especially important. You should be familiar with the concept of map scale, especially the relationship between graphic and fractional scales. You need to understand the concepts of equivalence and conformality. By the end of this chapter, you should be able to look at a world map and quickly judge its overall area and shape distortion. Finally, you should understand how to interpret various kinds of isolines.

KEY CONCEPTS

MAP SCALE (p. 30):

The *scale* of a map simply reflects how much Earth has been reduced for reproduction on a map.

Scale Types (p. 30): A *graphic scale* is a bar graph, graduated by distance. To use a graphic scale, measure a distance on the map, and then compare the measured distance to the bar graph to determine the actual distance represented.

Fractional scales use a fraction or ratio to compare the distance on a map to the actual distance on Earth. Keep in mind that the unit of measurement must be the same on both sides of the ratio. For example, on a map with a scale of 1:10,000 (also written 1/10,000), one centimeter on the map represents an actual distance of 10,000 centimeters on Earth. Similarly, one inch on such a map represents an actual distance of 10,000 inches on Earth.

Large and Small Map Scales (p. 31): Describing a map as either "large scale" or "small scale" is relative. *Large scale maps* (such as 1:24,000) show a small area of Earth, but in greater detail, than a *small scale map* (such as 1:1,000,000). Figure 2-4 (p. 32) shows Atlanta, Georgia, at four different map scales. As the diagram shows, a detailed city map is considered a relatively large scale map, while a map of the United States is considered a relatively small scale map.

MAP ESSENTIALS (p. 31):

Read this section for a discussion of important features of all maps.

MAP PROJECTIONS (p. 33):

It is impossible to convey the spherical surface of Earth on a flat map without distortion. This section explains the most important kinds of distortions, and how different types of *map projections* can be used to control these distortions.

Look at the diagrams of three major families of map projections (Figures 2-7, 2-8, and 2-9; pp. 34–35). Note that, in each case, there is one latitude or point at which the map is tangent to ("touches") Earth. In the examples shown, the *plane projection* touches at the North Pole, the *cylindrical projection* touches around the equator, and the *conic projection* touches around a parallel in the midlatitudes. These latitudes (called *standard parallels*) represent the location of least distortion for each of these projections. This is why plane projections are typically used to map polar regions, cylindrical projections to map equatorial latitudes, and conic projections to map the midlatitudes.

The Major Dilemma: Equivalence versus Conformality (p. 34): This is an important section of the chapter. The two key properties that cartographers often strive for in a map are *equivalence* (correct area relationships) and *conformality* (correct angular or shape relationships). It is impossible for a map to maintain both of these properties at the same time (and some maps maintain neither property).

As you study this section of the text, it will be helpful to have a globe at hand to compare how the shapes and sizes of the continents shown on different kinds of maps relate to their true relationships shown on a globe.

Equivalence (p. 35): In the simplest terms, an *equivalent* (or *equal area*) *map* shows correct area relationships across the entire map. This means that you can directly compare the spatial extent of a phenomenon (such as the distribution of forest cover) over all parts of a map. When comparing an equivalent world map (**Figure 2-10b**, shown below) to a globe, you will notice that while the relative areas of the continents are accurate, the shapes of the high latitude land masses are distorted.

Conformality (p. 35): A *conformal map* shows the correct angular relationships over the entire map. In practical terms, this means that conformal maps show the correct shapes of features in a limited area (although the true shapes of the continents can only be shown with a globe). When comparing a conformal world map (**Figure 2-10a**, below) to a globe, you will notice that while the shapes of the coastlines are quite accurate, the areas of the high latitude land masses are severely distorted.

There is no "ideal" map projection for all purposes. Rather, there are different kinds of map projections that are suitable for different purposes and for different parts of the world.

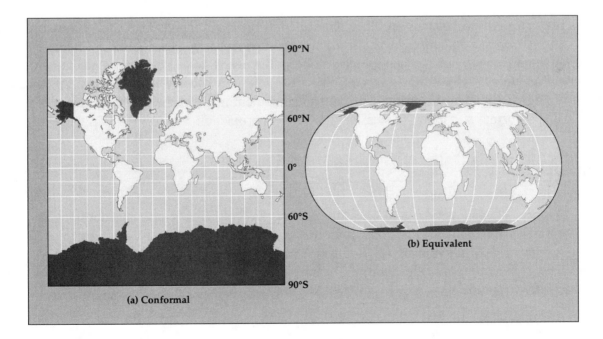

Figure 2-10: (a) Conformal map projection. (b) Equivalent map projection.

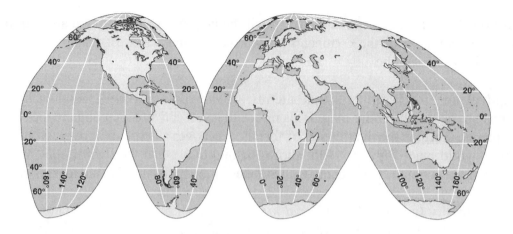

Figure 2-14: Goode's interrupted homolosine equal-area projection.

FAMILIES OF MAP PROJECTIONS (p. 35):

Mercator: The Most Famous Projection (p. 36): The most famous map projection is probably the Mercator (**Figure 2-10a**, shown on the previous page). The Mercator is a conformal projection that was originally designed for navigation; however, in the past it was widely—although inappropriately—adopted as a world map for classroom use.

Interrupted Projections (p. 38): One of the most innovative map projections used for world maps is *Goode's interrupted homolosine equal-area projection* (see **Figure 2-14** above). This projection is equivalent, but by "tearing" the globe in the ocean areas, the shapes of the continents are very accurate as well. In the study of physical geography we are usually more interested in comparing the distributions of phenomena, and so equivalent maps of the world are generally more useful than conformal maps. For this reason, the Goode's projection is used widely in the textbook.

ISOLINES (p. 39):

A common and very useful way of showing varying levels or concentrations of some phenomenon is with *isolines*—lines on a map that connect points of equal value. Isolines such as *isotherms* (showing equal temperature), *isobars* (showing equal atmospheric pressure), and *elevation contour lines* (showing equal elevation) are used throughout the text, and you should be familiar with their interpretation.

There are just a few basic rules pertaining to all isolines:

(a) An isoline connects points on a map where the value of some phenomenon is the same.

(b) Isolines are drawn at regular intervals (for example, for every 10° of temperature difference).

(c) Isolines are always closed lines—although they often close beyond the margins of a map.

(d) Isolines never cross each other.

(e) Where isolines are close together, they show a rapid horizontal change in the phenomenon; where they are far apart, they show a gradual horizontal change.

(f) Values inside a closed isoline are higher than those outside the closed isoline.

An example of isolines is illustrated in **Figure 2-17** (shown below; the complete diagram is found on page 40 of the textbook). A very good example of a map using isolines is Figure 2-16a (p. 40). This map uses *isohyets* to show precipitation amounts on the continent of Africa.

U.S. Geological Survey topographic maps that use contour lines to show elevation are discussed in "Focus: Topographic Maps" (p. 41) and in Appendix II (p. A3–A7).

THE GLOBAL POSITIONING SYSTEM (p. 41):

The *global positioning system* (or simply *GPS*) allows any location on Earth to be precisely and quickly determined. GPS is based on a system of satellites orbiting Earth. A small receiver on the ground (many are inexpensive handheld units) picks up the position signal transmitted by at least four of these satellites, and from these signals the exact location of the receiver can be determined in a matter of minutes.

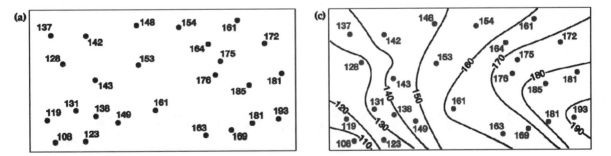

Figure 2-17a & 2-17c: Drawing isolines. (a) Each dot is a measuring station, and the number next to each dot is the value being measured. (c) Isolines drawn to show the overall pattern of the phenomenon being measured.

REMOTE SENSING (p. 44):

In the broadest sense, *remote sensing* involves the portrayal of Earth's surface with photographs taken from airplanes and satellites. However, some of the most significant recent advances in this field have involved the use of use of wavelengths of electromagnetic energy other than visible light (see Figure 2-22, p. 45).

Color and Color Infrared Sensing (p. 44): Note that by using *color infrared photography*, it is possible to clearly distinguish between living vegetation and other surfaces that are not vegetated but are green in color (see Figure 2-23, p. 46).

Multispectral Remote Sensing (p. 45): This section discusses satellite technology that records Earth in several different wavelengths of electromagnetic radiation. For example, Table 2-1 (p. 47) lists the bandwidths and most important applications of the images obtained with the multi-spectral scanner of the *Landsat Enhanced Thematic Mapper Plus* (see Figure 2-25, p. 48).

Radar and Sonar Sensing (p. 46): In contrast to "passive" imaging systems that record the natural radiation emitted or reflected from the surface (passive systems include visible light photography, as well as infrared and microwave recording systems), *radar* and *sonar* are "active" imaging systems. This means that a signal is emitted, and the reflection of this signal is recorded by the imaging system. The advantage of an active system, such as radar, is that it can work day or night, and can penetrate cloud cover to record the surface features (see Figure 2-27, p. 48).

GEOGRAPHIC INFORMATION SYSTEMS (p. 48):

This short section describes the rapidly expanding field of *geographic information systems* (*GIS*). GIS entails the use of computers to gather, store, and map spatial data. Relatively inexpensive software packages enable cartographers to integrate and plot a wide range of environmental or demographic characteristics on maps.

PROGRESSIVE CONTENT REVIEW

1. A _____ map scale uses a graduated line to indicate the graphic equivalent distance on Earth that is shown on a map. (p. 30)

2. A fractional scale of 1:10,000 means that a distance of 1 centimeter on the map represents _____ centimeters on Earth. (p. 31)

10,000

3. Compared to a map with a scale of 1:10,000, a map with a scale of 1:1,000,000 would be considered a _____ (large/small) scale map. (p. 31)

small

4. In an _____ map projection, the area relationships represented on Earth are constant over the whole map. (p. 35)

equivalent

5. In a _____ map projection, the angular relationships on Earth are accurately represented. (p. 35)

conformal

6. A map cannot be both conformal and _____. (p. 35)

equivalent

7. A loxodrome ("rhumb line") shows the true _____ _____ on a map. (p. 36)

compass heading

8. A Mercator projection is an example of a _____ (equivalent/conformal) map. (pp. 36-37)

conformal

9. An _____ is a line on a map that connects points of equal value. (p. 39)

isoline

10. An isotherm connects points of equal _____, while an isobar connects points of equal atmospheric _____. (p. 39)

temperature
pressure

11. The _____ is a satellite-based system used to determine positions on Earth's surface with extreme accuracy. (p. 41)

GPS (global positioning system)

12. _____ _____ is the acquisition of information without physical contact with Earth. (p. 44)

Remote sensing

13. _____ is the science of obtaining accurate measurements from aerial photographs. (p. 44)

Photogrammetry

14. In most cases, living vegetation can be distinguished from non-living surfaces of the same color with _____ _____ photography. (pp. 45-45)

color infrared

15. Thermal infrared sensing detects the radiant _____ of an object. (p. 45)   temperature

16. The "enhanced thematic mapper plus" of Landsat 7 is a _____ scanner and contains _____ wavelength bands. (p. 46)   Multispectral; 8

17. Infrared photography is an example of a _____ (passive/active) sensing system, while radar is an example of an _____ sensing system. (pp. 44–48)   passive

    active

18. _____ sensing systems are capable of mapping surface topography even through dense cloud cover. (pp. 46–48)   Radar

19. _____ are computer systems that are capable of integrating geographic data. (p. 48)   GIS (Geographic Information Systems)

SELF-TEST

1. On a map with a fractional scale of 1:100,000, one inch on the map represents how many inches on Earth?
   - (a) 1 inch
   - (b) 100 inches
   - (c) 100,000 inches
   - (d) 1/100,000th of an inch

2. Compared with a map with a scale of 1:1,000,000, a map with a scale of 1:10,000 would be considered:
   - (a) a large scale map.
   - (b) a small scale map.
   - (c) an equivalent map.
   - (d) a conformal map.

3. An equivalent map projection:
   - (a) shows area relationships accurately over the entire map.
   - (b) shows shapes accurately over the entire map.
   - (c) indicates magnetic compass correction with isogonic lines.
   - (d) cannot show all of Earth in one map.

4.   A conformal map projection:
       (a)   shows area relationships accurately over the entire map.
       (b)   can also be equivalent.
       (c)   can never be equivalent.
       (d)   cannot show all of Earth in one map.

5.   On a Mercator projection:
       (a)   the meridians and parallels cross at right angles.
       (b)   the meridians come together at the poles.
       (c)   the parallels come together at the poles.
       (d)   the parallels are not parallel to each other.

6.   What is the main limitation of using a Mercator projection as a general purpose world map?
       (a)   Shapes are severely distorted near the poles.
       (b)   Shapes are severely distorted near the equator.
       (c)   Area is severely distorted near the poles.
       (d)   Area is severely distorted near the equator.

7.   All straight lines drawn on a Mercator projection represent:
       (a)   the shortest route between two points.
       (b)   a path along a great circle.
       (c)   the true compass heading.
       (d)   the magnetic compass correction.

8.   A "isohyet" is a line joining points of equal:
       (a)   elevation
       (b)   temperature
       (c)   atmospheric pressure
       (d)   precipitation

9.   A "contour line" is a line joining points of equal:
       (a)   elevation
       (b)   temperature
       (c)   atmospheric pressure
       (d)   precipitation

10.   One advantage of vertical aerial photographs over oblique aerial photographs is that:
       (a)   more land area can be included in a single photograph.
       (b)   measurements of surface distances usually can be made more accurately.
       (c)   the elevation of the topography can be seen more readily.
       (d)   the colors of landforms are more accurately reproduced.

11.   One reason for using color infrared photography rather than conventional photography in remote sensing is that:
        (a)   it has better resolution of detail.
        (b)   it can penetrate cloud cover.
        (c)   it shows differences in elevation more accurately.
        (d)   living vegetation can be differentiated from non-living surfaces.

12.   Thermal infrared remote sensing shows:
        (a)   differences in elevation accurately.
        (b)   the temperature contrasts between features.
        (c)   the chemical composition of surface rocks.
        (d)   the wind direction.

13.   One reason for using an active remote sensing system (such as radar) is that:
        (a)   it can penetrate cloud cover.
        (b)   it has higher resolution than conventional photography.
        (c)   it can directly measure the temperature of the atmosphere.
        (d)   it can directly measure the temperature of the surface.

Answers to Self-Test:

1.	c	6.	c	11.	d
2.	a	7.	c	12.	b
3.	a	8.	d	13.	a
4.	c	9.	a		
5.	a	10.	b		

HINTS FOR TEXTBOOK STUDY QUESTIONS

1.   This question concerns the *distortions* of maps (as compared to globes), rather than the inability to show fine detail.

2.   See pages 30–31 in the text.

3.   Review the material on fractional map scales on page 31.

4.   Review the text material on page 31 and Figure 2-4 (p. 32).

5.   See Figure 2-10 (p. 19 in the Study Guide).

6.   See the textbook section "The Major Dilemma: Equivalence versus Conformality" on pages 34–35.

7.   See Figures 2-7, 2-8, and 2-9 and the textbook section "Families of Map Projections" on pages 34–38.

8.   See "Mercator: The Most Famous Projection" on pages 36–37.

9.   Consider the strengths and weaknesses of different projections, and the various kinds of information that can be mapped.

10.   See Figure 2-17 on page 21 of the Study Guide and the textbook section "Isolines" on pages 39–41.

11.   See page 39 in the textbook.

12.   Review the difference between color infrared and thermal infrared images (pp. 44–45 in textbook).

13.   Also review the difference between color infrared and thermal infrared images (pp. 44–45 in text).

14.   See the textbook sections on pages 45–48 and Figures 2-25 and 2-27 (p. 48).

15.   Review the textbook section on GPS beginning on page 41 and the section on GIS beginning on page 48.

ADDITIONAL STUDY QUESTIONS

1.   What are the advantages of using a map rather than an aerial photograph to study Earth's surface?

2.   Why would the Mercator projection be a poor choice for mapping the loss of forest cover around the world?

3.   Color infrared satellite photographs do not reproduce the color of Earth's surface accurately, but they are widely used. Why?

Hints for Additional Study Questions:

1.   Consider the selective nature of information presented on maps.

2.   When plotting forest cover, your main concern is the area involved.

3.   Infrared "sees" different characteristics of Earth than can the human eye.

Introduction to the Atmosphere

OVERVIEW

In Chapter 3 we begin the study of weather and climate. This chapter describes the composition and structure of the atmosphere, the basic elements or "ingredients" of weather and climate, and the most important "controls" or influences on weather and climate.

The operation of the atmosphere is complex. In subsequent chapters, the text will focus on the individual elements of weather and climate, such as temperature, pressure, wind, and moisture. All of these elements are interrelated. This chapter becomes the foundation for further study by providing an overview of these elements and their controls.

Take the time to understand the basic composition of the atmosphere and its vertical zones. Especially note the importance of the troposphere in our study of weather and climate. You will learn that the bulk of the atmosphere is very close to the surface of Earth, and that there are significant changes in the atmosphere, especially in temperature and pressure, with increasing elevation. You should also remember the most important controls of weather and climate. Chapter 3 helps you grasp the "big picture" of weather and climate.

KEY CONCEPTS

COMPOSITION OF THE ATMOSPHERE (p. 56):

Permanent Gases (p. 56): Figure 3-3 (p. 56) shows the relative proportions of the various gases in the atmosphere. The most abundant gases of the atmosphere are the permanent gases nitrogen (78%) and oxygen (21%)—these gases are relatively inactive in most weather processes.

Variable Gases (p. 56): Variable gases are found in very small quantities. Three of these variable gases—water vapor, carbon dioxide, and ozone—are very important in weather processes.

Particulates (Aerosols) (p. 57): The various kinds of solid and liquid particles suspended in the atmosphere are found in relatively small quantities, but are extremely important to processes such as the heating of the atmosphere and in the formation of clouds.

VERTICAL STRUCTURE OF THE ATMOSPHERE (p. 58):

Thermal Layers (p. 58): A number of vertical layers can be recognized in the atmosphere. The series of layers defined by temperature patterns is probably most important in our study of weather and climate.

The lowest thermal layer in the atmosphere is called the *troposphere*. Within the troposphere, temperature generally decreases with increasing altitude. This is shown in **Figure 3-5** (shown on the following page). Familiarize yourself with this kind of chart—you will need to interpret charts similar to this in subsequent chapters. Temperature is indicated along the bottom of the chart, and altitude is marked along the sides. The solid line indicates the average temperature at different elevations.

Notice that at the surface the average temperature is about 15°C (60°F), while at the *tropopause* (the top of the troposphere) at an altitude of approximately 14 kilometers (9 miles) the temperature has dropped to about -57°C (-70°F).

Pressure (p. 60): Figures 3-7 and 3-8 (p. 60) show that atmospheric pressure decreases rapidly with increasing altitude. Approximately 90% of the mass of the atmosphere is found within 16 kilometers (10 miles) of the surface.

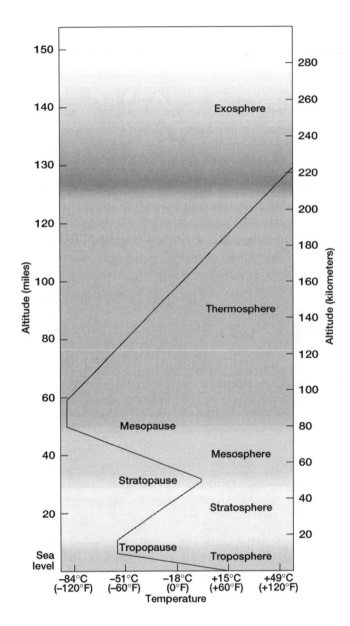

Figure 3-5: Thermal structure of the atmosphere.

HUMAN-INDUCED ATMOSPHERIC CHANGE (p. 61)

Depletion of the Ozone Layer (p. 62): Review the important role of the *ozone layer* as an absorber of ultraviolet radiation from the Sun. The human impact on the ozone layer is also illustrated in the animation ***Ozone Depletion***.

31

Air Pollution (p. 64): Note especially the formation of *photochemical smog* that has become common in many large cities around the world, and that human-produced ozone is one of the key components of photochemical smog.

WEATHER AND CLIMATE (p. 67):

The Elements of Weather and Climate (p. 67): The four elements of weather and climate—*temperature, pressure, wind,* and *moisture*—are the "ingredients" of weather. These elements are easy to describe but complex in their interrelationships (as we will see in the next few chapters).

The Controls of Weather and Climate (p. 67): The seven main controls of weather and climate mentioned in this section will be treated in much greater detail in the chapters to come. However, it is important to read this section carefully. It summarizes many of the most important concepts of weather and climate, such as the different heating characteristics of land and water, the basic circulation patterns of the oceans and the atmosphere, and the importance of mountain barriers. Keep these dominant influences on weather and climate in mind as you move through the following chapters.

The Coriolis Effect (p. 69): This is a good time to familiarize yourself with the *Coriolis effect* (also see the animation **Coriolis Effect**). The Coriolis effect is actually a "control" of some of the controls of weather and climate. Stated simply, because of the continuous rotation of Earth, the path of any free moving object (such as the wind or a rocket) will be deflected to the right in the Northern Hemisphere. The deflection is to the left in the Southern Hemisphere. The Coriolis effect exists because as an object is moving above Earth's surface, Earth is rotating underneath. The result is that the path traced out by this object appears to curve relative to the surface.

Note that regardless of the direction of movement, the deflection of the Coriolis effect is to the right in the Northern Hemisphere and to the left in the Southern Hemisphere. Further, the deflection is greatest at the poles and diminishes to zero deflection at the equator, and rapidly moving objects are deflected more than slowly moving objects.

While the Coriolis effect is described as an "apparent" deflection since the rotation of Earth is responsible for the deflection, the consequences of the Coriolis effect are very real. As we will see, both wind direction and the direction of ocean currents are strongly influenced by the Coriolis effect.

PROGRESSIVE CONTENT REVIEW

1. Nitrogen makes up _____ percent of the atmosphere by volume, while oxygen makes up about _____ percent. (p. 56)

    78
    21

2. Water vapor in the atmosphere is usually found in its greatest concentrations over _____ (polar/tropical) oceans. (pp. 56–57)

    tropical

3. Ozone is a good absorber of _____ solar radiation, and is found in its greatest concentrations at altitudes of about _____ to _____ kilometers (miles). (p. 57)

    ultraviolet

    15-48 km (9–30 mi.)

4. Solid particles in the atmosphere can both _____ and _____ solar energy. (pp. 57–58)

    absorb; reflect

5. In general the troposphere is deepest over the _____ (poles/equator) where it extends up to an altitude of about _____ kilometers (miles), and shallowest over the _____ where it extends up to an altitude of about _____ kilometers (miles). (p. 59)

    equator

    18 km (11 mi.); poles
    8 km (5 mi.)

6. Within the troposphere, temperature generally _____ with increasing altitude. (p. 59)

    decreases

7. The warmest part of the stratosphere is associated with the absorption of ultraviolet radiation in the _____ layer. (p. 59)

    ozone

8. As altitude increases, pressure _____. (p. 60)

    decreases

9. About 90% of the mass of the atmosphere is found within about _____ kilometers (miles) of the surface. (p. 60)

    16 km (10 mi.)

10. Within the lowest _____ kilometers (miles) of the atmosphere, the principal gases of the atmosphere have very uniform distribution. (pp. 61–62)

    80 km (50 mi.)

11. Human-produced chemicals known as _____ are evidently responsible for much of the depletion of the ozone layer. (p. 63)

    chlorofluorocarbons (CFCs)

12.   _____ refers to the short-run conditions of the atmosphere, while _____ refers to the long-term patterns of the atmosphere. (p. 67)

                                   Weather
climate

13.   The basic "elements" of weather and climate are _____, _____, _____, and _____. (p. 67)

                                   temperature; moisture; pressure; wind

14.   The amount of sunlight received throughout the year in a given location depends primarily upon its _____. (p. 68)

                                   latitude

15.   Maritime areas are generally _____ (warmer/cooler) in summer and _____ (warmer/cooler) in winter than continental areas. (p. 68)

                                   cooler
warmer

16.   Most winds in the middle latitudes blow from the _____ (east/west). (p. 68)

                                   west

17.   Generally, _____ (warm/cool) currents are found along the west coasts of continents. (p. 68)

                                   cool

18.   The windward side of a mountain usually receives _____ (more/less) precipitation than the leeward side. (p. 69; see Figure 3-21)

                                   more

19.   Because of the Coriolis effect the path of any freely moving object will be deflected to the _____ (right/left) in the Northern Hemisphere, and to the _____ (right/left) in the Southern Hemisphere. (pp. 69–71)

                                   right
left

20.   The Coriolis effect deflection is strongest at the _____ (equator/poles) and diminishes toward the _____. (p. 71)

                                   poles
equator

SELF-TEST

1.   The bulk of the atmosphere (by volume) consists of:
(a)   carbon dioxide and water vapor.
(b)   hydrogen and oxygen.
(c)   carbon dioxide and ozone.
(d)   nitrogen and oxygen.

2.   Approximately what percentage of the atmosphere (by volume) is carbon dioxide?
      (a)   10%   (b)   23%
      (c)   5%   (d)   less than 1%

3.   What is one role of carbon dioxide in the atmosphere?
      (a)   Becomes condensation nuclei for cloud formation.
      (b)   Blocks most incoming shortwave radiation.
      (c)   Helps absorb outgoing terrestrial infrared radiation.
      (d)   Increases the amount of ozone in the stratosphere.

4.   What is one role of solid particles in the atmosphere?
      (a)   They become condensation nuclei for cloud formation.
      (b)   They limit the amount of ozone formed in the stratosphere.
      (c)   They increase the amount of ozone in the stratosphere.
      (d)   They prevent cloud formation.

5.   What is one role of ozone in the atmosphere?
      (a)   Increases the cloud cover over the tropics.
      (b)   Becomes condensation nuclei for cloud formation.
      (c)   Reacts with sunlight to produce carbon dioxide.
      (d)   Absorbs incoming ultraviolet radiation in the stratosphere.

6.   Most water vapor in the atmosphere is found:
      (a)   near the surface.
      (b)   at the tropopause.
      (c)   in the ozone layer.
      (d)   in the mesosphere.

7.   As altitude increases, the pressure generally:
      (a)   increases.
      (b)   decreases.
      (c)   stays the same.

8.   Within the troposphere, temperature generally:
      (a)   is the same at all altitudes.
      (b)   decreases with increasing altitude.
      (c)   increases with increasing altitude.

9.   The troposphere is generally deepest:
        (a)   over the equator.
        (b)   over the poles.
        (c)   in the Northern Hemisphere during winter.
        (d)   over the oceans.

10.   The climate of a region is best thought of as representing the:
        (a)   the average weather conditions during the previous year.
        (b)   the extremes in weather conditions over many years.
        (c)   the average weather conditions over many years (including the extremes).
        (d)   the average weather conditions during summer months.

11.   In winter land tends to:
        (a)   cool faster but to a lesser extent than water.
        (b)   cool faster and to a greater extent than water.
        (c)   cool more slowly but to a greater extent than water.
        (d)   cool more slowly and to a lesser extent than water.

12.   The main surface currents in the major ocean basins assist in heat transfer around the world
        by moving:
        (a)   cool water from the tropics toward the poles.
        (b)   cool water from the poles toward the tropics and warm water from the tropics toward
                the poles.
        (c)   warm water from the poles toward the tropics.
        (d)   warm water from the Northern Hemisphere to the Southern Hemisphere.

Answers to Self-Test:

1.	d	6.	a	11.	b
2.	d	7.	b	12.	b
3.	c	8.	b		
4.	a	9.	a		
5.	d	10.	c		

HINTS FOR TEXTBOOK STUDY QUESTIONS

1.   Review the rapid decrease in atmospheric density with altitude.

2.   Consider both the gases and natural impurities in the atmosphere, as well as the relative concentrations of each.

3.   Especially consider the role of these components of the atmosphere in regulating temperature.

4.   This question has you consider changes in the concentration of water vapor with increasing altitude, as well as variations in water vapor concentration over different surfaces and at different latitudes. Take in to account the sources of water vapor in your answer as you contrast low altitudes with high altitudes, low latitude areas with high latitude areas, and continents with oceans.

5.   See Figure 3-5 (on p. 31 of the Study Guide).

6.   Figure 3-8 (p. 60) illustrates this pattern.

7.   For a discussion of this, see page 59.

8.   Review "Depletion of the Ozone Layer" (pp. 62–64) for a discussion of this topic.

9.   This phenomenon is discussed on page 64.

10.   This kind of air pollution is discussed on page 66.

11.   This important distinction is discussed on page 67 in the textbook.

12.   The four "elements" of weather and climate are discussed on page 67 in the textbook.

13.   In the next few chapters you will study the main "controls" of the elements of weather and climate. For now, a general discussion of the main controls can be found on pages 67–69 in the textbook.

14.   The Coriolis effect is well illustrated in the CD animation *Coriolis Effect*.

ADDITIONAL STUDY QUESTIONS

1. The total amount of carbon dioxide in the atmosphere has increased very slightly over the last 100 years, yet this is still causing great concern. Why?

2. Based on your understanding of Earth–Sun relations (from Chapter 1), explain why Earth's temperature generally decreases as you move from the equator toward the poles.

3. Why can't we easily determine if climate has changed based on just two or three years of unusual weather?

Hints for Additional Study Questions:

1. Consider the effects and importance of carbon dioxide in the atmosphere given its overall low level of concentration.

2. Remember the range of latitudes within which the Sun can strike Earth directly, as well as the seasonal changes in the solar angle and length of daylight.

3. Recall the definition of climate.

CHAPTER 4

Insolation and Temperature

OVERVIEW

Chapter 4 focuses on temperature, the first element of weather and climate that we will study. The chapter begins with a discussion of solar energy and a series of definitions of basic heating and cooling processes. The heating of Earth and the atmosphere is then discussed— especially focusing on the reasons for the unequal heating of Earth by the Sun (the fundamental basis of all weather and climate). The most important mechanisms for distributing heat around the planet are then presented. The chapter finishes with a discussion of global temperature patterns, which reflect both the unequal heating pattern of Earth, as well as the mechanisms of heat transfer, and an introduction to the issue of global warming.

Many of the patterns presented in subsequent chapters on weather and climate are rooted in the heating of the atmosphere. The basic processes of heating and cooling the atmosphere described briefly in the beginning of this chapter will be encountered again when pressure, wind, and moisture are discussed in the chapters that follow. It is important that you understand these processes before you move on to other chapters.

Several other topics are especially important in this chapter. First, understand how and why the troposphere is heated largely from below by Earth through processes such as the "greenhouse effect." Second, you should be able to relate the seasonal changes in Earth–Sun relations, to the annual heating patterns of Earth. Third, note the relationship of land–water contrasts to temperature patterns around the world. Finally, recognize the basic pattern of ocean currents, and how this transfer of heat serves to modify temperature patterns.

KEY CONCEPTS

ENERGY, HEAT, AND TEMPERATURE (p. 75):

This section defines terms used throughout our discussion of the atmosphere, such as energy, temperature, and heat.

SOLAR ENERGY (p. 78):

Electromagnetic Radiation (p. 78): It is important to remember that nearly all solar energy reaches Earth as *shortwave radiation* (mostly ultraviolet, visible, and short infrared wavelengths), while all of the energy radiated by Earth is *longwave radiation* (mostly thermal infrared wavelengths). This is illustrated in **Figure 4-6** (shown below). Notice that the peak intensity of incoming solar shortwave radiation is centered in the wavelength band of visible light.

Insolation (p. 80): "Insolation" is a contraction of the phrase, *in*coming *sol*ar radi*ation*. Remember that insolation consists of the shortwave radiation from the Sun.

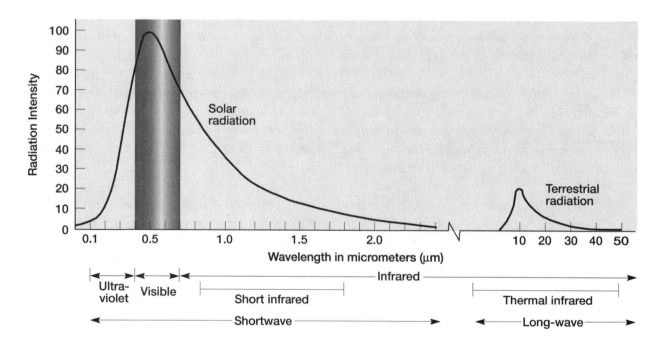

Figure 4-6: Comparison of solar and terrestrial radiation intensity.

BASIC HEATING AND COOLING PROCESSES IN THE ATMOSPHERE (p. 80):

Pay close attention to this discussion of basic heating and cooling processes. Knowledge of these processes is necessary in order to understand the heating of the atmosphere. Many of these processes will be mentioned again as we proceed through subsequent chapters on weather and climate.

Radiation (p. 80): Note that Earth radiates (emits) a great deal of energy, but at longer wavelengths than the *electromagnetic radiation* coming from the Sun (see Figure 4-6, shown on the previous page).

Absorption (p. 81): Most objects (including Earth's surface and atmosphere) show that they have absorbed ("taken in") electromagnetic radiation by an increase in temperature.

Reflection (p. 81): Distinguish between radiation and reflection. Earth both radiates energy (emits longwave radiation), and reflects energy (bounces away incoming shortwave radiation from the Sun and longwave radiation emitted by the atmosphere).

Scattering (p. 82): Scattering involves the deflection of selected wavelengths of light. The shortest wavelengths of visible light, especially violet and blue wavelengths, are easily scattered by the gas molecules in the atmosphere, while the longer wavelengths of visible light, such as orange and red, pass through with little scattering (Figure 4-9, p. 82). When you look up at the blue sky, you are seeing the scattering of blue light by the gas molecules in the atmosphere. When the Sun is low in the sky, most of the blue wavelengths of visible light have been scattered back to space, leaving only the longest wavelengths—orange and red (Figures 4-10 and 4-11, pp. 82–83).

Transmission (p. 83): This is a key section. Different substances have differing abilities to transmit radiation. This means that a substance may let one wavelength of electromagnetic radiation pass through but not another wavelength.

The Greenhouse Effect (p. 83): The *greenhouse effect* in the atmosphere is the result of the atmosphere's ability to easily transmit incoming shortwave radiation from the Sun, but not to easily transmit the outgoing longwave radiation emitted by Earth's surface. The *greenhouse gases* in the atmosphere are largely transparent to incoming shortwave radiation, but inhibit the transmission of outgoing terrestrial longwave radiation—these gases absorb much of the outgoing longwave radiation, and in turn, reradiate this energy in the lower atmosphere. The primary natural greenhouse gases in the atmosphere are (in order of importance) water vapor and carbon dioxide. Many other gases act as greenhouse gases, such as methane and particulates (although particulates are not actually a gas, some can absorb longwave radiation). Note that, compared to nitrogen and oxygen which make up the bulk of the atmosphere, these greenhouse gases are found in very small quantities in the atmosphere.

You should also distinguish between the ongoing natural warming of the atmosphere by the greenhouse effect and the likely human-produced *increase* in this warming through pollution. (See the textbook section "Global Warming and the Greenhouse Effect" on pages 102–104, and the animation *Global Warming* for a discussion of this topic.)

Conduction (p. 84): With the process of conduction, the discussion of heating and cooling processes in the text switches from processes involving electromagnetic radiation to processes involving the movement of "heat." Heat refers to the thermal energy that transfers from an object of higher temperature to an object of lower temperature.

The molecules in a substance are constantly vibrating or "jiggling" back and forth. The thermal energy in a substance is due to this random molecular motion. The temperature of an object is defined as the average *kinetic energy* (the energy of motion) of its molecules. When the molecules of an object are highly active and agitated the object is relatively hot. When the molecules of an object are not very active the object is relatively cool.

Conduction is the transfer of heat by way of molecule to molecule collision. In other words, thermal energy will be transferred between (or through) objects when the highly active molecules of a hot substance collide with the less active molecules of a cool substance (see Figure 4-14, p. 84). As thermal energy is transferred through molecular collisions, the temperature of both objects changes and tends to equalize. Conduction can transfer heat through many kinds of materials (such as metal and air). The lowest layer of the atmosphere is heated and cooled by conduction from the ground.

Convection (p. 85): Convection is the predominately vertical transfer of thermal energy in a moving liquid or gas—the liquid or gas moves and carries energy with it.

Convection is a process that will be mentioned many times in coming chapters. While the simplest example of convection is the circulation in a pan of boiling water, we are most interested in convection in the atmosphere. Heat is transferred through the atmosphere when currents of warm air rise from the surface. As warm air rises up from the surface, cooler air is pulled in from the sides. This air will then be warmed and will also begin to rise. In a well-developed *convection cell* (or *convective circulation cell*), the rising air eventually drops back down and is again heated and carried back up to higher elevations. In this way, heated air is transferred away from the surface of Earth.

Advection (p. 85): Advection refers to the horizontal transfer of heat, such as the movement of warm or cold air through wind.

Adiabatic Cooling and Warming (p. 85): This is a very important section. While mentioned only briefly here, adiabatic cooling and warming are keys to understanding the behavior of moisture in the atmosphere (Chapter 6). The adiabatic process in the atmosphere involves temperature changes as air expands or compresses. Remember two basic facts:

(1)   When air rises, it cools. As air rises, it comes under lower pressure and expands. This expansion of gas molecules over a greater volume requires energy. In effect, the energy is "spread out" through a greater volume and so the air cools.

(2)   When air descends, it warms. As air descends, it comes under higher pressure and compresses. As the air compresses, the energy is, in effect, "concentrated" into a smaller volume, and so the air warms (Figure 4-16, p. 86).

Remember, rising air will always cool adiabatically, and descending air will always warm adiabatically.

Latent Heat (p. 86): Another very important concept (that will be mentioned again in coming chapters) is that of *latent heat*. In the simplest terms, during evaporation, when water changes from a liquid to a gas, energy is "stored" as latent heat in the water vapor. When this water vapor condenses back to liquid form, this latent heat is released. This is important because evaporation is, in effect, a cooling process, and condensation is a warming process.

The heat "stored" in water vapor is simply the kinetic energy (the energy of movement) of the molecules. During the evaporation process, the faster or more "energetic" water molecules escape to become water vapor, and so the average kinetic energy of the remaining liquid water is reduced—and so the temperature of the liquid water is lowered. During condensation, the kinetic energy of the water vapor molecules being absorbed is given back to the liquid, increasing the temperature of the liquid water.

Note that latent heat is also released when water freezes, and is stored when ice melts.

THE HEATING OF THE ATMOSPHERE (p. 86):

The simple diagram of Earth's solar radiation budget (Figure 4-17, p. 87) summarizes a very complex process. Note that in the long run, there is a balance between the amount of solar energy received by Earth, and the amount of energy that leaves Earth.

Figure 4-18 (p. 87) shows the energy budget of Earth in more detail. In this diagram, "units" of energy are used to illustrate the flow of energy to and from Earth (the diagram begins with 100 "units" of energy coming from the Sun).

There are several important things to note about what happens to incoming solar radiation once it strikes the upper atmosphere. First, about 31% (31 "units") of incoming solar radiation is reflected and scattered back to space by the surface and by the atmosphere (this is the reflectance or *albedo* of Earth). Second, only about 24% of arriving solar energy is directly absorbed by the atmosphere (21 "units" by the atmosphere and 3 "units" by the ozone layer). Third, about 45% (45 "units") of arriving solar radiation passes through the atmosphere unchanged and is absorbed by Earth. Finally, once the radiation has been absorbed by Earth, the atmosphere is then heated by the surface through the greenhouse effect, through the latent heat stored in water vapor, and through conduction and convection. See the animation *Atmospheric Energy Balance* for a review of Earth's solar radiation budget.

VARIATIONS IN HEATING BY LATITUDE AND SEASON (p. 89):

This section covers a critical concept in meteorology: the unequal heating of Earth by the Sun is the fundamental factor responsible for producing variations in weather and climate.

Latitudinal and Seasonal Differences (p. 89): During this discussion of heating differences based on latitude, remember back to the basics of Earth–Sun relations (Chapter 1). Recall that the Sun's light can only strike Earth vertically (at an angle of 90°) between the Tropic lines (23.5° N and 23.5° S latitude). This means that in latitudes outside the Tropics, the Sun can never be directly overhead. The higher the latitude, the lower the noon Sun will be in the sky.

Notice in **Figure 4-19** (shown below) that in equatorial latitudes the Sun will have a higher *angle of incidence* and so the intensity of incoming solar energy will be much greater (each "beam" of sunlight will cover a smaller surface area) than in higher latitudes. Also notice that this greater concentration of solar heating based on the angle of incidence is reinforced by atmospheric obstruction (Figure 4-21, p. 90). In other words, high latitudes receive less solar heating during a year than low latitudes because they have less-direct angles of incidence and the solar energy must pass through a greater thickness of atmosphere. (Note also that variations in the length of day during the year influence the seasonal heating patterns at various latitudes.)

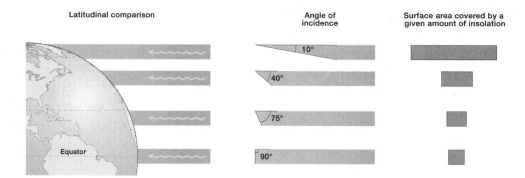

Figure 4-19: The angle at which solar rays hit Earth's surface varies with latitude. The larger the angle, the more concentrated the energy and therefore the more effective the heating.

Latitudinal Radiation Balance (p. 90): Note the seasonal shift of this heating. Figure 4-23 (p. 91) shows the distribution of insolation in December and June. Notice that in December (the Northern Hemisphere winter) the latitudes of most intense insolation are in the Southern Hemisphere, while in June (the Northern Hemisphere summer), the latitudes of most intense insolation are in the Northern Hemisphere.

LAND AND WATER CONTRASTS (p. 92):

A key concept in the study of weather and climate is that of land/water temperature contrasts. Land and water react differently to heating and cooling, and in turn, land and water influence the temperature of the atmosphere differently.

In short, land heats and cools faster and to a greater extent than water. This has very important implications. The hottest and coldest places on Earth are over land. In summer, the interiors of large land masses will heat up much more than coastal areas, while in winter, the interiors of land masses will cool off much more than coastal areas (for example, see Figure 4-26, p. 93). As you study land and water contrasts, be sure that you understand the reasons for these heating and cooling differences (Figure 4-25, p. 93).

MECHANISMS OF HEAT TRANSFER (p. 94):

Were it not for two key mechanisms of heat transfer around the world, the tropics would be much warmer and the polar regions much colder than they actually are. The most important mechanism for moving heat from the tropics toward the poles is the general circulation of the atmosphere, covered in Chapter 5. A second important mechanism is the general circulation of the oceans, covered in this chapter.

Oceanic Circulation (p. 94): Take the time to learn the basic pattern of ocean currents. This pattern is very important when trying to understand global temperature distribution as well as climate patterns around the world.

The basic pattern is the same in the five main ocean basins of the world (North and South Atlantic, North and South Pacific, and the Indian Ocean). Figure 4-28 (p. 95) is a map of major ocean currents. Focus on the overall circular pattern found in each of these basins. Begin by looking at the pattern in the northern Atlantic Ocean. Notice that near the equator, the water is moving toward the west, then at the margin of the basin the current curves toward the North Pole. Before the water reaches the pole, it turns south back toward the equator. In the Northern Hemisphere ocean basins, this circulation is in a clockwise direction, while in the Southern Hemisphere basins it is counterclockwise (due in part to the Coriolis effect).

Also notice the temperature of the currents (red lines represent relatively warm water, and blue lines relatively cool water). Warm water is moved from the equator toward the poles, while cool water is brought back toward the equator. This overall pattern is repeated in all five ocean basins. In general, warm water is moving along the east coasts of the major continents toward the poles, and cool water is moving along the west coasts of continents back toward the equator.

See the animation *Ocean Circulation Patterns* for additional information about the circulation of ocean currents.

VERTICAL TEMPERATURE PATTERNS (p. 98):

Several important terms are introduced here.

Environmental Lapse Rate (p. 98): The *environmental lapse rate* refers to the observed temperature change that takes place as we increase altitude in the troposphere—the environmental lapse rate varies from place to place and from time to time.

Average Lapse Rate (p. 98): The *average lapse rate* (6.5°C per 1000 meters or 3.6°F per 1000 ft.) refers to the average decrease in temperature that takes place as we increase altitude in the troposphere. The main reason for this can be understood by remembering that the troposphere is largely heated from below—the warmest part of the troposphere is the part closest to the surface. Keep in mind that the average lapse rate simply refers to the overall change in temperature with increased altitude in the atmosphere; it does *not* refer to the temperature change that will take place within a specific parcel of moving air (we will come back to this distinction in Chapter 6).

Temperature Inversions (p. 98): A *temperature inversion* is a common, but generally short-lived, deviation from the average lapse rate. In other words, for periods of time, and over limited areas, temperature may actually increase with increasing altitude. Figure 4-30 (p. 98) charts these circumstances. Notice in example (a) that with increasing altitude, temperature decreases. This is the normal situation and reflects the average lapse rate. In example (b) near the surface, temperature increases as we move to higher altitudes. This is a temperature inversion (however, at a higher altitude, this trend reverts to the more usual situation, and temperature begins to decrease as expected).

GLOBAL TEMPERATURE PATTERNS (p. 99):

It is valuable to study the maps in this section (**Figure 4-32** and **Figure 4-33** shown on the following page) showing the average January and July surface temperatures (adjusted to sea level). Temperature is mapped using *isotherms*, lines that connect points of equal temperature (see Chapter 2 for a review of how to interpret isolines).

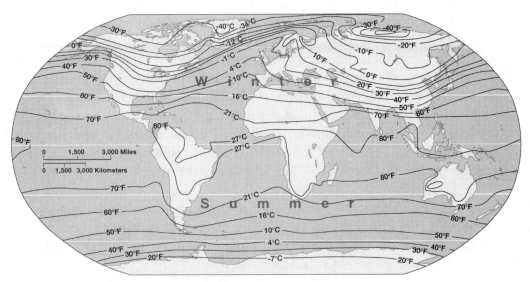

Figure 4-32: Average January sea-level temperatures.

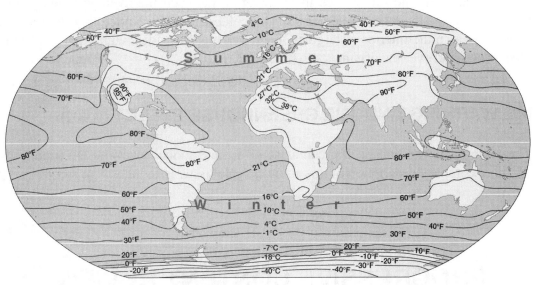

Figure 4-33: Average July sea-level temperatures.

Generally, temperatures should be warmest at the equator, and cooler as we move toward the poles. That means that the isotherms should generally run parallel to the lines of latitude (running west to east across the map). Notice that this is generally the case over the oceans, but not over the continents. These deviations from the hypothetical pattern reflect three important factors: the season, ocean currents, and land/water contrasts.

For example, look at the map of average July temperatures (Figure 4-33). Follow the 21°C (70°F) isotherm in the Northern Hemisphere from west to east (from left to right across the map). Notice that the isotherm generally runs west to east until it approaches the west coast of North America. Along the west coast it is deflected toward the equator by the cool water of the California Current (21°C [70°F] temperatures are found closer to the equator here). The isotherm shifts toward the North Pole over western North America since this is summer, and the interior of the continent is warmer than the ocean (21°C [70°F] temperatures are found farther from the equator here). The isotherm moves across the Atlantic Ocean almost exactly west to east, but is again deflected toward the North Pole over the warm interior of the Eurasian landmass. The isotherm shifts to the south again once it reaches the Pacific Ocean along the right side of the map.

Figure 4-34 (p. 101) shows the general shift of isotherms crossing a hypothetical Northern Hemisphere continent during different seasons. In July, the isotherm shifts to the north because the interior of the continent is warmer than the oceans, while in January, the isotherm shifts to the south since the interior of the continent is colder than the oceans.

Annual Temperature Range (p. 102): The significance of land/water contrasts to global temperature patterns is reflected in the *average annual temperature range* shown in Figure 4-35 (p. 102). This map plots the differences in temperature between the average temperature of the warmest month, and the average temperature of the coldest month. Notice that the most extreme temperature range is in the interior of large continents at high latitudes, while the smallest range is found in the tropics and over the oceans.

GLOBAL WARMING AND THE GREENHOUSE EFFECT (p. 102):

The topic of human-enhanced greenhouse effect and global warming is introduced in this section. A more complete description of this environmental issue is found in Chapter 8.

PROGRESSIVE CONTENT REVIEW

1. The solar energy that reaches Earth is called _____. (p. 80)   insolation

2. Most of the energy from the Sun arrives at Earth as _____   shortwave
    (shortwave/ longwave) radiation, while nearly all of the
    energy emitted by Earth is _____ radiation. (p. 80)   longwave

3. Hotter objects radiate mostly _____ (shortwave/longwave) radiation, while cooler objects radiate mostly _____ radiation. (pp. 80–81)

    shortwave
    longwave

4. Objects generally show the absorption of energy with a(n) _____ (increase/ decrease) in temperature. (p. 81)

    increase

5. In the visible portion of the electromagnetic spectrum, dark-colored objects are generally better at _____ (absorbing/ reflecting) radiation than lighter colored objects. (p. 81)

    absorbing

6. In the atmosphere _____ wavelengths of visible light are the most easily scattered wavelengths. (p. 82)

    shorter (blue)

7. In general, the atmosphere is efficient in transmitting _____ (shortwave/longwave) radiation from the Sun, but not very efficient in transmitting _____ radiation from Earth's surface. (pp. 83–84)

    shortwave

    longwave

8. _____ is the transfer of heat energy by molecular collision. (p. 84)

    Conduction

9. When air rises and expands it _____ (warms/cools), while when air descends and compresses it _____. (p. 85)

    cools
    warms

10. During _____, energy is stored as latent heat, and during _____ this heat is released. (p. 86)

    evaporation
    condensation

11. About _____ percent of incoming solar radiation is reflected back to space. (pp. 86–87)

    31

12. About _____ percent of incoming solar radiation passes through the atmosphere and is absorbed by Earth's surface. (p. 87)

    45

13. Longwave radiation emitted from the surface heats the atmosphere through the_____ _____. (p. 87)

    greenhouse effect

14. Because of differences in the angle of incidence of incoming solar radiation, _____ (high/low) latitude regions of Earth receive less intense insolation overall during a year than _____ latitude regions. (p. 89)

    high

    low

15. In the high latitudes, solar radiation has a greater distance to travel through the _____ to reach the surface than in the low latitudes. (pp. 89–90)

atmosphere

16. In the winter, high latitude regions have _____ (more/fewer) hours of daylight than in summer. (p. 90)

fewer

17. In the low latitudes there is a general solar energy _____ (surplus/deficit), while in the high latitudes there is a general solar energy _____. (pp. 90–92)

surplus

deficit

18. Land heats _____ (slower/faster) and to a greater extent than water because water has a _____ (higher/lower) specific heat. (pp. 92–93)

faster
higher

19. In general, the hottest and coldest places on Earth are found in the middle of _____ (oceans/continents). (p. 93)

continents

20. The most important mechanism of heat transfer around the world is the general circulation of the _____. (p. 94)

atmosphere

21. Ocean currents in the major Northern Hemisphere ocean basins generally circulate in a _____-wise direction. (p. 95)

clock-

22. Major ocean currents along the east coasts of continents are _____ (warm/cool) and moving toward the _____ (equator/poles), while currents along the west coasts of continents are _____ and moving toward the _____. (p. 95)

warm; poles

cool; equator

23. The average lapse rate in the troposphere is a temperature decrease of _____ degrees for every 1000 meter (1000 foot) increase in altitude. (p. 98)

6.5°C/1000 m
(3.6°F/1000 ft.)

24. An _____ temperature inversion occurs when cool air at the surface flows under warm air. (p. 99)

advectional

25. In general, the surface temperature of Earth _____ (increases/decreases) moving from the equator toward the poles. (p. 100)

decreases

26. The interiors of large high latitude continents have a _____ (large/small) average annual temperature range. (p. 102)

large

27.   The 0.6°C (1.0°F) global temperature increase observed over
        the 20th century is likely the result of _____ gases released by   greenhouse
        human activity. (pp. 102–103)

SELF-TEST

1.   Most solar energy reaches Earth as:
       (a)   shortwave radiation.   (b)   longwave radiation.
       (c)   radio waves.   (d)   microwaves.

2.   Most terrestrial radiation is:
       (a)   shortwave radiation.   (b)   longwave radiation.
       (c)   radio waves.   (d)   microwaves.

3.   When electromagnetic radiation is reflected:
       (a)   the wavelengths become longer.
       (b)   the wavelengths become shorter.
       (c)   the wavelengths remain unchanged.
       (d)   the intensity of radiation increases.

4.   In Earth's atmosphere, which wavelength of light is most easily scattered?
       (a)   Visible red
       (b)   Infrared
       (c)   Visible blue
       (d)   All wavelengths are scattered equally.

5.   In the atmosphere, carbon dioxide:
       (a)   easily transmits both longwave and shortwave radiation.
       (b)   easily transmits longwave but not shortwave radiation.
       (c)   easily transmits shortwave but not longwave radiation.
       (d)   transmits neither shortwave nor longwave radiation.

6.   The vertical circulation of warm air away from the surface, which pulls in cool air from the
       sides, is called:
       (a)   convection.   (b)   conduction.
       (c)   advection.   (d)   absorption.

7.   Rising air:
     (a)   compresses and warms.   (b)   expands and warms.
     (c)   compresses and cools.   (d)   expands and cools.

8.   Descending air:
     (a)   compresses and warms.   (b)   expands and warms.
     (c)   compresses and cools.   (d)   expands and cools.

9.   "Latent heat" is:
     (a)   stored during condensation.
     (b)   stored during evaporation.
     (c)   released during evaporation.
     (d)   released from the air as pressure increases.

10. Approximately what percentage of total solar energy arriving at Earth is absorbed directly by the atmosphere before it reaches the surface?
     (a)   Less than 1%   (b)   48%
     (c)   24%   (d)   73%

11. Approximately what percentage of total solar energy arriving at Earth is reflected back out to space by the atmosphere or the surface?
     (a)   Less than 1%   (b)   31%
     (c)   66%   (d)   80%

12. The "greenhouse effect" refers to:
     (a)   the absorption of solar shortwave radiation by carbon dioxide.
     (b)   the absorption of terrestrial longwave radiation by carbon dioxide, water vapor, and particulates.
     (c)   the absorption of ultraviolet radiation by the ozone layer.
     (d)   the absorption of terrestrial longwave radiation by nitrogen and oxygen.

13. High latitude regions of Earth receive *less* total insolation during a year than equatorial latitudes because:
     (a)   the length of day is always shorter in high latitudes than at the equator.
     (b)   the Sun strikes the surface less directly (the Sun is always lower in the sky) in high latitudes.
     (c)   the atmosphere is thinner in high latitudes.
     (d)   the equator is never cloudy.

14. What is one reason that a body of water heats more slowly than land?
    (a) Sunlight cannot penetrate water.
    (b) Water has a lower specific heat than land.
    (c) Water is mobile.
    (d) Land can absorb energy deeper below the surface than water.

15. Because of the differential heating of land and water:
    (a) the coldest places on Earth are over water.
    (b) the hottest places on Earth are over water.
    (c) the hottest and coldest places on Earth are over land.
    (d) the hottest places are over land and the coldest places are over water.

16. In general, along the west coasts of continents there is an ocean current that is:
    (a) cool and moving toward the poles.
    (b) cool and moving toward the equator.
    (c) warm and moving toward the poles.
    (d) warm and moving toward the equator.

17. What can cause a temperature inversion?
    (a) the heating of the ground during a hot summer day.
    (b) high humidity during a hot summer day.
    (c) warm air moving underneath cool air.
    (d) cool air moving underneath warm air.

18. On a global temperature map, isotherms will generally run west to east:
    (a) across large midlatitude land masses during the winter.
    (b) across large midlatitude land masses during the summer.
    (c) across the oceans all year.

19. Referring to the map of average July temperatures (Figure 4-33, p. 47 of the Study Guide), why is the 60° isotherm in the Northern Hemisphere deflected toward the equator along the west coast of North America?
    (a) heating of land during summer.
    (b) cooling of land during summer.
    (c) cool ocean current.
    (d) warm ocean current.

20. Which location will tend to have the greatest average annual temperature range?
    (a) a small island on the equator.
    (b) a small island in the high latitudes.
    (c) in the middle of a continent in the high latitudes.
    (d) in the middle of a continent on the equator.

Answers to Self-Test:

1.	a	6.	a	11.	b	16.	b
2.	b	7.	d	12.	b	17.	d
3.	c	8.	a	13.	b	18.	c
4.	c	9.	b	14.	c	19.	c
5.	c	10.	c	15.	c	20.	c

HINTS FOR TEXTBOOK STUDY QUESTIONS

1.   See pages 75–76 for a discussion of these concepts.

2.   See the discussion of temperature and kinetic energy on page 76.

3.   This is an important distinction. See Figure 4-6 on page 40 of the Study Guide.

4.   This is discussed on page 80 in the textbook.

5.   These are important processes to understand. See pages 80–83.

6.   This is described on page 81.

7.   Scattering is a special type of reflection—the differences are described on pages 81–82.

8.   See Figure 4-10 (p. 82).

9.   This is an important question for you to answer. It is first discussed on page 83 in the textbook.

10.   Figures 4-14 and 4-15 (pp. 84–85) may help you distinguish between these two processes.

11.   The results of conduction in the atmosphere are first introduced on page 85.

12.   The consequences of conduction in the atmosphere are first introduced on page 85.

13.   This is another important question. See Figure 4-16 (p. 86).

14.   This question concerns latent heat—first discussed on page 86.

15.   This is another important question. Although the ultimate source of energy for the atmosphere is the Sun, consider the processes that actually heat the troposphere. Review the section "The Heating of the Atmosphere" (p. 86) if you are unsure of your answer.

16.   This term is discussed in the section "The Heating of the Atmosphere" (p. 86).

17.   Consider how and from where the troposphere is heated.

18.   Again, consider what processes are responsible for heating the troposphere.

19.   Especially consider the consequences of variations in the angle of incidence and atmospheric obstruction.

20.   Again, consider the importance of the angle of incidence, along with seasonal variations in day length.

21.   This is another important topic. The four main factors are discussed beginning on page 92 in the textbook.

22.   This topic is introduced on page 94.

23.   This is considered on page 94.

24.   See Figure 4-28 (p. 95).

25.   You must know the basic ocean current patterns. Study the "Basic Pattern" and map (Figure 4-28) on page 95 in the textbook.

26.   You should be clear on the difference between "environmental lapse rate" and "average lapse rate"—see page 98.

27.   These are defined on page 98.

28.   Both kinds of inversions develop when cold air is found below warm. See page 99 in the textbook for a description.

29.   You may want to review the section on isolines in Chapter 2.

30.   To answer this question, you'll need to consider the factors that influence global temperature patterns—see pages 99–101.

31.   Although this is shown in Figure 4-35 (p. 102), you should review the reasons for this pattern.

32.   This discussion begins on page 102.

ADDITIONAL STUDY QUESTIONS

1.   How would air movement within the troposphere be different if the lower atmosphere were directly heated by the Sun?

2.   Why is there such a large annual temperature range in the middle of continents in the high latitudes, compared with the middle of continents at the equator?

3.   Why is it mistaken to say that we must "stop the greenhouse effect" in the atmosphere?

4.   Why does variation in Earth's distance to the Sun have virtually nothing to do with the variation of temperatures experienced as the seasons change?

Hints for Additional Study Questions:

1.   Consider the role of convection in establishing wind systems.

2.   Compare the seasonal variation of heating at the equator with the seasonal variation of heating at higher latitudes.

3.   Distinguish between the natural, ongoing heating processes of the atmosphere and the potential human-produced intensification of these heating processes.

4.   Electromagnetic radiation from the Sun easily travels through the vacuum of space; heating of Earth is largely dependent upon the angle of incidence of solar radiation.

CHAPTER 5

Atmospheric Pressure and Wind

OVERVIEW

Chapter 5 focuses on the second and third elements of weather and climate: pressure and wind. The first half of the chapter describes how atmospheric pressure is measured and mapped, the factors that influence air pressure, and the wind movement associated with high and low pressure cells. The second half of the chapter focuses on the general circulation patterns of the atmosphere, with a description of the major wind and pressure systems around the world. The chapter concludes with a discussion of the most important modifications of the general circulation pattern, as well as localized wind systems and El Niño.

The material in Chapter 5 on pressure and wind is another part of our foundation for understanding the patterns of weather and climate presented in upcoming chapters. Two topics deserve special consideration. First, the wind direction patterns associated with high and low pressure cells are a key to understanding storms (discussed in Chapter 7). Second, an understanding of the general circulation pattern of the atmosphere is fundamental to both recognizing and explaining global climate patterns.

KEY CONCEPTS

THE NATURE OF ATMOSPHERIC PRESSURE (p. 107):

This section discusses the concept of air pressure, especially the idea that atmospheric pressure is an active force of air molecules exerted in all directions.

Factors Influencing Atmospheric Pressure (p. 107): This topic can be confusing at first. The complication is that atmospheric pressure, temperature, and density (how tightly air molecules are packed together) are all closely related. If one factor changes, the other two may also change. We can, however, make a few generalizations about the kinds of conditions that tend to produce either high or low pressure near the surface. The following are generalizations and not absolute laws:

1.   Ascending (rising) air tends to produce low pressure near the surface. Lows caused by strongly rising air are called "dynamic lows."

2.   Warm surface conditions tend to produce low pressure near the surface. Lows caused by warm surface conditions are called "thermal lows."

3.   Descending (subsiding) air tends to produce high pressure near the surface. Highs produced by strongly descending air are called "dynamic highs."

4.   Cold surface conditions tend to produce high pressure near the surface. Highs produced by cold surface conditions are called "thermal highs."

We will see examples of all four of these circumstances subsequently, but keep in mind that there are exceptions to these tendencies.

Mapping Pressure With Isobars (p. 109): Familiarize yourself with *isobars* (lines on a map showing equal pressure), and the terms *high*, *low*, *ridge*, and *trough*.

Figure 5-4 (p. 109) is an isobar map showing pressure measured in *millibars* (mb). For comparison, 1013.25 mb is the average sea-level pressure. Generally, 1020 mb would be relatively high pressure, while 995 mb would be relatively low pressure at the surface.

THE NATURE OF WIND (p. 110):

Direction of Movement (p. 110): Read this section carefully. It describes the three factors that determine wind direction: the *pressure gradient*, the *Coriolis effect*, and *friction*. **Figure 5-6** (shown below) shows the wind direction resulting from the balance of these factors in the Northern Hemisphere. The text focuses on the wind directions associated with high and low pressure cells, although the principles apply to wind direction in general.

Air tends to flow "down the pressure gradient" (moving as directly as possible from high to low pressure), crossing the isobars at right angles. This is shown in Figure 5-6a. But this rarely happens over any great distance because the Coriolis effect will deflect the path of this moving air to the right in the Northern Hemisphere (and to the left in the Southern Hemisphere).

Where the propelling force of the pressure gradient and the deflection of the Coriolis effect are balanced, wind will blow parallel to the isobars. This is shown in Figure 5-6b. This is the case for wind in the upper atmosphere, above about 1000 meters (3300 feet), and is known as *geostrophic wind*. The end result is that wind tends to circulate around upper elevation high or low pressure areas.

(a) Pressure Gradient Force only:

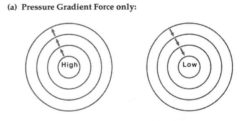

(b) Upper Atmosphere—Pressure Gradient Force and Coriolis Effect:

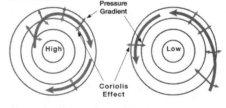

Figure 5-6: Factors influencing wind direction (Northern Hemisphere examples). (a) If the pressure gradient were the only factor influencing wind direction, wind would blow perpendicular to the isobars. (b) Where the pressure gradient and the Coriolis effect are balanced (in the upper atmosphere) winds blow parallel to the isobars, resulting in geostrophic wind. (c) Near the surface, friction slows the wind (which reduces the Coriolis effect deflection) and so wind takes an intermediate path, diverging in a clockwise direction from a high, and converging in a counterclockwise direction into a low.

(c) Lower Atmosphere—Pressure Gradient Force, Coriolis Effect, and Friction:

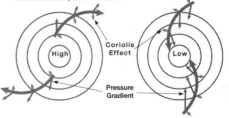

Near the surface, the friction of the air dragging against the ground slows the wind. As the wind speed is reduced, there is less Coriolis effect (the faster an object moves, the greater the Coriolis effect deflection), and so the wind takes an intermediate course (Figure 5-6c).

The animation ***Development of Wind Patterns*** will be very helpful as you learn this material.

Cyclones and Anticyclones (p. 111): You must know the wind patterns associated with low pressure cells (*cyclones*) and high pressure cells (*anticyclones*). These wind patterns become keys to understanding the general circulation patterns of the atmosphere, as well as many of the storms discussed in Chapter 7.

There are eight possible wind circulation patterns around pressure cells (Figure 5-8, p. 112). These eight patterns represent the various combinations of high or low pressure, upper or lower atmosphere, and Northern or Southern Hemisphere. If you remember the Northern Hemisphere cases, you can simply reverse the direction of circulation and you will have produced the Southern Hemisphere cases.

Northern Hemisphere patterns:

(a)   *High pressure near the surface*—diverging (blowing out of the high), clockwise.

(b)   *High pressure in the upper atmosphere*—clockwise, geostrophic (whirling around parallel to the isobars).

(c)   *Low pressure near the surface*—converging (blowing in to the low), counter-clockwise.

(d)   *Low pressure in the upper atmosphere*—counterclockwise, geostrophic.

Note also that there is a prominent, and important, vertical component of air movement in cyclones and anticyclones. Figure 5-9 (p. 114) shows that after air converges into a cyclone near the surface, it rises. On the other hand, air descends into an anticyclone and then diverges out along the surface. Review the animation ***Cyclones and Anticyclones*** to see the three-dimensional aspect of cyclones and anticyclones.

Wind Speed (p. 114). Wind speed is highest where there is a "steep" pressure gradient (where the isobars are close together), and is slowest where there is a "gentle" pressure gradient (where the isobars are far apart). The relationship between relative wind speed and pressure gradient is well illustrated in Figure 5-10 (p. 114).

THE GENERAL CIRCULATION OF THE ATMOSPHERE (p. 114):

There are just seven main components in this pattern, with the Northern and Southern Hemisphere being mirror images of each other. You need to know the approximate latitudes of each of these components. While you can simply memorize these wind and pressure systems, it is much better if you understand the reasons for them.

You can think of these components as being part of two groups. First, study the four wind and pressure systems centered on the equator (the intertropical convergence zone, the trade winds, the subtropical highs, and the westerlies).

The key to these four components is the pair of *Hadley cells* (**Figure 5-13**, shown below). These large and fairly persistent convection cells are driven by the heating in the area of greatest insolation in the equatorial latitudes. Air rises in the middle of the convection cells, creating the low pressure band and area of unstable, rainy weather known as the *intertropical convergence zone* or simply the *ITCZ*. This rising air then cools and descends at about 30° north and south latitude, creating the areas of persistent high pressure, dry weather and stability, known as the *subtropical highs* ("STH"; **Figure 5-18**, shown on the following page).

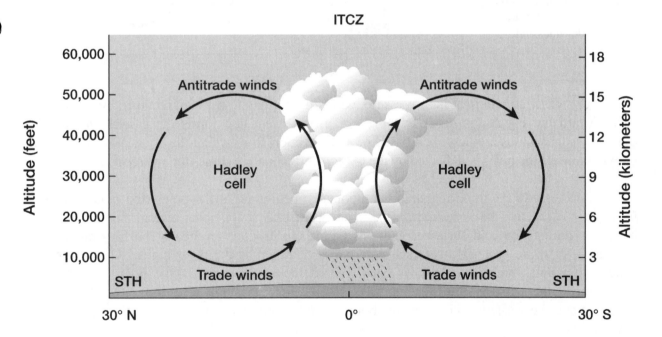

Figure 5-13: The Hadley cells. Equatorial air rises in the ITCZ to about 12 kilometers (40,000 feet) before descending in the STHs at approximately 30° north and south latitude.

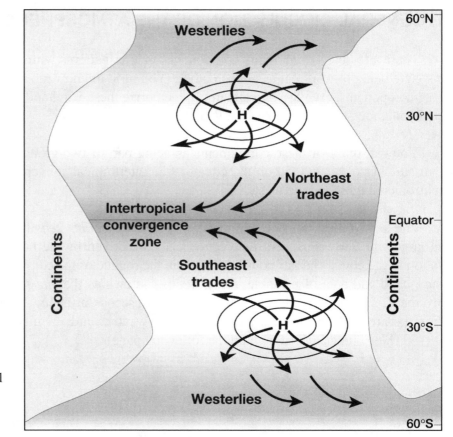

Figure 5-18: The subtropical highs are the source of the surface trade winds and westerlies.

Out of these ridges of high pressure, winds blow mainly in two directions. Wind blowing back toward the equator is deflected by the Coriolis effect and forms the easterly *trade winds* (remember that winds are described based on the direction from which the wind blows). The wind blowing toward the poles is deflected by the Coriolis effect and becomes the *westerlies*.

Next, study the three remaining components, beginning at the poles (the *polar highs*, the *polar easterlies*, and the *subpolar lows*). The north and south polar regions are areas of low insolation and so the cold surface conditions there help produce an area of fairly persistent high pressure—these are centered over each pole and are known as the polar highs. Out of the large anticyclonic polar highs, wind blows back toward the midlatitudes in the polar easterlies (the deflection of the wind by the Coriolis effect results in the easterly direction). Where the polar easterlies and the westerlies converge at about 55°–60° north and south latitude, the subpolar lows develop.

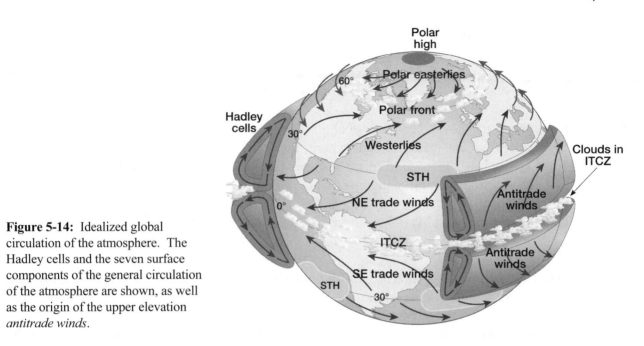

Figure 5-14: Idealized global circulation of the atmosphere. The Hadley cells and the seven surface components of the general circulation of the atmosphere are shown, as well as the origin of the upper elevation *antitrade winds*.

Figure 5-14 (shown above) shows the symmetrical pattern of these seven components, and their approximate latitudes, while a cross-section of these wind and pressure systems is shown in Figure 5-26 (p. 123). Be sure to view the animation ***Global Atmospheric Circulation*** when studying this material.

As a summary of these wind and pressure systems, note the location and key characteristics of each. Moving from the equator toward the poles we find:

1.   **ITCZ (Intertropical Convergence Zone)** (p. 121)—centered on the equator; an area of rising air; unstable conditions; frequent cloudiness and rain.

2.   **Trade Winds** (p. 117)—from near the equator to about 25° N and S; steady winds blowing from the east.

3.   **Subtropical Highs** (p. 116)—centered about 25°–30° N and S; location of descending air from the Hadley cell produces persistent high pressure areas; these 3200 kilometer (2000 mile) diameter anticyclones are best developed over the oceans (the heating and cooling of the land masses disrupts them over the continents); areas of persistent clear skies and dry conditions (see the satellite image in Figure 5-22, p. 121).

4.   **The Westerlies** (p. 121)—from about 30° to about 60° N and S; winds blowing from the west; the midlatitudes are dominated by these winds; the polar front *jet stream* is in the upper atmosphere and is the high velocity "core" of the westerlies (Figure 5-23,

p. 122); the jet stream has a strong influence on surface weather conditions, especially when it begins to meander north and south in what are called *Rossby waves* (Figure 5-25, p. 123). The animation ***The Jet Stream and Rossby Waves*** illustrates the development of Rossby Waves.

5.   **Polar Front** (p. 124)—centered at about 50° to 60° N and S; area of storminess and unsettled weather; formed where the cold polar easterlies meet the warmer westerlies. Figure 5-26 (p. 123) shows the collision of the westerlies (coming out of the subtropical high) with the polar easterlies (coming out of the polar high).

6.   **Polar Easterlies** (p. 124)—from near the poles to about 60° N and S; cold dry winds blowing out of polar highs.

7.   **Polar Highs** (p. 124)—centered over the poles; areas of cold stable air; diverging out of a fairly persistent anticyclone.

This is good time to review the animation ***Ocean Circulation Patterns***, which illustrates the relationship between global wind patterns and global ocean current patterns.

MODIFICATIONS OF THE GENERAL CIRCULATION (p. 125):

Two kinds of variations in the general pattern of wind and pressure are important for an understanding of both precipitation patterns (Chapter 6) and climate patterns (Chapter 8).

Seasonal Variations in Location (p. 126): As the latitude of the vertical rays of the Sun shifts north and south with the seasons, the location of greatest insolation also shifts (refer back to "The Annual March of the Seasons" in Chapter 1 if you need to review the reasons for this shift). As a consequence, the latitude of wind and pressure systems (which are set up by the heating from the Sun) shift to the north in the Northern Hemisphere summer, and to the south in the Northern Hemisphere winter.

The wind and pressure systems in the tropics and subtropics tend to shift more than wind and pressure systems in the high latitudes. This shift is clearly visible over the Atlantic Ocean in Figure 5-19 (p. 120), showing the trade winds in January and July.

The shifts of the ITCZ and subtropical highs have special significance in patterns of climate. The ITCZ brings rain into areas, while the STH brings dry conditions (Figure 5-30, p. 126, shows the maximum northerly and southerly shifts of the ITCZ). You should view the animation ***Seasonal Pressure and Precipitation Patterns*** several times during your study of the atmosphere—first when you study seasonal shifts of the wind and pressure systems here in Chapter 5, and again when you study global precipitation patterns in Chapter 6.

Monsoons (p. 126): *Monsoons* represent major deviations in the general circulation pattern in some parts of the world. These seasonal wind reversals significantly influence precipitation patterns along the coastlines in some low latitude regions, such as South Asia. Generally, the onshore flow in summer brings rain, while the offshore flow in winter brings dry conditions (Figure 5-33, p. 128). Keep these regions in mind when we discuss precipitation patterns in the next chapter.

LOCALIZED WIND SYSTEMS (p. 128):

Notice the role of heating and cooling of land in producing both *Sea and Land Breezes* (p. 128), and *Valley and Mountain Breezes* (p. 130). As land heats during the day it creates warm, rising air and low pressure over land, while the cooling of land at night tends to create high pressure.

EL NIÑO–SOUTHERN OSCILLATION (p. 131):

El Niño is a periodic tropical and subtropical phenomenon that occasionally influences global weather. Figure 5-39a (p. 133) shows the equatorial Pacific Ocean and the normal surface ocean current that is pushed by the trade winds from east to west. During El Niño years the trade winds diminish (or even reverse direction). This reduces the *upwelling* of cold ocean water off the west coast of South America (Figure 5-39b) and leads to much warmer surface water than usual. The atmospheric and oceanic changes associated with El Niño are often tied to heavy precipitation in some parts of the world, and drought in others (Figure 5-41, p. 136). *La Niña* refers to a circumstance when the ocean conditions are the opposite of El Niño—much cooler water than usual off the west coast of South America.

See the animation *El Niño* for a more detailed look at the patterns associated with this phenomenon.

PROGRESSIVE CONTENT REVIEW

1. With increasing altitude, atmospheric pressure _____ decreases (increases/decreases). (p. 108)

2. Very warm surface conditions or strongly rising air are most
    likely to produce _____ (high/low) pressure near the surface,   low
    while very cold surface conditions or strongly descending air
    are most likely to produce _____ (high/low) pressure near   high
    the surface. (p. 109)

3. An _____ is a line on a map that connects points of equal   isobar
    pressure. (p. 109)

4. A parcel of air will tend to move from _____ (low/high)   high
    pressure toward _____ pressure. (p. 110)   low

5. The Coriolis effect will deflect the path of wind to the _____   right
    the Northern Hemisphere, and to the _____ in the Southern   left
    Hemisphere. (p. 110)

6. Upper elevation wind moving parallel to the isobars is known
    as _____ wind. (pp. 110–111)   geostrophic

7. In the lowest 1000 meters (3300 feet) of the atmosphere, in
    addition to the pressure gradient and Coriolis effect, _____   friction
    influences wind direction. (p. 111)

8. A high pressure center is known as an _____ and a low   anticyclone
    pressure center as a _____. (p. 112)   cyclone

9. The wind pattern of a cyclone near the surface in the
    Northern Hemisphere will be _____ (converging/diverging)   converging
    in a _____-wise direction. (p. 112).   counterclock-

10. The wind pattern of an upper atmosphere anticyclone in the
    Southern Hemisphere will be _____ in a _____-wise   geostrophic; counter-
    direction. (p. 112)   clock-

11. The vertical component of air movement is _____ (rising/   rising
    descending) within cyclones and _____ within anticyclones.   descending
    (p. 114)

12. Wind speed will be greatest where the pressure gradient is
    _____ (gentle/steep). (p. 114)   steep

13. As a generalization, wind speed tends to _____ (decrease/ increase) at higher elevations. (p. 114)

increase

14. The _____ _____ are large convection cells centered in the area of the equator. (p. 115)

Hadley cells

15. The _____ are pressure systems usually found at about 30° north and south latitude. (pp. 116-117)

STH (subtropical highs)

16. The vertical movement of air associated with the subtropical highs is _____ air. (p. 117)

descending (subsiding)

17. The weather associated with the subtropical highs is usually _____. (p. 117)

sunny/clear/dry

18. The _____ _____ originate from the wind diverging from the subtropical highs moving back toward the equator. (pp. 117– 118)

trade winds

19. The trade winds blow predominantly from the _____ (west/east). (p. 118)

east

20. The intertropical convergence zone (ITCZ) is a region of generally _____ pressure and rising air. (p. 121)

low

21. The weather in the ITCZ typically includes _____. (p. 121)

thunderstorms/cloudy/ rainy conditions

22. The _____ originate from the wind diverging from the subtropical highs moving toward the poles. (p. 121)

westerlies

23. The polar front jet stream of the westerlies is typically found at an elevation of about _____ kilometers (feet) and is a zone of _____ (low/high) speed winds. (p. 122)

10 km (35,000')
high

24. The wandering path of the jet stream is reflected in the _____ waves. (p. 122)

Rossby

25. Over both poles, there is a persistent cell of _____ pressure known as the _____ _____. (p. 124)

high
polar high

26.   The polar easterlies tend to be cold and _____ (wet/dry).   dry
(p. 124)

27.   The polar front represents the boundary between the cold
winds of the _____ _____ and the relatively warmer winds of   polar easterlies
the _____. (p. 124)   westerlies

28.   During the Northern Hemisphere summer, global wind and
pressure systems will shift somewhat to the _____. (p. 126)   north

29.   The heavy rains of the South Asian monsoon are associated
with the _____ (onshore/offshore) wind flow during the   onshore
_____ season. (p. 126)   summer

30.   During the day, wind in coastal areas tends to blow _____   onshore
(onshore/offshore). (p. 128).

31.   _____ winds develop in cold, high elevation areas when   Katabatic
dense air descends rapidly. (p. 130)

32.   During an El Niño, ocean water along the west coast of South
America is _____ (cooler/warmer) than usual, while during a   warmer
La Niña, the water is _____ (cooler/warmer) than usual. (pp.   cooler
133–134)

SELF-TEST

1.   As altitude increases, pressure:
     (a)   decreases.
     (b)   increases.
     (c)   remains the same.

2.   A "ridge" is an area of:
     (a)   low pressure.
     (b)   high pressure.
     (c)   rainy weather.
     (d)   rising air.

3. In the Northern Hemisphere, the wind pattern associated with an upper atmosphere low pressure cell will be:
   (a) divergent, clockwise.
   (b) convergent, counterclockwise.
   (c) geostrophic, clockwise.
   (d) geostrophic, counterclockwise.

4. In the Southern Hemisphere, the wind pattern associated with a surface low pressure area will be:
   (a) divergent, clockwise.
   (b) convergent, clockwise.
   (c) convergent, counterclockwise.
   (d) geostrophic, counterclockwise.

5. In the Northern Hemisphere, air:
   (a) descends into a surface anticyclone, then diverges clockwise.
   (b) descends into a surface anticyclone, then diverges counterclockwise
   (c) converges clockwise into a surface anticyclone, then rises.
   (d) converges counterclockwise into a surface anticyclone, then rises.

6. The subtropical highs are areas of:
   (a) descending air.
   (b) rising air.
   (c) frequent cloudiness and rain.
   (d) strong horizontal wind flow.

7. The ITCZ is characterized by:
   (a) strong horizontal wind flow.
   (b) frequent cloudiness and rain.
   (c) clear, sunny weather.
   (d) descending air.

8. The trade winds:
   (a) are found between 35° and 65° north and south latitude.
   (b) generally blow from west to east.
   (c) generally blow from east to west.
   (d) are not very steady or predictable.

9.   The westerlies:
      (a)   generally diverge out of the subtropical highs.
      (b)   generally blow from east to west.
      (c)   are found between the equator and 25° north and south latitude.
      (d)   originate from the polar high.

10.   The polar front jet stream of the westerlies:
      (a)   is typically found at an elevation of 900 meters (3000 feet).
      (b)   rarely meanders in the north-south direction.
      (c)   has little influence on the surface weather patterns.
      (d)   is the high elevation, high velocity core of the westerlies.

11.   Over the polar regions, there is typically:
      (a)   a persistent cyclone.
      (b)   a persistent anticyclone.
      (c)   air rising all year.
      (d)   air rising during the winter.

12.   The polar easterlies originate from:
      (a)   the subtropical high.
      (b)   the ITCZ.
      (c)   the polar highs.
      (d)   the polar front.

13.   The polar front:
      (a)   is formed where the westerlies collide with the polar easterlies.
      (b)   is formed where the trade winds collide with the westerlies.
      (c)   is a region of persistently clear and sunny weather.
      (d)   is a region of descending air.

14.   Between December and June, the subtropical highs:
      (a)   shift to the western sides of the major ocean basins.
      (b)   shift somewhat to the north.
      (c)   shift somewhat to the south.
      (d)   lose strength.

15.   During the summer, the South Asian monsoon:
      (a)   brings dry conditions and winds blowing off the ocean.
      (b)   brings dry conditions and winds blowing off the continent.
      (c)   brings rainy conditions and winds blowing off the ocean.
      (d)   brings rainy conditions and winds blowing off the continent.

16. During the winter, the East Asian monsoon:
    (a) brings dry conditions and winds blowing off the ocean.
    (b) brings dry conditions and winds blowing off the continent.
    (c) brings rainy conditions and winds blowing off the ocean.
    (d) brings rainy conditions and winds blowing off the continent.

17. Why is it common for wind to blow from the ocean toward the land during a sunny day?
    (a) The ocean heats quickly, creating low pressure.
    (b) The ocean cools quickly, creating low pressure.
    (c) The land heat up quickly, creating low pressure.
    (d) The land heats up quickly, creating high pressure.

18. El Niño refers to:
    (a) heavy rain occurring in the midlatitudes every few years.
    (b) the cooling of west coast waters during the summer.
    (c) the occasional warming of the ocean off the west coast of South America, near the equator.
    (d) droughts that occur in tropical rainforests.

Answers to Self-Test:

1.	a	6.	a	11.	b	16.	b
2.	b	7.	b	12.	c	17.	c
3.	d	8.	c	13.	a	18.	c
4.	b	9.	a	14.	b		
5.	a	10.	d	15.	c		

HINTS FOR TEXTBOOK STUDY QUESTIONS

1. See Figure 5-3 (p. 108).

2. Review "Factors Influencing Atmospheric Pressure" on page 107 of the textbook.

3. Again, review "Factors Influencing Atmospheric Pressure" on page 107 of the textbook.

4.   The generalizations made on page 109 of the textbook should be helpful here.

5.   Distinguish between the *units* of measure and the isolines shown on a map. These terms are defined in the section "Mapping Pressure with Isobars" (p. 109).

6.   These terms are also discussed in "Mapping Pressure with Isobars" (p. 109).

7.   This is very important. If you're not sure, review "The Nature of Wind" beginning on page 110 in the textbook. Also review the animation ***Development of Wind Patterns***.

8.   In "The Nature of Wind" section, review the balance between the pressure gradient and the Coriolis effect in the upper atmosphere and near the surface. Also see Figure 5-6 on page 59 of the Study Guide. Also review the animation ***Development of Wind Patterns***.

9.   You must know these basic patterns. See Figure 5-8 on page 112 in the textbook.

10.   Consider which wind direction influencing factor is different in the Northern Hemisphere and in the Southern Hemisphere.

11.   Again, review the "The Nature of Wind" beginning on page 110 in the textbook.

12.   See Figure 5-9 on page 114 of the textbook if you're not sure.

13.   Figure 5-10 (p. 114) may help.

14.   Table 5-1 (p. 114) shows the pattern; read the associated text as well.

15.   Part of the answer to this is straight forward: consider what would *slow* the winds near the surface. There are other factors as well.

16.   See Figure 5-14 (on page 63 of the Study Guide) and review the textbook on pages 115–116. Also review the animation ***Global Atmospheric Circulation***.

17.   Figure 5-18 (on page 62 of the Study Guide) shows the general location of these components.

18.   This is discussed in the textbook beginning on page 116.

19.   This question is concerned with the total area influenced by the trades. Look at a globe.

20.   A good discussion of jet streams (along with some nice diagrams) begins on page 122 in the textbook.

21. See Figure 5-25 (p. 123).

22. These components are shown in Figure 5-14 (on page 63 of the Study Guide), and discussed in the textbook on page 124.

23. Wind direction is not the only difference. See Figure 5-14 (on page 63 of the Study Guide).

24. Figure 5-30 and the associated text on page 126 is a good starting point.

25. Figure 5-33 (p. 128) illustrates the basics of monsoons, but you should also review the associated text as well.

26. See Figure 5-35 (p. 129).

27. Compare Figure 5-35 (p. 129) with Figure 5-36 (p. 130).

28. Review the "Normal Pattern" in the Pacific Ocean, beginning on page 132.

29. Figure 5-39 (p. 133) illustrates some of these differences.

ADDITIONAL STUDY QUESTIONS

1. In what ways are the "Hadley cells" responsible for four of the major wind and pressure systems of the general circulation pattern of the atmosphere?

2. Suggest one reason why the subtropical highs are most persistent over the ocean near the west coasts of continents?

3. Why do most winter storms move across the United States from west to east?

4. Using the map showing the position of the trade winds (Figure 5-19, p. 120) explain the pattern shown: (a) Why are the trade winds best developed over the ocean? (b) What accounts for the shifts in location from January to July?

5. Why are localized wind systems usually associated with inland and coastal areas but not with the middle of ocean basins?

Hints for Additional Study Questions:

1.   See Figures 5-13, 5-14 and 5-18 (on pages 61–63 of the Study Guide).

2.   Consider the pattern of ocean currents.

3.   Notice which wind system dominates the midlatitudes.

4.   Consider both land/sea differences in heating, and changing Earth–Sun relations throughout the year.

5.   Note the importance of topography, or pressure changes associated with the heating and cooling of land, in the formation of each of the localized wind systems.

CHAPTER 6

Atmospheric Moisture

OVERVIEW

Chapter 6 discusses the final element of weather and climate: moisture in the atmosphere. Although this chapter is ultimately aimed at explaining precipitation patterns, much of Chapter 6 focuses on water as a gas in the atmosphere. This foundation is necessary since an understanding of the behavior of water vapor in the atmosphere is fundamental to an understanding of the processes that can lead to condensation, cloud formation and precipitation.

Several topics deserve special attention. First, the concept of relative humidity—particularly the relationship between relative humidity and temperature—is crucial to an understanding of cloud formation and precipitation. Second, the adiabatic process in the atmosphere, especially the fact that rising air cools adiabatically, is perhaps the most important concept of the chapter. As you will see, adiabatic temperature changes strongly influence the stability of the air, the types of clouds that form, and the mechanisms that produce clouds and rain. Finally, the reasons behind worldwide precipitation patterns (shown in Figure 6-34, pp. 170–171) must be grasped. A basic understanding of global precipitation patterns is needed before patterns of climate (Chapter 8) can be understood.

KEY CONCEPTS

THE NATURE OF WATER: COMMONPLACE BUT UNIQUE (p. 141):

The Water Molecule (p. 142): Many of the special properties of water are related to the characteristics of the water molecule itself. Notice in Figures 6-2 and 6-3 (p. 142) that water molecules can be attracted to each other through *hydrogen bonds*, and such hydrogen bonding explains a number of special properties of water, such as:

- Water expands when it freezes to form ice. We will see in Chapter 15 that this property of water allows it to become a powerful force in the breakdown, or *weathering*, of rock.
- Water has high *surface tension* (it easily sticks to itself); it is able to move upward through narrow pore spaces or through narrow tubes. This *capillary action* (or *capillarity*) means that water can move up and down through soil, as well as up through plant roots and stems.

PHASE CHANGES OF WATER (p. 143):

This section explains the important concept of *latent heat*. As you can see in Figure 6-6 (p. 145), when water changes state from ice to liquid and from liquid to gas, energy must be added to the water that does not increase its temperature—this heat energy is known as latent heat. When water changes back from gas to liquid and from liquid to ice, this energy must be released. This is why evaporation is a cooling process (latent heat is "stored" in water vapor during evaporation) and condensation is a warming process (latent heat is "released" during condensation).

The animation ***Phase Changes of Water*** illustrates the changes in temperature and the exchange of latent heat involved with changes of state between solid, liquid, and gas.

EVAPORATION (p. 146):

The source of moisture for clouds and rain is the *water vapor* that has evaporated from the surface. Note that the rate of evaporation depends on a number of factors. In general, the rate of evaporation will be relatively low when the temperature is low, when the air is already close to saturation, or when the air is still. The rate of evaporation will be greater when the temperature is high, when the air is relatively dry, or when it is windy.

MEASURES OF HUMIDITY (p. 149):

Four measures of the amount of water vapor in the air (the "humidity") are discussed here. Three of these measures (*absolute humidity*, *specific humidity*, and *vapor pressure*) describe the actual amount of water vapor in the air, while the fourth (*relative humidity*) describes how close the air is to being saturated with water vapor.

Absolute Humidity (p. 149): Absolute humidity describes the actual amount of water vapor in the air, expressed as the mass (the "weight") of water vapor for a given volume of air. Absolute humidity is usually expressed in grams of water vapor per cubic meter of air (g/m^3).

Specific Humidity (p. 149): Like absolute humidity, specific humidity describes the actual amount of water vapor in the air. However, with specific humidity the amount of water vapor in the air is expressed as the mass of water vapor for a given mass of air. Specific humidity is usually expressed in grams of water vapor per kilogram of air (g/kg).

Vapor Pressure (p. 149): Vapor pressure describes the actual amount of water vapor in the air in terms of the contribution of water vapor to the total pressure of the air.

These three different measures of actual water vapor content of the air are useful to meteorologists under different circumstances. For example, when monitoring changes within a rising parcel of air specific humidity is usually used—as a parcel of air rises it expands, and with an increase in volume the absolute humidity changes but the specific humidity does not.

Relative Humidity (p. 149): Relative humidity does not describe the actual amount of water vapor in the air. Rather, it describes how close the air is to being saturated with water vapor. The relative humidity is a ratio (expressed as a percentage) that compares the actual amount of water vapor in the air (the absolute humidity, specific humidity, or vapor pressure) to the water vapor *capacity* of the air. The capacity is the maximum amount of water vapor that could be in the air at a given temperature.

Relative humidity is calculated with a simple formula:

$$RH = \frac{\text{Actual Water Vapor in Air}}{\text{Capacity}} \times 100$$

For example, if the specific humidity of a parcel of air is 10 g/kg and the capacity of the parcel is 20 g/kg, the relative humidity is:

$$\frac{10 \text{ g/kg}}{20 \text{ g/kg}} \times 100 = 50\% \text{ RH}$$

The key to understanding relative humidity is recognizing the relationship between temperature and the water vapor capacity of the air. Warm air has a higher water vapor capacity than cold air (see Figures 6-9 and 6-10, pp. 149–150). Because of this, the relative humidity of a parcel of air will change when the temperature changes. For example, when the temperature of air decreases, so does its water vapor capacity. This means that as temperature decreases, relative humidity increases. If a parcel of air is cooled enough, its water vapor capacity will match its actual water vapor content and the air will be saturated (100% relative humidity). At this point, condensation and cloud formation are possible.

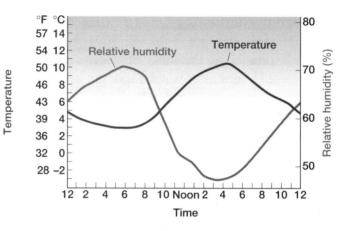

Figure 6-11: Typically there is an inverse relationship between temperature and relative humidity. As the temperature increases toward midafternoon, the relative humidity decreases. As the temperature decreases after midafternoon, the relative humidity increases. Thus, relative humidity tends to be lowest in midafternoon and highest just before dawn.

The relationship between temperature and relative humidity is well illustrated in **Figure 6-11** (shown above). This chart shows the inverse relationship between temperature and relative humidity during a typical day. This pattern is generally true even though the absolute humidity also may change during the course of a day.

The temperature-relative humidity relationship is one of the most important in our study of weather. As we will see, by far the most common way that air becomes saturated is by a decrease in temperature.

Dew Point Temperature (p. 151): The *dew point temperature* refers to the temperature to which a parcel of air must cool in order to reach 100% relative humidity.

CONDENSATION (p. 151):

Condensation is a rather complex process. It takes a great deal of condensation to produce water drops large enough to become visible as clouds, let alone to fall as precipitation. Note also that microscopic particulates, known as *condensation nuclei*, must be present in order for condensation to take place.

ADIABATIC PROCESSES (p. 153):

This is a crucial section. Adiabatic cooling and warming were mentioned in Chapter 4 in the discussion of basic heating and cooling processes. The expansive cooling of rising air (adiabatic cooling) and the compressive warming of descending air (adiabatic warming) are keys to the formation of clouds and precipitation, as well as the development of arid regions of the world.

We said earlier that the most common way that air reaches 100% relative humidity is by cooling. We now add an important addendum to this. By far, the most common way that air is cooled enough to make clouds and rain is through adiabatic cooling—the cooling that takes place as air rises.

Before a rising parcel of air is saturated, it will cool at the *dry adiabatic rate* (DAR, or the *dry adiabatic lapse rate*) of about 10°C per 1000 meters (5.5°F per 1000 feet). As air rises it cools, and so its relative humidity increases (because cooling decreases the water vapor capacity of air). At some point, this parcel of air will have cooled enough to reach the dew point. The elevation at which the dew point temperature is reached is called the *lifting condensation level*, and at this point, condensation and cloud formation may begin. If a parcel of air continues to rise as condensation takes place, the air will continue to cool adiabatically, but it will cool more slowly than before. Saturated air (in which condensation is taking place) cools at the *saturated adiabatic rate* (SAR, or *saturated adiabatic lapse rate*) of about 6°C per 1000 meters (3.3°F per 1000 feet), although the SAR can vary considerably from this.

It is important to understand the reason that rising saturated air cools more slowly than rising unsaturated air. Remember from Chapter 4 and earlier in this chapter that evaporation is a cooling process. When water evaporates (changes from liquid to gas), latent heat is stored, and this in effect cools the air. When water vapor condenses back to liquid, this latent heat is released and the air is warmed. So, as saturated air rises, it cools adiabatically but the latent heat being released counteracts some of this cooling. Adiabatic temperature changes are illustrated in the animation ***Adiabatic Processes and Atmospheric Stability***.

Note that descending air warms adiabatically. As descending air begins to warm, its water vapor capacity increases and so descending saturated air will quickly become unsaturated. For this reason, descending air cannot make clouds—this explains the dry conditions associated with the descending air of anticyclones such as the subtropical highs discussed in Chapter 5. See **Figure 6-16** (shown on the following page) for an illustration of the adiabatic temperature changes associated with a hypothetical parcel of air passing up and over a mountain range.

CLOUDS (p. 155):

Figure 6-18 (p. 157) shows the 10 principal types of clouds. Note that these cloud types reflect two sets of variables: characteristic elevations (or *cloud families*) and the three general shapes ("forms") of clouds—*cirriform*, *stratiform*, and *cumuliform*.

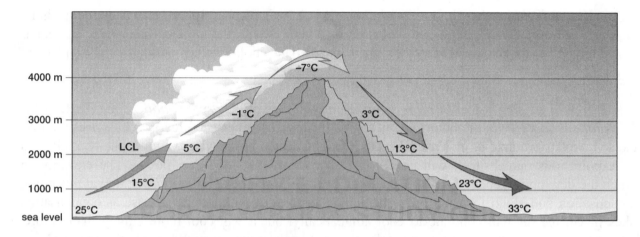

Figure 6-16: Temperature changes in a hypothetical parcel of air passing over a 4000 meter (13,100 foot) high mountain (assuming no evaporation as the air descends down the lee side of the mountain). The lifting condensation level (LCL) of the parcel is 2000 meters, the dry adiabatic rate is 10°C/1000 m and the saturated adiabatic rate is 6°C/1000 m. Notice that because of the release of latent heat during condensation on the windward side of the mountain, by the time the air has descended back down to sea level on the leeward side, it is warmer than before it started up the windward side.

THE BUOYANCY OF AIR (p. 159):

Atmospheric Stability (p. 159): The stability of air is another important concept in this chapter. Understanding the basics of stability is easy. In short, *unstable air* will rise on its own, whereas *stable air* will not. The key to stability is temperature (although other factors influence stability as well). If a parcel of air is warmer than the surrounding air, it will be unstable and will rise on its own. If a parcel of air is the same temperature (or cooler) than the surrounding air, it will be stable and will not rise on its own—stable air will only rise if it is forced.

In order to more fully explain stability, the textbook then proceeds with a more involved description. First, we must distinguish between the *environmental lapse rate* presented in Chapter 4 and the "adiabatic" rates presented here. The environmental lapse rate reflects the temperature of the atmosphere at different altitudes—sometimes called the *vertical temperature gradient*. The environmental lapse rate averages about 6.5°C per 1000 meters (3.6°F per 1000 feet). This means that, on average, as we move up through the troposphere, the temperature will be about 6.5°C cooler for every 1000 meters (3.6°F cooler for each 1000 feet) we climb. However, from day to day and from place to place, the actual vertical temperature gradient frequently deviates from this average rate.

The dry adiabatic rate (DAR) and the saturated adiabatic rate (SAR) reflect the temperature change within a specific parcel of moving air. The distinction between the average lapse rate and the adiabatic rates is illustrated in Figure 6-15 (p. 154). In the context of stability, we can think of the environmental lapse rate as showing the temperature of the surrounding air through which a parcel of air is moving and changing temperature adiabatically (following the DAR or SAR). This is illustrated in **Figure 6-25b** (shown below). The column of temperatures at the far left in the diagram shows the vertical temperature gradient of the atmosphere (in this hypothetical example, 12°C/km). The arrows and oval bubbles with temperatures over the buildings show a rising parcel of air. The rising parcel of air cools following the DAR until the lifting condensation level is reached at 2000 meters; the parcel then cools following the SAR.

If, at a given altitude, a parcel of air is warmer than that of the surrounding air, the parcel will be unstable and rise on its own. However, if at a given altitude the parcel of air is cooler than the surrounding air, the parcel will be stable. In Figure 6-25b, notice that the parcel of rising air is *unstable*—at every altitude shown, the rising parcel of air is warmer than the surrounding air, and so will rise on its own. These relationships are also shown in graph form in Figure 6-25b to the right of the diagram.

See page 163 in the text for two other related diagrams. Figure 6-25a shows stable conditions: at every altitude the rising parcel of air is cooler than the surrounding air. Figure 6-25c shows the third possibility of *conditionally unstable*. Rising air may be stable near the surface, but if it is forced to rise, after condensation begins to take place and latent heat is released, a parcel of air may become unstable.

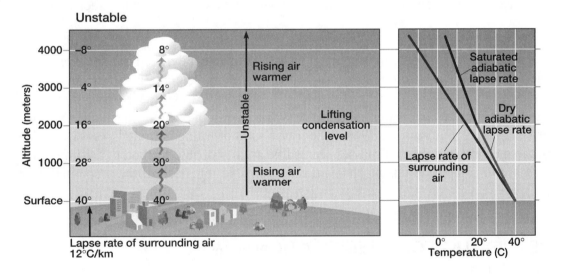

Figure 6-25b: The relationship between the lapse rate of the surrounding air (in this example, 12°C/1000 m.) and the adiabatic rates followed by a rising parcel of air. The parcel of rising air cools first at the DAR (10°C/1000 m) until the lifting condensation level is reached. Above the lifting condensation level, the rising parcel of air cools at the SAR (6°C/1000 m). At every altitude, the temperature of the rising parcel of air is higher than the temperature of the surrounding air (shown on the far left of the diagram), so the parcel of air is unstable and will rise on its own.

81

The animation *Adiabatic Processes and Atmospheric Stability* is worth reviewing. It allows you to observe changes in atmospheric stability that result from differences in the lapse rate of the surrounding air.

Visual Determination of Stability (p. 162): Note that the types of clouds present often reflect the stability of the atmosphere. Puffy, cumuliform clouds generally indicate unstable conditions, while flat layers of stratiform clouds generally indicate stable conditions.

PRECIPITATION (p. 162):

Hail (p. 166): Note that *hail* forms under conditions of instability. Unstable, rising air helps produce the strong updrafts necessary to carry water droplets high into the upper parts of a *cumulonimbus cloud* where *supercooled* water droplets are present (Figure 6-31, p. 166).

ATMOSPHERIC LIFTING AND PRECIPITATION (p. 167):

The adiabatic cooling that results when air rises is the main process that leads to the formation of most clouds and precipitation (see Figure 6-32, p. 167). Two mechanisms that can initiate this uplift have already been mentioned: *convective lifting* caused by warm (unstable) air rising from the surface, and *convergent lifting*, when opposing winds come together, such as in the ITCZ.

Two other mechanisms of uplift are important as well. Air may be forced to rise when it hits a mountain barrier. This *orographic lifting* tends to produce distinct precipitation patterns that relate to the topography (see Figure 6-33, p. 168). Because of orographic lifting, the windward sides of mountains tend to be wetter than the leeward sides—we will see examples of this in Chapter 8, when we look at deserts that develop in *rain shadows*. The fourth kind of lifting is frontal. *Frontal lifting* that results from the meeting of unlike air masses seems like an improbable method of cooling much air, but as we will see in Chapter 7, this mechanism is responsible for much of the precipitation in the midlatitudes.

GLOBAL DISTRIBUTION OF PRECIPITATION (p. 169):

It is worth spending some time looking at the series of maps in this section. The map showing average annual precipitation (Figure 6-34, pp. 170–171) reflects the overall distribution of precipitation around the world. Relate the controls of weather and climate to the areas of the world that receive high annual precipitation and the areas that receive low annual precipitation. The most important controls are:

(a)   The dominant wind and pressure systems: Notice that high amounts of precipitation are generally found in the latitudes dominated by the ITCZ (approximately 10° north to 10° south latitude), while dry conditions prevail along the west coasts of continents next to the subtropical highs (about 25°–30° north and south latitude).

(b)   Ocean currents: Ocean currents may either stabilize the air with cool water (along many west coasts), or increase the moisture availability and instability with warm water (along many east coasts).

(c)   Mountain barriers: Mountain ranges typically have a wet windward side and a dry leeward side (remember from Chapter 5 that the wind generally blows from the west in the midlatitudes and from the east in tropical latitudes.

(d)   Variations in sources of moisture: This is conspicuous in the relatively dry areas in the interiors of mid- and high-latitude continents.

Seasonal variations in precipitation are shown in the pair of world maps (Figure 6-35, p. 172) and the pair of U.S. maps (Figure 6-36, p. 173). For example, in the world maps, the northward shift of the ITCZ in July brings summer rain to areas just north of the equator, while the southward shift of the ITCZ in January brings summer rain to areas just south of the equator. These seasonal shifts are well illustrated in the animation *Seasonal Pressure and Precipitation Patterns*.

Precipitation Variability (p. 171): *Precipitation variability* refers to the usual deviation from average precipitation from year to year. For example, a town in an arid region might on average receive 25 centimeters (10 inches) of rain per year. However, it is very unlikely that this town will receive exactly 25 centimeters of rain every year. The town might receive 35 centimeters (13 inches) in one year, but just 15 centimeters (6 inches) the next, although the long-term average is still 25 centimeters (10 inches). Precipitation variability is the expected departure from average precipitation in any given year, expressed as a percentage. (In our example, 35 centimeters [13 inches] would represent a 40% departure from the average of 25 centimeters [10 inches]).

Notice on the precipitation variability map (Figure 6-37, p. 174) that the areas of the world with the greatest precipitation variability are the desert regions, while the wet regions of the tropics have very low variability.

ACID RAIN (p. 172):

Note the relationship between the occurrence of acid rain and the release of pollutants discussed in the section, "Air Pollution," in Chapter 3 (p. 64).

PROGRESSIVE CONTENT REVIEW

1.   A _____ _____ forms because the negatively charged oxygen side of one water molecule is attracted to the positively charged hydrogen side of another water molecule. (p. 142)

hydrogen bond

2.   When water freezes, its volume _____ (increases/decreases). (p. 143)

increases

3.   _____ refers to the ability of water to climb upward in narrow openings. (p. 143)

Capillarity

4.   Water has a _____ (high/low) specific heat. (p. 143)

high

5.   Water vapor can be converted directly to ice by the process of _____ (p. 144)

sublimation

6.   The energy stored by evaporating water molecules is known as the _____ _____ of vaporization. Because of this, evaporation is a _____ (warming/cooling) process. (pp. 144–145)

latent heat
cooling

7.   The _____ cycle refers to the unending transfer of water between the atmosphere, oceans, and land masses. (p. 146)

hydrologic

8.   The pressure exerted by water vapor in the air is called the _____ _____. The higher the temperature of the air, the _____ (lower/ higher) the maximum vapor pressure. (p. 146)

vapor pressure
higher

9.   In addition to temperature, the degree of _____ influences the rate of evaporation. (p. 147)

windiness

10. _____ is the process of water vapor entering the air from plants. Collectively, _____ is the transfer of moisture from the land areas (including plants) to the atmosphere. (p. 147)

Transpiration
evapotranspiration

11. Absolute humidity is expressed as the _____ of water vapor in a given _____ of air. (p. 149)

mass ("amount")
volume

12. Specific humidity is expressed as the _____ of water vapor in a given _____ of air. (p. 149)

mass
mass

13. _____ humidity is the ratio of the actual amount of water vapor in the air, to the amount of water vapor that would be in saturated air at that temperature. (pp. 149–150)

Relative

14. The water vapor capacity of air will change if the _____ changes. (pp. 149–150)

temperature

15. When the temperature decreases, the water vapor capacity of air will _____ (increase/decrease), and so the relative humidity will _____. (p. 150)

decrease
increase

16. The dew point temperature is the _____ at which a parcel of air becomes saturated. (p. 151)

temperature

17. The "sensible temperature" will seem high when the air temperature is high and the relative humidity is _____. (p. 151)

high

18. Condensation cannot take place in saturated air unless _____ _____ are present. (p. 153)

condensation
nuclei

19. Supercooled water is still _____ at temperatures below freezing. (p. 153)

liquid

20. Rising unsaturated air will cool at approximately _____ degrees per 1000 meters (1000 feet). (p. 153)

10°C/1000 m
(5.5°F/1000')

21. The lifting condensation level is the _____ at which a rising parcel of air becomes saturated. (p. 153)

altitude

22. Rising saturated air will cool adiabatically at approximately _____ degrees per 1000 meters (1000 feet). (p. 153)

6°C/1000 m
(3.3°F/1000')

23. Rising saturated air cools at a slower rate than rising unsaturated air because _____ _____ is being released during condensation. (p. 153)

latent heat

24. Descending air generally warms at the _____ (saturated/dry) adiabatic rate. (pp. 153–154)

dry

25.   _____ clouds are thin, wispy clouds composed of ice crystals and are found at high elevations. (p. 155)   Cirriform

26.   _____ clouds are massive, puffy, and often have flat bottoms. (p. 155)   Cumuliform

27.   Advection fog forms when warm, moist air passes over a _____ (warm/cool) surface. (p. 158)   cool

28.   Air is considered _____ if it rises on its own. When a parcel of air is heated so that it is warmer than the surrounding air, it will be _____. (p. 161)   unstable

unstable

29.   The presence of _____ clouds usually indicates unstable conditions, while the presence of _____ clouds usually indicates fairly stable conditions. (p. 162)   cumuliform

stratiform

30.   _____ is the type of precipitation produced when water vapor is converted directly to ice. (pp. 165–166)   Snow

31.   _____ lifting and precipitation involves the spontaneous uplift of warm air from the surface. (p. 167)   Convective

32.   Air that is forced to rise over a topographic barrier can produce _____ precipitation. The dry, _____ (windward/ leeward) side of a mountain range is called a _____ _____. (p. 168)   orographic; leeward

rain shadow

33.   _____ lifting and precipitation can occur when unlike air masses meet. (pp. 168–169)   Frontal

34.   The areas dominated by the subtropical highs most of the year tend to have _____ (high/low) amounts of precipitation. (p. 169)   low

35.   The _____ (summer/winter) is the time of maximum precipitation for most of the world. (p. 171)   summer

36.   Regions of high average annual precipitation tend to have _____ (high/low) precipitation variability. (pp. 171–172)   low

SELF-TEST

1. Heat stored during the evaporation of water is released when:
   (a) the relative humidity drops below 50 percent.
   (b) the relative humidity rises above 50 percent.
   (c) the air is saturated and condensation takes place.
   (d) the air becomes stable.

2. Which conditions are most likely to allow rapid evaporation to take place?
   (a) Cold air temperatures.
   (b) Air that is very close to saturation.
   (c) Warm air temperatures.
   (d) Very calm conditions (no wind).

3. If the water vapor content of an unsaturated parcel of air remains the same, but the temperature decreases, the *relative* humidity will:
   (a) increase. (b) decrease. (c) remain the same.

4. If the vapor content of an unsaturated parcel of air remains the same, but the temperature decreases, the *absolute* humidity will:
   (a) increase. (b) decrease. (c) remain the same.

5. If the temperature of an unsaturated parcel of air remains the same, but the absolute humidity (vapor content) increases, the *relative* humidity will:
   (a) increase. (b) decrease. (c) remain the same.

6. If the temperature of an unsaturated parcel of air remains the same, but the vapor content increases, the *absolute* humidity will:
   (a) increase. (b) decrease. (c) remain the same.

7. As a parcel of unsaturated air rises, its relative humidity will:
   (a) increase. (b) decrease. (c) remain the same.

8. As a parcel of air descends, its relative humidity will generally:
   (a) increase. (b) decrease. (c) remain the same.

9. If air is saturated, but no condensation nuclei are available and cooling continues:
   (a) the air will become supersaturated (no condensation).
   (b) the relative humidity will begin to decrease.
   (c) large drops of water will begin to condense out.

10. Radiation fog can form when:
    (a) air is warmed from the surface on a hot summer day.
    (b) air is lifted up a mountain barrier.
    (c) cool air moves over a warm ocean current.
    (d) the air is chilled by the surface on a cold winter night.

11. If a parcel of air is warmer than the surrounding air, the parcel will be:
    (a) stable.   (b) unstable.
    (c) conditionally stable.   (d) conditionally unstable.

12. An unstable parcel of air will most likely produce:
    (a) cumulus clouds.   (b) stratus clouds.
    (c) cirrus clouds.   (d) advection fog.

13. Why does rising saturated air cool more slowly than rising unsaturated air?
    (a) Saturated air cannot rise as quickly as unsaturated air.
    (b) Clouds absorb a great amount of heat from the air.
    (c) Latent heat is being stored during condensation.
    (d) Latent heat is being released during condensation.

14. The formation of hail usually takes place when the atmosphere is:
    (a) stable.   (b) very stable.   (c) unstable.

15. Rain shadows form:
    (a) on the windward side of a mountain.
    (b) on the leeward side of a mountain.
    (c) where moist air passes over a cool ocean current.
    (d) where dry air passes over a warm ocean current.

16. Referring to the map of world precipitation (Figure 6-34, pp. 170–171), what is a main reason that Indonesia (0° latitude, 120° E longitude.) receives so much rain?
    (a) Influence by subtropical highs all year.
    (b) Influence by subtropical highs in summer.
    (c) Marine influence from westerlies all year.
    (d) Influence by the ITCZ all year.

17.   Referring to the map of world precipitation (Figure 6-34, pp. 170–171), what is a main reason that central and western Australia (30° S latitude, 120° E longitude) receive so little rain?
   (a)   Influence by subtropical highs all year.
   (b)   Influence by subtropical highs in summer.
   (c)   Marine influence of westerlies all year.
   (d)   Influence by ITCZ all year.

18.   In general, which area will have the greatest precipitation variability?
   (a)   Regions of very high annual precipitation.
   (b)   Regions of moderate annual precipitation.
   (c)   Regions of very low annual precipitation.

19.   In general, which area will have the least precipitation variability?
   (a)   Regions of very high annual precipitation.
   (b)   Regions of moderate annual precipitation.
   (c)   Regions of very low annual precipitation.

Answers to Self-Test:

1.	c	6.	a	11.	b	16.	d
2.	c	7.	a	12.	a	17.	a
3.	a	8.	b	13.	d	18.	c
4.	c	9.	a	14.	c	19.	a
5.	a	10.	d	15.	b		

HINTS FOR TEXTBOOK STUDY QUESTIONS

1.   See Figure 6-3 (p. 142).

2.   This is discussed on page 143 of the textbook.

3.   Figure 6-4 (p. 143) illustrates one result of surface tension.

4.   Figure 6-6 (p. 145) illustrates this process, but read through the associated section of text to review the concept of latent heat.

5.   This is related to question 4 above; see Figure 6-5 (p. 144) for a diagram showing the exchange of latent heat involved when water changes phases between liquid and gas.

6.   See "Evaporation" beginning on page 146.

7.   This is discussed on page 147.

8.   It is important to note the ways in which absolute humidity and specific humidity are similar. It is especially important to understand how the relationship of the water vapor *content* of the air to the water vapor *capacity* of the air determines the relative humidity.

9.   This term is defined on p. 149.

10.   See Figure 6-9 on page 149.

11.   See the fractions shown on page 150.

12.   Figure 6-11 (shown on page 78 of the Study Guide) illustrates this relationship.

13.   Again, Figure 6-11 (shown on page 78 of the Study Guide) illustrates this relationship.

14.   You need to understand the concept of relative humidity before you can fully understand the idea of the dew point.

15.   You should understand what "sensible temperature" means, as well as why humidity influences sensible temperature. A discussion of this is found on page 151.

16.   Review the condensation process, beginning on page 151.

17.   Review question 16 above for the role condensation nuclei play in the condensation process.

18.   This question really refers to water droplets becoming supercooled (p. 153).

19.   Think about the altitudes of most clouds you see in the sky and remember that the surface is the source of water vapor for the atmosphere—how can moist air near the surface end up in a cloud high above the surface?

20.   What happens to the temperature of rising air?

21.   At the lifting condensation level the air has cooled to what temperature?

22.   Above the lifting condensation level two heating/cooling processes are taking place, while below, there is only one.

23.   Figure 6-16 (on page 80 of the Study Guide) may help you understand this process. Remember what happens to the temperature of descending air, and, therefore, to its water vapor capacity.

24.   This is discussed on pages 155–156. Be sure to look at the photographs and diagram of cloud types (Figures 6-17 and 6-18, pp. 156–157).

25.   Again, this is discussed on pages 155-156. See Figure 6-18 on page 157.

26.   See Figure 6-20 (p. 158).

27.   This is discussed beginning on page 159. It is also worth looking at the diagrams in Figure 6-25 (p. 163 in the textbook; Figure 6-25b is also reproduced on page 81 of the Study Guide).

28.   See question 27 above.

29.   This is illustrated in Figure 6-25c (p. 163).

30.   The text discusses "Visual Determination of Stability" on page 162.

31.   Figure 6-31 (p. 166) is a good starting point. Think about what would produce the strong updrafts associated with hail formation.

32.   See Figure 6-32 (p. 167).

33.   See Figure 6-32b (p. 167) and Figure 6-16 (on page 80 of the Study Guide).

34.   Consider the location and characteristics of the ITCZ, the trade winds, the subtropical highs, and the westerlies to these areas. Consider global wind and pressure patterns, as well as major mountain ranges.

35.   Note the position of the ITCZ in each map.

36.   This term is defined on page 171.

37.   Compare the map of precipitation variability (Figure 6-37, p. 174) to the map of average annual precipitation (Figure 6-34, pp. 170–171).

38.   This is discussed beginning on page 172.

ADDITIONAL STUDY QUESTIONS

1.   Why do desert regions experience greater precipitation variability than humid areas?

2.   Why is it misleading to call the average amount of precipitation received in an arid or semiarid area "normal" precipitation?

3.   Why are changes in relative humidity generally more important in producing clouds and precipitation than changes in absolute humidity or specific humidity?

4.   Explain how the release of latent heat can make air unstable.

5.   Why does descending air typically warm following the dry adiabatic rate?

Hints for Additional Study Questions:

1.   Consider a dry area that receives an average of 25 centimeters (10 inches) of precipitation per year, and a wet area that receives an average of 200 centimeters (80 inches) of precipitation per year. Calculate the departure from average that would result if both locations were to receive 12.5 centimeters (5 inches) less precipitation in a year (as might happen if each location received five fewer thunderstorms in a year).

2.   Review the concept of precipitation variability.

3.   Consider the most common ways that air becomes saturated.

4.   Remember that a parcel of air that is warmer than the surrounding air will be unstable.

5.   Consider what happens to the water vapor capacity of air (and therefore the relative humidity) when it begins to descend and warm.

CHAPTER 7

Transient Atmospheric Flows and Disturbances

OVERVIEW

In Chapter 7, we begin to integrate concepts learned in the four previous chapters of the text. This chapter focuses on storms and other temporary disturbances in the atmosphere. It begins by looking at air masses and fronts, which are two key components of the most important kind of midlatitude storm: the midlatitude cyclone. The chapter then discusses hurricanes, thunderstorms, and tornadoes.

Two kinds of storms deserve special attention in this chapter. Midlatitude cyclones are a prominent feature of the midlatitudes, and tropical cyclones (hurricanes) are a prominent feature of the tropics and subtropics. As you learn about these two kinds of storms, you will utilize your knowledge of temperature, wind, pressure, and moisture. You will see that the concepts of adiabatic cooling, latent heat, stability, as well as the direction of wind flow associated with different pressure systems, are all important as we explain these atmospheric disturbances.

One last point to keep in mind: The various kinds of storms discussed in this chapter should not be thought of as unusual deviations from "normal" weather. Depending on the location, certain kinds of storms are expected and regular features of the weather and climate.

KEY CONCEPTS

AIR MASSES (p. 179):

The starting point for understanding midlatitude storms is the *air mass*. Air masses are large parcels of air with uniform characteristics in the horizontal dimension. They can form when the atmosphere is quiet for a few days and a uniform surface imparts its characteristics to the air above. The map of North American air masses (Figure 7-2, p. 180) shows the most common source regions.

Note the relationship between the location of the *source region*, and the characteristics of the air masses that develop there. For example, air masses forming over high latitude land areas will be cold and dry, while those forming over high latitude maritime areas will be cool and moist.

Also note that air masses rarely form in the midlatitudes (where the westerlies tend to keep the atmosphere too active for air masses to develop). However, the midlatitudes do become the meeting place of contrasting air masses.

FRONTS (p. 182):

When unlike air masses meet (such as when a cold air mass meets a warm air mass), they don't mix readily. Instead, an abrupt boundary develops between them, called a *front*. On one side of a front, the characteristics of the air will be quite different from the air on the other side, especially with regard to temperature.

Warm Fronts (p. 183): When a warm air mass is advancing and displacing a cold air mass, a *warm front* develops. As the warm air mass pushes against the cold air mass, the warm air is forced to rise. The rising air cools adiabatically, and clouds and precipitation usually result. Notice in Figure 7-6, (p. 184) that the boundary of the warm front can often be recognized by different types and elevations of clouds.

Cold Fronts (p. 183): When a cold air mass is advancing and displacing a warm air mass, a *cold front* develops. The cold air pushes underneath the warm air, forcing the warm air to rise. The steeper slope of a cold front (Figure 7-8, p. 184) causes air to rise more abruptly, and this tends to produce a more concentrated zone of cloudiness and precipitation than along a warm front.

The movement of fronts is well illustrated in the animation ***Cold Fronts and Warm Fronts***.

We will now utilize the concepts of unlike air masses and fronts in our study of major atmospheric disturbances.

MIDLATITUDE CYCLONES (p. 185):

The *midlatitude cyclone* is the most important storm of the midlatitudes. The heart of a midlatitude cyclone is a large area of low pressure, perhaps 1600 kilometers (1000 miles) across. Remember from our discussion of pressure and wind that the wind pattern associated with lows near the surface is converging counterclockwise (in the Northern Hemisphere). Refer back to Figure 5-8 (p. 112) if you need a review. This pattern is a key to understanding the weather patterns associated with these storms. The converging pattern of wind pulls together two unlike air masses—relatively cool air from the higher latitudes, and relatively warm air from the subtropics. Where these unlike air masses meet in a midlatitude cyclone, fronts develop.

Characteristics (p. 185): Look at the map of a well-developed midlatitude cyclone over the United States (**Figure 7-9**, shown on the following page). Pressure is mapped using isobars. Notice that the lowest pressure is in the heart of the storm where the cold front (shown as a line with triangles) meets the warm front (shown as a line with half-circles), but that low pressure extends as a trough along the length of the cold front as well.

Notice the wind pattern associated with this low pressure area. The southeast quadrant of the storm is called the *warm sector*, since the southerly and southeasterly winds in this portion of the storm are in the warm air mass. To the west and north of the two fronts is the *cool sector*, produced by the cold air mass at the surface.

Figure 7-9b shows a cross section through the midlatitude cyclone shown in Figure 7-9a (both shown on the following page). This is an idealized drawing of the conditions as you travel from the cold sector into the warm sector (at the cold front) and then back into the cold sector (at the warm front). Notice that both the cold front and the warm front are advancing in the same direction (from left to right in the diagram). The cold front is moving faster than the warm front. Eventually, the cold front catches up with the warm front.

Notice also that at the surface, a midlatitude cyclone is mostly cold air, but at higher altitudes, it is mostly warm air. The cloudiness and precipitation of midlatitude cyclones results as warm air is forced to rise over the cold air. This ongoing uplift results in the adiabatic cooling that produces clouds and precipitation.

Consider the weather changes that take place with the passing of a cold front. Using Figure 7-9 for reference, imagine that you are standing in the warm sector, between the cold and warm fronts. The cold front is approaching you from the west:

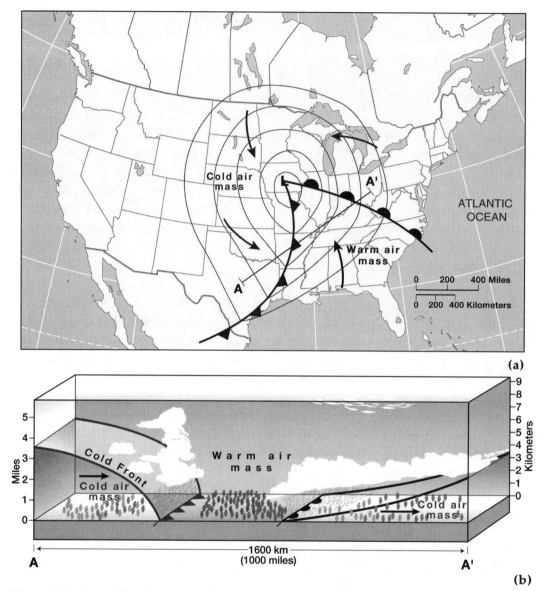

Figure 7-9: A map (a) and a cross section (b) of a typical mature midlatitude cyclone. Arrows indicate wind direction in (a) and the direction of frontal movement in (b).

(a)   As the cold front passes there will be an abrupt drop in temperature, since the cold front is a sharp boundary between a cold air mass and a warm air mass.

(b)   Since the cold front is associated with a trough of low pressure extending south from the heart of the storm, as the front approaches, pressure will decline steadily to its lowest point at the front. Then, as the cold front passes and the trough moves away, pressure will begin to increase steadily.

(c)   There is a shift in wind direction as well. Because of the overall converging counterclockwise wind pattern (in the Northern Hemisphere), winds in the warm sector come from the south (the situation before the cold front), and from the west or northwest after the front passes.

(d)   The unsettled weather and precipitation associated with the cold front are due to the adiabatic cooling of warm air as it is lifted along the front.

Movements (p. 187): The four movements of a midlatitude cyclone (Figure 7-11, p. 188; **Figure 7-11c** is shown below) are linked with the life cycle of a storm. The converging pattern of wind results from the circulation around and into a low pressure cell, and the movement of the whole storm is a consequence of the general circulation pattern of the westerlies. Both of these movements are clearly illustrated in the satellite image movies used on television weather reports.

The fact that cold fronts advance faster than warm fronts becomes the key to understanding the dissipation of a midlatitude cyclone.

Life Cycle (p. 187): The stages in the life of a midlatitude cyclone are shown in Figure 7-12 (p. 189). Note that as the cold front gradually gains on the warm front, the area of warm air at the surface (the warm sector) becomes smaller. When the cold front catches the warm front— forming an *occluded front*—all of the warm air has been lifted off the ground (Figure 7-15, p. 191). After occlusion, the mechanism for producing clouds and rain has been shut down, and the storm usually dies out. The animation ***Midlatitude Cyclones*** shows the life cycle of a midlatitude cyclone, including the process of occlusion.

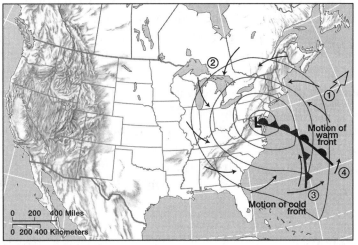

Figure 7-11c: The four varieties of motion in a typical midlatitude cyclone: (1) the entire storm moves in flow of westerlies; (2) cyclonic airflow; (3) cold front advances; (4) warm front advances. The cold front generally advances faster than the warm front; when the cold front catches the warm front, the storm begins to occlude (shown here in Figure 7-11c).

(c) Day 3

MIDLATITUDE ANTICYCLONES (p. 191):

These migrating cells of high pressure are really "non-storms" since they bring clear, stable, and dry weather. They are often associated with midlatitude cyclones (Figure 7-18, p. 192), sometimes alternating with cyclones across the band of the westerlies.

The Chapter 6 box, *Focus: GOES Weather Satellites* (p. 148), offers an introduction to the interpretation of the satellite images we see on television weather reports. Storms such as midlatitude cyclones are usually easy to recognize in these satellite images.

MAJOR TROPICAL DISTURBANCES: HURRICANES (p. 193):

Tropical cyclones, known as *hurricanes* in the United States, are the most significant storms of the tropics and subtropics. The low pressure pattern of a hurricane is mapped with isobars in Figure 7-21 (p. 194).

Characteristics (p. 194): Notice that these storms are much smaller than midlatitude cyclones, but that the pressure gradient is much steeper. The wind pattern of a hurricane is converging counterclockwise (in the Northern Hemisphere), but the pattern has a much more spiraling, whirling pattern than midlatitude cyclones. Hurricanes are also characterized by very high wind speeds (tropical cyclones are officially classified as hurricanes when wind speeds reach 64 knots (119 kph; 74 mph). You will remember that when we discussed midlatitude cyclones we did not make any generalizations about wind speed, just wind direction.

Two factors are the keys to the power of hurricanes. First, hurricanes depend on warm tropical water to survive. They will begin to die when they reach cooler water or when they move over land (although strong hurricanes can certainly produce great destruction for a period of time after they have reached land). Second, the "fuel" for hurricanes comes from the release of latent heat. Remember that evaporation involves the storing of heat and that condensation releases this heat back into the atmosphere. The warm air over the tropical oceans has high water vapor content. As this warm, moist air is drawn up into the low pressure cell of a hurricane, it rises and cools adiabatically. As more and more water condenses out of this air, more and more latent heat is released. This heat increases the instability inside the hurricane, causing air to rise still faster. This pulls more warm, moist air into the storm, which is uplifted in great updrafts, releasing still more latent heat. The end results are powerful updrafts and high-speed horizontal winds, as well as heavy precipitation.

Figure 7-22 (shown on the following page) is a cross section of a hurricane, showing the air being pulled into the hurricane, and then spiraling up toward the top of the storm. Note that the *eye* of the hurricane is an area of calm and mostly clear skies. The animation ***Hurricanes*** illustrates the patterns of airflow within a well-developed hurricane.

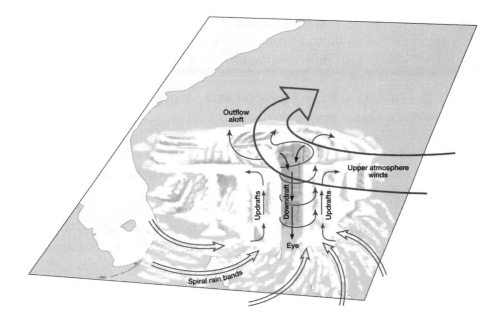

Figure 7-22: Idealized cross section through a well-developed hurricane.

Origin (p. 195): Hurricanes develop out of preexisting low pressure disturbances, and require warm ocean water and the lack of *wind shear* (a significant change in wind direction or speed with increasing altitude) in order to form.

Movement (p. 197): Keep in mind the general location of hurricane formation (Figure 7-23, p. 195), and the general direction of hurricane movement. Figure 7-24 (p. 197) shows the main hurricane tracks around the world. Hurricanes generally move with the flow of the trade winds, but they can move toward the poles some distance, especially in the area of a warm ocean current (such as along the east coasts of North America and Eurasia).

Damage and Destruction (p. 198): While high-speed wind and heavy rains account for some of the damage brought by hurricanes, in many cases the greatest destruction comes from *storm surges* (Figure 7-26, p. 198). A storm surge is rapidly advancing surge of water, as much as 7.5 meters (25 feet) high, pushed on shore by the hurricane. *People and the Environment: Hurricane Katrina* (p. 196) describes the destruction brought by Hurricane Katrina in August 2005.

LOCALIZED SEVERE WEATHER (p. 200):

Thunderstorms (p. 200): In *thunderstorms*, the release of latent heat during the condensation of rising air is a key mechanism in producing, or at least intensifying, the high instability in these storms. As shown in chart of "Average number of days per year with thunderstorms" (Figure 7-29, p. 201), most thunderstorms take place over land in the tropics where the high moisture and high temperature commonly produce unstable conditions. *Lightning* forms through the separation of electrical charges in cumulonimbus clouds (Figure 7-32, p. 203).

Tornadoes (p. 204): Most *tornadoes* occur in the spring and early summer when air mass contrasts are usually greatest. Differences in wind speed with increasing altitude (a circumstance that can generate *wind shear*) may create a rolling horizontal column of air that is tilted and uplifted within a severe thunderstorm, forming a *mesocyclone* (Figure 7-34, p. 206). It is from such mesocyclones that many tornadoes develop. The animation ***Tornadoes*** illustrates the development process of tornadoes.

Notice on the map showing the anticipated distribution of tornadoes around the world (Figure 7-36, p. 207), that most develop in the Great Plains of the United States. Also see *Focus: Forecasting Severe Storms with NEXRAD* (p. 202) and *Focus: Forecasting Severe Storms with the Oklahoma Mesonetwork* (p. 205*)* for a discussion of the development of tornadoes and severe thunderstorms.

PROGRESSIVE CONTENT REVIEW

1. An _____ _____ is a large parcel of air with uniform properties in the horizontal dimension. (p. 179)

    air mass

2. _____ polar air masses tend to be cold and dry. Maritime _____ air masses tend to be warm and wet. (p. 181)

    Continental
    tropical

3. When unlike air masses meet, a _____ is formed. (p. 182)

    front

4. When a warm air mass is advancing over a cold air mass, a _____ front is formed. (p. 183)

    warm

5. The slope of a cold front is usually _____ (more gentle/steeper) than the slope of a warm front. (p. 183)

    steeper

6. When two air masses meet, but neither air mass is advancing, a _____ front is formed. (p. 185)

    stationary

7. A midlatitude cyclone is a _____ pressure system, with a diameter of about _____ kilometers (miles). (p. 185)

    low
    1600 km (1000 mi.)

8. A well-developed midlatitude cyclone typically has a _____ front and a _____ front that separate the _____ sector from the _____ sector. (p. 186)

    warm
    cold; warm
    cold

9. Most of the precipitation associated with a midlatitude cyclone develops along the _____, and the cold front tends to produce _____ (more/less) intense precipitation than the warm front. (p. 186)

    fronts
    more

10. Midlatitude cyclones generally move from _____ to _____ across the midlatitudes. (p. 187)

    west to east

11. In the Northern Hemisphere, the wind direction ahead of a cold front in the warm sector of a midlatitude cyclone tends to be from the _____. (p. 187)

    south

12. The cold front of a midlatitude cyclone tends to move _____ (faster/ slower) than the storm itself, while the warm front tends to move _____ than the storm itself. (p. 187)

    faster

    slower

13. Most midlatitude cyclones develop in the region of the _____ _____. (p. 187)

    polar front/
    subpolar low

14. When a cold front catches a warm front an _____ front forms. This dissipates the storm since all of the _____ air has been lifted off the ground. (p. 188)

    occluded
    warm

15. A midlatitude anticyclone is a migrating _____ pressure system. (p. 191)

    high

16. Anticyclones have no fronts because the wind pattern is _____ at the surface. (p. 191)

    diverging

17. In the winter, midlatitude anticyclones are generally characterized by _____ temperatures. (p. 191)

    low

18. An _____ _____ is a weak migrating low pressure system in the tropics. (p. 191)

    easterly wave

19. Hurricanes (tropical cyclones) are _____ in size than midlatitude cyclones. (p. 193)

    smaller

20.	The eye of a hurricane is usually about _____ kilometers (miles) in diameter and is characterized by _____ weather. (p. 195)	16–40 km (10–25 mi.) calm/clear
21.	The energy for hurricanes comes from the release of _____ _____ during condensation. (p. 194)	latent heat
22.	Hurricanes can only form over tropical _____. (p. 195)	oceans
23.	Once a hurricane has formed, it will usually follow the flow of the _____ winds generally toward the _____ (east/west). (p. 197)	trade; west
24.	Most hurricanes form during the _____ season. (pp. 197–198)	late summer/fall
25.	Thunderstorms are characterized by rapid _____ (vertical/horizontal) air movement and instability. (p. 200)	vertical
26.	Thunderstorms are most common in areas with _____ (high/low) temperatures and _____ (high/low) humidity. (p. 201)	high high
27.	Most thunderstorms occur in the _____ regions of the world. (p. 201)	equatorial
28.	Tornadoes are characterized by very intense _____ (high/low) pressure, with a very _____ pressure gradient. (p. 204)	low steep/extreme
29.	Tornadoes are most common during the _____ season. (p. 207)	spring/early summer

SELF-TEST

1. An air mass is *least* likely to form over:
   (a) an ocean.
   (b) arctic tundra.
   (c) a desert.
   (d) a mountain range.

2. A continental polar air mass is likely to be:
   (a) warm and wet
   (b) warm and dry
   (c) cold and wet
   (d) cold and dry

3. A maritime tropical air mass is likely to be:
   (a) warm and wet
   (b) warm and dry
   (c) cold and wet
   (d) cold and dry

4. When a warm air mass meets a cold air mass, usually:
   (a) they will mix quickly, making all of the air cool.
   (b) a front will form between them.
   (c) a zone of gradual transition will form between them.
   (d) they will repel each other and move back to their source regions.

5. Why is rain usually more intense along a cold front than along a warm front?
   (a) The slope of a warm front is steeper.
   (b) The slope of a cold front is steeper.
   (c) Cold fronts move more slowly than warm fronts.
   (d) Warm fronts only form over land.

6. Ahead of the cold front in the warm sector of a well-developed midlatitude cyclone in the Northern Hemisphere, the wind is most likely to be from the:
   (a) northwest
   (b) south
   (c) northeast
   (d) west

7. As a cold front passes, the temperature is likely to:
   (a) decrease quickly
   (b) increase quickly
   (c) decrease gradually
   (d) increase gradually

8. As a cold front approaches, the pressure is likely to:
   (a) decrease abruptly
   (b) increase abruptly
   (c) decrease gradually
   (d) increase gradually

9. What causes clouds and precipitation along a cold front?
   (a) Increasing vapor content by evaporation from the surface.
   (b) Adiabatic warming of descending air.
   (c) Adiabatic cooling of rising air.
   (d) Increasing relative humidity as pressure increases.

10. Occlusion occurs in a midlatitude cyclone when:
    (a)   the storm passes over land.
    (b)   the storm stops moving in the westerlies.
    (c)   the warm front begins to move faster than the cold front.
    (d)   the cold front catches up with the warm front.

11. Why does an occluded front usually indicate the end of a midlatitude cyclone?
    (a)   Clouds can't form in cold air near the surface.
    (b)   The mechanism for lifting air to produce clouds and rain has ceased.
    (c)   All of the water vapor has condensed out of the warm air.
    (d)   The warm air and cold air have mixed, producing cool air.

12. Why do midlatitude anticyclones generally bring clear weather in winter?
    (a)   Air is converging into an anticyclone.
    (b)   The cold air of midlatitude anticyclones is usually unstable.
    (c)   Strong winds prevent the formation of fronts.
    (d)   Anticyclones consist of descending, stable air.

13. Why don't fronts develop in hurricanes?
    (a)   The high winds prevent front formation.
    (b)   All of the air associated with hurricanes is warm and moist.
    (c)   Fronts can't exist over the ocean.
    (d)   Heavy rain prevents front formation.

14. Why do hurricanes generally move from east to west?
    (a)   They move toward the subtropical highs.
    (b)   They move toward areas of colder ocean water.
    (c)   They generally flow with the westerlies.
    (d)   They generally flow with the trade winds.

15. Hurricanes will usually lose strength when:
    (a)   they pass over a warmer region of the ocean.
    (b)   they move over land.
    (c)   the air entering the storm becomes unstable.
    (d)   they pass over a small tropical island.

16. Hurricanes in the North Atlantic/Caribbean region:
    (a)   mostly occur in late summer and fall.
    (b)   mostly occur in early spring.
    (c)   mostly occur in winter.
    (d)   occur with equal frequency in every month of the year.

17. Why do most thunderstorms occur over land in summer?
    (a)   Land heats up during the day in summer.
    (b)   The moisture from the oceans produces stable conditions.
    (c)   Air becomes stable over warm land.
    (d)   The winds tend to blow from land to ocean during the summer.

18. Tornadoes are characterized by:
    (a)   a gentle pressure gradient.
    (b)   an extreme pressure gradient.
    (c)   rapidly descending air.
    (d)   very low relative humidity.

Answers to Self-Test:

1.	d	6.	b	11.	b	16.	a
2.	d	7.	a	12.	d	17.	a
3.	a	8.	c	13.	b	18.	b
4.	b	9.	c	14.	d		
5.	b	10.	d	15.	b		

HINTS FOR TEXTBOOK STUDY QUESTIONS

1. First, you should define an air mass. Next, consider how and where air masses form, and how the source regions influence the temperature and moisture characteristics of air masses.

2. Consider what it takes to create an air mass: a uniform surface and a quiet atmosphere for a few days. Where are those preconditions unlikely?

3. See question 2 above. Again, consider why the preconditions necessary to form an air mass are unlikely in the Rocky Mountains. What usually prevents the atmosphere from remaining quiet in a mountainous area?

4. Look at the mP air masses in the Pacific and Atlantic in Figure 7-2 (p. 180). Imagine the atmosphere is in motion. In which direction will each of those air masses go?

5.   Figure 7-5 (p. 183) may help. Pay attention to the temperatures of the air masses and to the direction arrows in the diagrams.

6.   See Figure 6-32c (p. 167).

7.   Figure 7-9 (on page 96 of the Study Guide) can help here.

8.   Again, see Figure 7-9.

9.   Consider the places in a midlatitude cyclone where air is rising.

10.   This is an important question. Figure 7-11 is a good starting point for studying this (p. 188; Figure 7-11c is shown on page 97 of the Study Guide).

11.   Figure 7-12 (p. 189) and Figure 7-15 (p. 191) may help here. Consider what mechanism is responsible for creating clouds and rain in a midlatitude cyclone, and how this changes with occlusion.

12.   Another important question. Page 187 in the textbook has a quick summary of these changes, but you need to understand *why* these changes are taking place. Look at Figure 7-9 (on page 96 of the Study Guide) and imagine that this storm is moving from west to east.

13.   See Figures 7-13 and 7-14 (p. 190) and the associated text.

14.   If the answer isn't clear, look at the map in Figure 7-17 (p. 192).

15.   This is discussed on page 191.

16.   See Figure 7-18 (p. 192) and its associated text.

17.   Consider both the definition of a front, and why fronts develop in midlatitude cyclones.

18.   See Figure 7-19 (p. 192) and the text on pages 191–193.

19.   This is covered in the textbook beginning on page 193.

20.   See Figure 7-22 (on page 99 of the Study Guide) and the text on page 195.

21.   Consider both the definition of a front and the parts of the world where tropical cyclones form—with a tropical cyclone, one necessary condition of front formation is missing.

22.   The map of hurricane origin points (Figure 7-23 on p. 195) may help. See the associated text beginning on page 195.

23.   The general tracks are shown in Figure 7-24 (p. 197). Consider why most hurricanes move in these directions.

24.   See question 22 above—what conditions necessary for hurricane formation and survival disappear once a hurricane makes landfall?

25.   Again, see question 22 above. The map of global ocean currents (Figure 4-28, p.95) may help.

26.   See Figure 7-26 (p. 198) and Figure 7-27 (p. 200).

27.   Consider the role that tropical cyclones play in some of the precipitation patterns studied in Chapter 6.

28.   This is graphically shown in Figure 7-28 (p. 201), but see the associated text for a complete description.

29.   Why are unstable conditions more likely to develop over land than over water?

30.   A description of this begins on page 204 of the textbook.

31.   See Figure 7-34 (p. 206).

ADDITIONAL STUDY QUESTIONS

1.   How does a midlatitude cyclone produce rain even if all of the air associated with the storm is stable?

2.   Why are hurricanes unlikely to strike the coast of California?

3.   Why are hurricanes more common in the summer and fall, while midlatitude cyclones are more common in winter?

Hints for Additional Study Questions:

1.   Even stable air will rise if it is forced to do so.

2.   Consider the wind directions, pressure systems, and ocean currents in the region.

3.   Two very different mechanisms of storm formation are involved. One involves contrasts of warm and cold air masses, and the other involves the release of latent heat stored by evaporation over warm oceans.

CHAPTER 8

Climatic Zones and Types

OVERVIEW

This chapter is the culmination of our study of the atmosphere. The goal of Chapter 8 is to help you recognize basic patterns of climate around the world, and to help you understand why these patterns exist.

The chapter begins by introducing the Köppen climate classification system. The Köppen system groups all climates of the world into one of 15 types. Each climate type is given a descriptive name and a letter code. The text describes the location, characteristics, and controls of each of these 15 categories of climate. The text also provides maps and climographs (charts showing average monthly temperature and precipitation patterns) for each climate type.

The chapter concludes with a discussion of climate change: how scientists recognize climate change, some of the mechanisms of climate change, and a description of the current evidence of human-induced global warming.

At first glance, it might seem that comprehending all of the material in this lengthy chapter would be an impossible task. However, it is important to keep in mind that Chapter 8 introduces very little new material in the section "World Distribution of Major Climate Types." Other than describing climographs and the Köppen system of climate classification, this section mostly involves illustrating and organizing what you already know about weather and climate.

Rather than offering guidelines for memorizing the details of the 15 climate types, this chapter of the Study Guide will help you utilize your knowledge of the elements and controls of weather to comprehend the main reasons for the locations and characteristics of each type of climate. The key to understanding climate patterns is recognizing the relationships between the characteristics, locations, and controls of weather and climate.

KEY CONCEPTS

THE KÖPPEN CLIMATE CLASSIFICATION SYSTEM (p. 212):

The Modified Köppen System (p. 212): The text has categorized all climates into 15 types, based on the *modified Köppen system*, the most widely-used climate classification system. In the Köppen system, each climate is given a descriptive name, as well as a code based on two or three letters. In this system, the first letter refers to the major climate group, the second letter usually refers to the precipitation pattern, and the third letter refers to the temperature pattern. The names and letter codes for the 15 climate types covered in the text, organized by major climate group, are listed below. Note that some climate types include several letter code variations.

Group A – Tropical Humid Climates
1. Tropical Wet   (Af)
2. Tropical Savanna   (Aw)
3. Tropical Monsoon(Am)

Group B – Dry Climates
4. Subtropical Desert   (BWh)
5. Subtropical Steppe   (BSh)
6. Midlatitude Desert   (BWk)
7. Midlatitude Steppe   (BSk)

Group C – Mild Midlatitude Climates
8. Mediterranean   (Csa and Csb)
9. Humid Subtropical   (Cfa and Cwa)
10. Marine West Coast   (Cfb and Cfc)

Group D – Severe Midlatitude Climates
11. Humid Continental   (Dfa, Dwa, Dfb and Dwb)
12. Subarctic   (Dfc, Dwc, Dfd and Dwd)

Group E – Polar Climates
13. Tundra   (ET)
14. Ice Cap   (EF)

Group H – Highland Climates
15. Highland Climates   (H)

Appendix V (pp. A18–A19) provides definitions for each of the letters used in the Köppen system, including specific temperature or precipitation cutoff points. While some instructors do not require that you memorize each of these definitions, a general understanding of the meaning of the letters will be helpful in your study of climate.

The following is a highly generalized description of the meaning of most letters used in the Köppen system, but not their exact definitions. Note that upper and lower case letters have different meanings in some cases.

Modified Köppen System Letter Codes

First Letters (major climate group):

A – Tropical Humid Climates:	Low latitude, warm, wet.
B – Dry Climates:	Hot or cold deserts and steppes.
C – Mild Midlatitude Climates:	Warm or hot summers, mild winters.
D – Severe Midlatitude Climates:	Severe (cold) winters.
E – Polar Climates:	Very high latitude, cold climates.
H – Highland Climates:	High mountain areas, where altitude is the dominant climate control.

Second Letters (refers to precipitation):

A, C, & D Climates only:
- f – Wet all year
- m – Monsoon precipitation pattern
- w – Winter dry season
- s – Summer dry season

B Climates only:
- W – Desert
- S – Steppe

Third Letters (refers to temperature):

C & D Climates only:
- a – Hot summers
- b – Warm summers
- c – Cool summers
- d – Very cold winters

B Climates only:
- h – Hot desert or steppe
- k – Cold desert or steppe

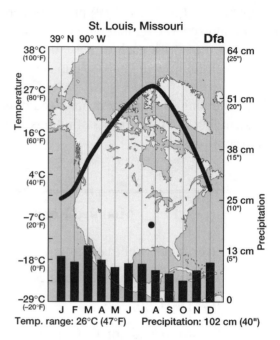

Figure 8-5: Climograph for St. Louis, Missouri.

Climographs (p. 215): You should understand the information presented in *climographs* (or *climatic diagrams*) before proceeding with the chapter (**Figure 8-5**, the climograph for St. Louis, Missouri, is shown above).

On climographs, the months of the year are indicated along the bottom of the chart (by the first letter of each month). The average monthly temperature is plotted with a solid line, and is indicated by the scale along the left side of the chart (in °C and °F). The average monthly precipitation is indicated with bars. The precipitation scale (in centimeters and inches) is found along the right side of the chart.

In the sample climograph above, note that the average January temperature in St. Louis is about -2°C (28°F), the average July temperature is about 27°C (80°F), and each month receives about 8 to 13 centimeters (3 to 5 inches) of precipitation.

WORLD DISTRIBUTION OF MAJOR CLIMATIC TYPES (p. 215):

Notice that as we discuss the locations of the five basic climate groups, we are generally moving from the equator toward the poles. The A climates are found in the tropics, many of the B climates in the subtropics, the C climates in the lower midlatitudes, the D climates in the higher midlatitudes, and finally the E climates near the poles.

As you study this section, take advantage of the "Summary Tables" for each major climate group (for example, the Summary Table for Group A is Table 8-3, p. 217). These summary tables list the general location, temperature and precipitation characteristics, and dominant controls of all of the climate types presented. In addition, the sample climographs will help you visualize the temperature and precipitation patterns for each climate. You should also refer to the map of climatic regions (Figure 8-4, pp. 214–215) to locate the major areas of each climate as you proceed through the chapter.

Your goal as you study the following sections of the text should be to understand the basic characteristics, locations, and controls of each climate type. You should especially try to understand the relationship between the characteristics, locations and controls of each climate type.

Tropical Humid Climates (Group A) (text p. 216; table p. 217): Group A climates are quite distinctive. There are virtually no other climates found in equatorial latitudes (except for some Highland climates). The three types of A climate differ mostly in the pattern of precipitation.

Tropical Wet Climate (Af) (p. 217): This equatorial climate is easy to distinguish. Note the temperature lines in the climographs (Figure 8-7b, p. 218). The temperature is nearly the same all year, with an average of about 27°C (80°F). Also note the high level of precipitation every month of the year (the *f* in Af means "wet all year"). The most basic control of Af climates is the heating and convection common in equatorial regions—especially the influence of the intertropical convergence zone (ITCZ) throughout the year.

Tropical Savanna Climate (Aw) (p. 219): Looking at the map of climate types (pp. 214–215), notice that Aw climates generally fringe the Af and Am climates to the north and south, and are more widespread than the other A climates. The climographs (Figure 8-10b, p. 220) show the characteristic high temperature of A climates, and a summer rainy season (the *w* in Aw means "winter dry"). The dominant control of Aw climates is the migration of the ITCZ, which brings rain north of the equator in the Northern Hemisphere summer, and south of the equator in the Southern Hemisphere summer (see Figure 6-35, p. 172). Notice that while both the Aw and Am have distinct rainy seasons, the total precipitation for the tropical monsoon climates is much greater than for tropical savanna climates.

Tropical Monsoon Climate (Am) (p. 221): The climographs (Figure 8-12b, p. 221) reveal that while the temperature pattern is similar to Af, there is a very pronounced rainy season with very high total precipitation—usually 250 centimeters (100 inches) per year, or more. These climates are found in the areas of tropical monsoon wind reversals (the *m* in Am means "monsoon"). See pages 126–128 in the textbook for a review of monsoons.

Dry Climates (Group B) (text p. 222; table p. 223): In the Köppen system, the dryness of a climate depends on the balance between moisture and temperature. There are two basic categories of dry climates, the hot, subtropical deserts and steppes, and the cool (or cold) midlatitude deserts and steppes. Not only do these two categories of dry climates differ in their yearly temperature patterns but also in their dominant climatic controls.

Subtropical Desert Climate (BWh) (p. 223): Look for BWh climates along the west coast of continents at about 20°–30° north and south latitude. These areas correspond to the position of the subtropical highs—areas of subsiding, stable air, made more persistent by the presence of cool ocean currents (Figure 8-15, p. 224). Notice in the climographs (Figure 8-16b, p. 225) that the summer temperatures in BWh climates are higher than in the equatorial Group A climates.

The subtropical steppes (BSh) typically fringe BWh areas, and are simply more moderate versions of the desert climate.

Midlatitude Desert Climate (BWk) (p. 226): Look for the BWk climates in the interiors of large continents, or in areas where prevailing winds are blocked by mountain barriers (producing a rain shadow). The key to the dryness of these climates is that these regions are removed from sources of moisture. Notice in the climographs (Figure 8-21b, p. 228) that these areas often have winter temperatures that are below freezing.

The midlatitude steppes (BSk) typically fringe the BWk climates.

Mild Midlatitude Climates (Group C) (text p. 227; table p. 229): The three variations of Group C climates (as well as the two variations of Group D to follow) are quite easy to distinguish and understand if you keep in mind the dominant climate controls. These controls are highlighted in each climate group's Summary Table (p. 229 for Group C; p. 235 for Group D).

You can easily remember the general distribution pattern of C and D climates in North America by noting the example cities on the four "corners" of the conterminous United States given for each climate type. This "four corners" pattern repeats itself at comparable latitudes on the other continents as well.

Mediterranean Climate (Csa, Csb) (p. 229): Mediterranean climates are very distinctive (as shown by their climographs, Figure 8-24b, p. 230). They have dry summers and wet winters (the *s* means "summer dry"), and mild temperatures throughout the year. No other climate type is defined by such a dry-summer precipitation pattern. Mediterranean climates only occur along the west coasts of continents at about 35° north and south latitude. The summer dry season is due to the stable conditions brought by the migration of the subtropical high toward the poles in summer, while the winter rain comes from midlatitude cyclones that can move through in the westerlies when the subtropical high migrates toward the equator in winter.

Mediterranean climates are found at the southwest corner of the United States—for example, Los Angeles, California.

Humid Subtropical Climate (Cfa, Cwa) (p. 231): Humid subtropical climates are found at about the same latitude as mediterranean climates, but along the east coast of continents (and extending some distance inland as well). Winter precipitation typically comes from migrating midlatitude cyclones (often the same storms that bring winter rain to the mediterranean climate regions to the west). The rainfall in summer (Figure 8-27b, p. 232) is due largely to the presence of warm ocean currents and onshore wind flows, which can bring unstable conditions and thunderstorms. In North America and Asia, summer rains also can result from the influence of tropical cyclones.

Humid subtropical climates are found at the southeast corner of the United States—for example, Atlanta, Georgia.

Marine West Coast Climate (Cfb, Cfc) (p. 233): Marine west coast climates are found poleward of the mediterranean climates along the west coast of continents. The mild temperatures and moderate rainfall throughout the year (Figure 8-30b, p. 234) are easy to explain. These areas receive the moderating influence of a cool ocean current, and remain within the band of the westerlies all year (which brings moist marine air and migrating midlatitude cyclones).

Marine west coast climates are found at the northwest corner of the United States—for example, Seattle, Washington.

Severe Midlatitude Climates (Group D) (text p. 235; table p. 235): Severe midlatitude climates are the product of strong continental influences, and are found only in the Northern Hemisphere (there are no continents in comparable latitudes in the Southern Hemisphere).

Humid Continental Climate (Dfa, Dfb, Dwa, Dwb) (p. 235): Humid continental climates are found at about the same latitude as marine west coast climates, but on the east coast of continents (and extending inland to about mid-continent). These regions are in the band of the westerlies all year, so they receive strong continental influence from the interior (the westerlies can bring this continental influence all the way to the east coast). Notice the temperature curves in the climographs (Figure 8-32b, p. 236); temperatures are high in summer but below freezing in winter.

Humid continental climates are found at the northeast corner of the United States—for example, New York City.

Subarctic Climate (Dfc, Dfd, Dwc, Dwd) (p. 237): The severe winters experienced in regions of subarctic climate are explained by their high latitudes and positions in the interiors of continents. Notice that the annual temperature ranges of subarctic climates (Figure 8-35b, p. 238) can exceed 56°C (100°F), the widest of any climate type.

Continuing with our location examples of climate types in North America, we can add a fifth "corner"—subarctic climates are found in central Canada, for example, around Hudson Bay.

Polar Climates (Group E) (text p. 239; table, p. 239): The two types of polar climates are easy to explain and recognize. In both cases they are far removed from sources of warmth. The cold air can hold little moisture, so precipitation is very sparse.

Tundra Climate (ET) (p. 239): Note in the climographs (Figure 8-37b, p. 240) that the average temperature of the warmest month in tundra climates is below 10°C (50°F), and that there is low total precipitation.

Ice Cap Climate (EF) (p. 242): By definition, in ice cap climates the average temperature of the warmest month is less than 0°C (32°F). In some ice cap locations, there may be virtually no precipitation during the year (Figure 8-38b, p. 242).

Highland Climate (Group H) (p. 243): Highland climates are not defined in the same way as other climates in the Köppen system. Highland climates are those in which altitude is the dominant control. There are many variations of highland climate. For example, equatorial highland regions, such as high in the Andes in South America, have mild (or even very low) temperatures, but exhibit very little temperature change during the year. In contrast, the high mountain areas within mediterranean climate zones will be influenced by midlatitude cyclones during the winter and will exhibit a summer dry season (see Figure 8-41, p. 244).

GLOBAL PATTERNS IDEALIZED (p. 245):

Figure 8-44 (shown on the following page) is a chart showing the general distribution of A, B and C climates by latitude. This chart shows the pattern along the west coast of continents, so Cfa and BWk/BSk climates are not shown. The influence of the seasonal migration of the ITCZ and subtropical highs along the west coast of continents is quite clear. Also review the animation *Seasonal Pressure and Precipitation Patterns* when studying the characteristics and controls of these climates.

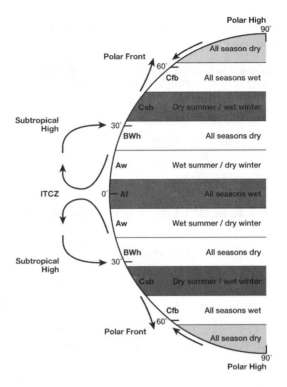

Figure 8-44: Idealized seasonal precipitation patterns and climates along the west coast of continents. Note that the progressions north and south of the equator are mirror images. Much of this pattern is due to the seasonal shifts of the ITCZ and the subtropical highs.

It is worth noticing the diagram of Köppen climatic types on a hypothetical continent (Figure 8-45, p. 246). This map shows the presumed pattern of climate that would develop on a large continent, assuming that there is no interference from factors such as mountain ranges. If you compare this diagram to the map showing the actual distribution of climate (Figure 8-4, pp. 214–215), you'll see that for a given latitude and position on a continent, the hypothetical pattern quite closely matches the actual pattern.

Climatic Distribution in Africa: A Practically Perfect Pattern (p. 246): This section of the text discusses the continent of Africa, where the actual pattern of climate nearly matches the predicted pattern.

GLOBAL CLIMATE CHANGE (p. 247):

This section of the chapter introduces the study of global climate change. Notice that the patterns that stand out in the climate record depend in part on the time scale used (Figure 8-47, p. 248).

Determining Climates of the Past (p. 248): Oxygen isotope analysis has become an important tool for studying climates of the past. Both more-common ^{16}O (oxygen atoms containing 8 protons and 8 neutrons) and less-common ^{18}O (oxygen atoms containing 8 protons and 10 neutrons) exist naturally in many different kinds of molecules such as water (H_2O) and calcium carbonate ($CaCO_3$), but the ratio of ^{18}O to ^{16}O in these compounds varies depending on a number of environmental conditions. For example, water molecules containing lighter ^{16}O evaporate more easily than those containing ^{18}O, and so during an ice age, when lots of water is locked up on land as ice, the concentration of ^{18}O in the oceans increases—and this is reflected in the $^{18}O/^{16}O$ ratio in ocean floor sediments.

Causes of Long-Term Climate Change (p. 251): A number of mechanisms of climate change are discussed here, including variations in Earth-Sun relations (such as *Milankovitch cycles*), and changes in greenhouse gas concentrations. It is especially important to note the *feedback mechanisms* that can be at work. For example, with a warming climate polar snow and ice melt and this reduces the reflectance of the surface, thus increasing absorption of solar energy—so leading to increased warming.

Evidence of Current Global Warming (p. 253): This section is an extension of the topic of human-enhanced greenhouse effect and global warming first introduced in Chapter 4 (p. 102). Note that the latest report of the Intergovernmental Panel on Climate Change (IPCC) released in 2007 offers stronger evidence than previous reports that humans are indeed altering global climate through the release of greenhouse gases such as carbon dioxide.

PROGRESSIVE CONTENT REVIEW

---

1. The Köppen climate classification system is based on the average annual and monthly _____ and _____ values. (p. 212)

    temperature; precipitation

2. A climograph plots the average _____ temperature and precipitation for a weather station. (p. 215)

    monthly

3. Tropical humid ("A") climates are only found within about _____ degrees of latitude north and south of the equator. (p. 216)

    15°–20°

4. Tropical humid climates are characterized by _____ (high/low) temperatures throughout the year. (p. 216)

5. Tropical wet (Af) climates have the _____ (largest/smallest) annual temperature range of all climates. (p. 217)

    smallest

6. In Af climates, rainfall occurs throughout year and usually comes in the form of _____. (p. 218)

    thunderstorms/ convective storms

7. Tropical savanna (Aw) climates are typically found in locations north and south of _____ climates. (p. 219)

    Af

8. In Aw climates, most rainfall comes in the _____ (summer/winter). (p. 219)

    summer

9. The rainy season of Aw climates is closely associated with the migration of the _____ pressure zone. (p. 219)

    ITCZ

10. Tropical monsoon (Am) climates are characterized by very heavy rainfall during the _____ (summer/winter) monsoon. (p. 221)

    summer

11. Dry ("B") climates cover _____ (more/less) land area than any other single climate group. (p. 222)

    more

12. The greatest areas of dry climates occur in the _____ (equatorial/subtropical/mid-) latitudes. (p. 222)

    subtropical

13. The "dryness" of a climate not only depends on the amount of precipitation, but also on the _____. (p. 222)

    temperature

14. Subtropical desert (BWh) climates are generally found on the _____ (east/west) coasts of continents at about _____ degrees north and south latitude. (table on p. 223)

    west; 25–30

15. The dryness of BWh climates is largely the result of the location of the _____ _____ pressure systems. (p. 223)

    subtropical high

16. Midlatitude desert (BWk) climates are primarily found in the middle of _____ or in the _____ _____ of a major mountain. (table on p. 223; p. 226)

    continents; rain shadow

17. Compared with subtropical deserts, midlatitude deserts have _____ (cold/warm) winters. (pp. 226–227)

    cold

18. Mediterranean (Cs) climates are found along the _____ (east/west) coasts of continents, at about _____ degrees north and south latitude. (p. 229)

west
35

19. Cs climates receive virtually all precipitation in the _____ (summer/winter). (p. 229)

winter

20. The dry summer conditions of the Cs climates are associated with the migration of the _____ _____ pressure system. (p. 231)

subtropical high

21. Humid subtropical (Cfa) climates are found at about the same latitude as the _____ climates but along the eastern side of continents. (p. 231)

mediterranean

22. The peak in rain during late summer/autumn typical of Cfa climates in North America, is largely due to rainfall associated with _____ _____. (pp. 232–233)

tropical cyclones

23. Marine west coast (Cfb) climates are found between about _____ and _____ degrees north and south latitude along the west coasts of continents. (p. 233)

40; 65

24. The dominant controls of marine west coast climates are _____ (inland/coastal) locations and the _____ winds all year. (p. 233)

coastal; westerly

25. Severe midlatitude ("D") climates are only found in the _____ Hemisphere. (p. 235)

Northern

26. Even along the east coast, D climates receive little maritime influence because the dominant wind flow is from the _____. (p. 235)

west

27. Compared with humid subtropical (Cfa) climates, humid continental (Dfa) climates have _____ (colder/warmer) winters. (p. 236)

colder

28. Subarctic (Dfc) climates have the _____ (largest/smallest) annual temperature range of all climates. (p. 238)

largest

29. Polar ("E") climates have no month with an average temperature above _____ degrees. (p. 239)   10°C (50°F)

30. The equatorward boundary of tundra (ET) climates generally corresponds to the poleward limit of _____ growth. (pp. 239–240)   tree

31. In icecap (EF) climates, no month has an average temperature above _____ degrees. (pp. 242–243)   0°C (32°F)

32. In highland (H) climates, _____ is the most important climatic control. (p. 243)   altitude

33. Water molecules with the oxygen isotope _____ ($^{18}O/^{16}O$) evaporate more easily than those with _____ ($^{18}O/^{16}O$), leaving a relatively greater quantity of water with _____ ($^{18}O/^{16}O$) in the oceans during an ice age. (p. 249) ^{16}O
^{18}O
^{18}O

34. Volcanic ash ejected into the atmosphere by Mount Pinatubo in 1991 _____ (increased/decreased) global temperatures over the following year. (p. 251)   decreased

SELF-TEST

1. Tropical wet (Af) climates have a small annual temperature range because:
   (a) it is rainy throughout the year.
   (b) cloud cover all year moderates the seasons.
   (c) thunderstorms are common.
   (d) the noon sun is high in the sky every day of the year.

2. Most rain in tropical wet (Af) climates comes from:
   (a) frontal lifting of air.
   (b) convective lifting of air.
   (c) tornadoes.
   (d) monsoon wind reversals.

3. What is the main reason that tropical savanna (Aw) climates have rain in summer?
   (a) Influence of the ITCZ all year.
   (b) Influence of the ITCZ in summer.
   (c) Influence of warm ocean currents.
   (d) Influence of the subtropical highs in summer.

4. The dry winters of Aw climates are associated with:
   (a) the influence of the ITCZ.
   (b) the influence of warm ocean currents.
   (c) the westerlies.
   (d) the influence of the subtropical highs.

5. What is the primary control of subtropical desert (BWh) climates?
   (a) Locations in the middle of continents.
   (b) The influence of the ITCZ all year.
   (c) The influence of the subtropical highs all year.
   (d) The influence of the subtropical highs in winter and ITCZ in summer.

6. Which of the following factors contributes to the dryness of subtropical desert climates along the west coasts of continents?
   (a) Cool ocean current.
   (b) Warm ocean current.
   (c) Westerlies blowing off ocean all year.
   (d) Westerlies blowing off ocean during the winter.

7. What is a primary control of midlatitude desert (BWk) climates?
   (a) Locations in the middle of continents.
   (b) The influence of the ITCZ all year.
   (c) The influence of warm ocean currents.
   (d) The ITCZ in summer.

8. Why do mediterranean (Cs) climates have dry summers?
   (a) Influence of the ITCZ in summer.
   (b) Influence of the trade winds in summer.
   (c) Influence of the subtropical highs in summer.
   (d) Midlatitude cyclones do not develop during the summer.

9. What is the primary source of precipitation in mediterranean climates?
   (a) Thunderstorms
   (b) Hurricanes.
   (c) Tornadoes.
   (d) Midlatitude cyclones.

10. Why do marine west coast (Cfb) climates have moderate temperatures throughout the year?
    (a) Marine influence all year.
    (b) Continental influence all year.
    (c) Marine influence in summer and continental influence in winter.
    (d) Continental influence in summer and marine influence in winter.

11. Which of the following is most likely to bring late summer precipitation to the humid subtropical (Cfa) climates in North America?
    (a) Hurricanes.
    (b) Midlatitude cyclones.
    (c) Subtropical highs.
    (d) Cool ocean currents.

12. Which of the following is *not* an important control of humid continental (Dfa) climates?
    (a) Westerly winds throughout the year.
    (b) The subtropical high.
    (c) Midlatitude cyclones in winter.
    (d) Continental influences.

13. Why are no D climates found in the Southern Hemisphere?
    (a) There are no warm ocean currents in the Southern Hemisphere.
    (b) There are no cool ocean currents in the Southern Hemisphere.
    (c) No large Southern Hemisphere land masses are located at 50° to 60° south latitude.
    (d) The westerlies are less reliable in the Southern Hemisphere.

14. Why do ice cap (EF) climates receive so little precipitation?
    (a) The air is too cold to hold much water vapor.
    (b) These areas are dominated by low pressure all year.
    (c) These areas are very windy all year.
    (d) A subtropical high stabilizes the air in summer.

15. In terms of climate, an increase in elevation is *most* similar to:
    (a) an increase in latitude (moving toward the poles).
    (b) a decrease in latitude (moving toward the equator).
    (c) moving from the coast to the interior of a large continent.
    (d) moving from the interior to the coast of a large continent.

16. Refer to the climate map (Figure 8-4, pp. 214–215). What is the most likely reason that southern Japan is Cfa, while northern Japan is Dfa?
    (a) Cfa area is in the trades, while Dfa is in the westerlies.
    (b) Cfa area is influenced by the subtropical high in summer.
    (c) Cfa area is influenced by the subtropical high all year.
    (d) Dfa area is higher in latitude.

17. Which of the following represents the climate with the hottest summer?
    (a) Dfa
    (b) Csb
    (c) Cfb
    (d) Cfc

18. Which of the following represents the climate with the coolest summer?
    (a) Dfa
    (b) Csb
    (c) Cfb
    (d) Cfc

Answers to Self-Test:

1.	d	6.	a	11.	a	16.	d
2.	b	7.	a	12.	b	17.	a
3.	b	8.	c	13.	c	18.	d
4.	d	9.	d	14.	a		
5.	c	10.	a	15.	a		

HINTS FOR TEXTBOOK STUDY QUESTIONS

1. Consider the kind of data needed to classify climates with the Köppen system, as well as the virtues of this system. This is introduced beginning on page 212.

2. See Table 8-2 on page 216 for a summary of this.

3. Look at any climograph in this chapter. You should consider the two types of data shown in a climograph, as well as the basis of these data ("average" versus "maximum," and so on).

4.   See Table 8-2 (p. 216) and the associated text.

5.   For this question you may want to begin with the summary tables for each major climate group (for example, the "A" climates are shown in Table 8-3 on page 217); next look at the representative climographs for each; finally, review the distribution pattern of these climates on the map of global climate distribution (Figure 8-4, pp. 214–215).

6.   Figure 6-35 (p. 172) showing July and January global precipitation may help. Also review the climate summary table on p. 206.

7.   For a review of this see Table 8-4 (p. 223).

8.   Consider the importance of the clear skies that generally prevail in regions of subtropical desert, as well as the seasonal variations in the length of day and angle of the noon Sun.

9.   These deserts generally develop because of stable conditions that prevent the uplift of air. In terms of climate controls, what is different about the east and west coasts of continents?

10.   Look at the global map of climate regions (Figure 8-4; pp. 214–215) and locate the other BWh regions of the world. In terms of climate controls, what circumstances allow moisture to enter the subtropical latitudes from the east in North America, South America, southern Africa, and Australia, but not in northern Africa? This is discussed in the text on page 223.

11.   Figure 8-44 (on p. 117 of the Study Guide) may help here. Also see Table 8-5 (p. 229).

12.   Consider why locations at the same latitude as marine west coast climates, but on the eastern sides of continents, have very cold winters.

13.   Why are these regions removed from ocean influence (in terms of climate)? Also see the hint for question #12 above.

14.   Note how the dominant wind direction regulates the amount of continental influence in both locations.

15.   Consider both the variation in insolation throughout the year, and the continental locations.

16.   In order to have precipitation, there must be water vapor *in the air*. What would limit the amount of water vapor in these regions?

17.   A discussion of this is on page 249.

18. Consider information about both temperature and the gas composition of the atmosphere. A discussion of this begins on page 249 in the textbook.

19. You may want to review Earth–Sun relations (beginning on page 15 in the textbook) before reviewing the material on page 251.

20. Look at the photograph of sea ice in Figure 8-49 (p. 252) and consider how the reflectance of the surface would change if more sea ice melts.

21. This is discussed on page 252.

22. Some of these factors are discussed on page 253.

ADDITIONAL STUDY QUESTIONS

1. Why will a subtropical desert (BWh) that receives 25 centimeters (10 inches) of precipitation a year be a "drier" climate than a subarctic climate (Dfc) that also receives 25 centimeters of precipitation a year?

2. Why are mediterranean climates generally restricted to coastal areas?

Hints for Additional Study Questions:

1. Consider the importance of temperature to the overall dryness of a region.

2. Consider which climate control factor is responsible for the dry summers of the mediterranean climates. Why doesn't this influence generally extend inland into the continent for great distances?

CHAPTER 9

The Hydrosphere

OVERVIEW

Chapter 9 focuses on the distribution and importance of water on Earth. The chapter first describes the hydrologic cycle which entails the movement of water, in its various forms, between the surface of Earth and the atmosphere. The chapter continues by discussing water in the oceans, the movement of ocean waters (tides and currents), water permanently frozen as ice, and water both on the land surface in rivers and lakes, as well as below the surface.

You will see that many of the topics introduced in this chapter relate to material in other chapters of the text. For example, an understanding of the hydrologic cycle is necessary to fully comprehend the operation of ecosystems (Chapters 10 and 11). The characteristics of water underneath the surface are important for an understanding of soil formation (Chapter 12) and solution topography (Chapter 17). The work of streams is discussed in Chapter 16. Permanent ice will be discussed in the section on glacial landforms (Chapter 19). And finally, the characteristics of the ocean waters and the consequences of tidal movement will be addressed again when discussing the shaping of coastal landforms (Chapter 20).

KEY CONCEPTS

THE HYDROLOGIC CYCLE (p. 261):

Over 97% of the water on Earth is found in the oceans. The water on the land surfaces, water in the atmosphere, and water in living things accounts for only about one-quarter of one percent of all water. However, these waters are crucial for all forms of terrestrial life, as well as precipitation and the most important erosional processes on the surface of Earth.

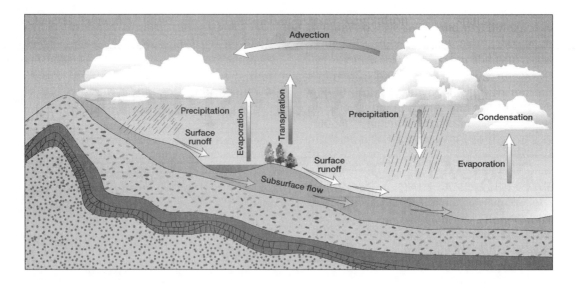

Figure 9-2: The hydrologic cycle.

The general *hydrologic cycle*, involving the processes of evaporation and transpiration, condensation, precipitation, and surface and subsurface flow, are illustrated in **Figure 9-2** (shown above), and in the animation *Hydrologic Cycle*.

THE OCEANS (p. 263):

Chemical Composition (p. 266): Note how the salinity of ocean waters varies by location: ocean water tends to have the highest salinity in the subtropics where evaporation is high, and the lowest salinity in equatorial regions and polar regions where the inflow of fresh water is greatest.

MOVEMENT OF OCEAN WATERS (p. 267):

Tides (p. 267): Note in the diagram (**Figure 9-6**, shown on the following page) that the highest of the high tides (*spring tides*; diagram 2) occur when Earth, Sun, and Moon are all aligned, while the lowest of the high tides (*neap tides*; diagram 3) occur when the Moon and the Sun are at right angles with respect to Earth. Also review the animation *Tides*.

Currents (p. 268): See Figure 9-10 for description of the *global conveyor-belt circulation*. Notice that cold, dense water sinks in the North Atlantic, joins deep, cold water near the Antarctic, and eventually rises as a shallow warm current in the Indian and North Pacific Ocean basins before flowing back to the North Atlantic. You may also want to review the animation *Ocean Circulation Patterns*.

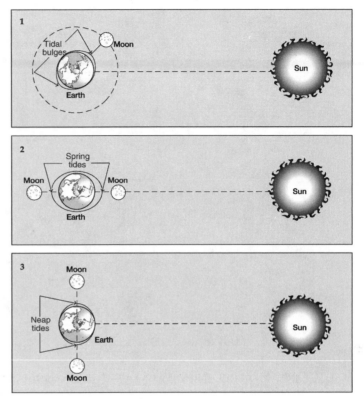

Figure 9-6: Juxtaposition of the Sun, Moon, and Earth accounts for variations in Earth's tidal range. (1) Normal tidal range. (2) Highest high tides (spring tides). (3) Lowest high tides (neap tides).

PERMANENT ICE—THE CYROSPHERE (p. 271):

Permanently frozen water is found both on land and in the oceans (Figures 9-11, 9-13, and 9-14, pp. 271–273). Most of this ice is found on land in glaciers, including the ice sheet that covers most of Antarctica, ice caps on Arctic islands, as well as alpine glaciers in mountain areas of the world.

Oceanic ice includes water that freezes directly from the ocean (*ice packs*), as well as glacial ice from land that is resting in the ocean (an *ice shelf*). Note that all forms of oceanic ice consist of fresh water, even if frozen from salt water (when ocean water freezes, very little dissolved salt is retained).

SURFACE WATERS (p. 273):

Note that lakes are relatively temporary surface features. Most are destined to disappear when they fill up with sediments deposited by in-flowing streams, or when they are drained by out-flowing streams.

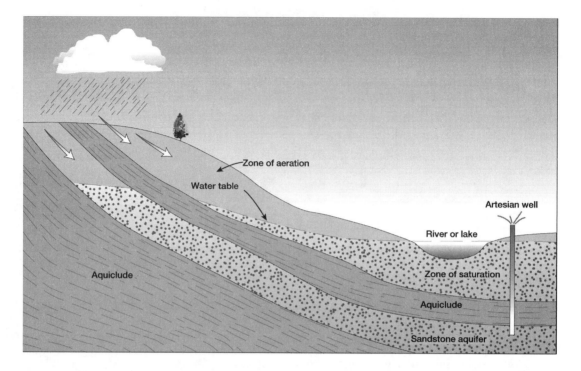

Figure 9-22: An aquifer is a rock structure that is permeable and/or porous enough to hold water. An artesian system develops where surface water penetrates the aquifer in the recharge area and infiltrates downward. It is confined to the aquifer by impermeable strata (aquicludes) above and below.

UNDERGROUND WATER (p. 280):

The total amount of water found underground exceeds that contained in surface streams and lakes. As we will see in subsequent chapters, patterns of subsurface water are important factors in the distribution of plants (Chapters 10 and 11), the development of soils (Chapter 12), and the development of landforms (Chapter 17).

Zone of Aeration (p. 281): Several underground hydrologic zones are described in the text (**Figure 9-22**, shown above). The *zone of aeration* is closest to the surface. This zone tends to contain many clay particles and holds varying amounts of *soil water*.

Zone of Saturation (p. 281): Below the zone of aeration is the *zone of saturation*. Within this zone, all openings in the bedrock or sediments are fully saturated with water. The top of this saturated groundwater zone is called the *water table* and its depth varies with the level of precipitation in the region and with the topography. Water wells must be drilled into the zone of saturation, and will fill up to the level of the water table. The animation, ***Groundwater Cone of Depression***, illustrates that when groundwater is pumped extensively from one well an adjacent well may go dry.

Zone of Confined Water (p. 282): In some areas there is another hydrologic zone below the zone of saturation. If an impermeable layer of rock (called an *aquiclude*) is located beneath the surface, groundwater will be unable to seep down into permeable layers below. However, water may be able to fill permeable layers beneath this aquiclude and form a layer of groundwater known as an *aquifer* by seeping in from the sides (coming from some distance away where there is no aquiclude to interfere with the infiltration of groundwater from above). The resulting aquifer is in a *zone of confined water*. These aquifers are occasionally under pressure, and so when wells tap into this zone, the water may be able to flow to the surface without pumping, producing an *artesian well*.

Groundwater Mining (p. 283): This section discusses the consequences of pumping groundwater faster than it is replenished naturally.

PROGRESSIVE CONTENT REVIEW

1.   At any one time, less than _____ percent of all water in the world is actively moving through the hydrologic cycle. (p. 261)

1

2.   The oceans contain about _____ percent of all water on Earth. (p. 261)

97

3.   Most evaporation takes place over the _____ of the world. (p. 262)

oceans

4.   Oceans cover about _____ percent of Earth's surface. (p. 262)

71

5.   The salinity of the ocean is relatively _____ (high/low) in areas of high rainfall and near the mouths of major rivers. (p. 266)

low

6.   The water temperature along the east coast of a continent (along the western margins of an ocean) is usually _____ than along the west coast. (p. 266)

warmer

7.   In most coastal areas of the world, the tides will rise for about _____ hours and then fall for about _____ hours. (p. 267)

6; 6

8. Surface ocean currents are caused primarily by _____. (p. 269)   wind

9. In the global conveyor-belt circulation, water _____ (sinks/rises) in the North Atlantic Ocean before flowing south toward Antarctica. (p. 269)   sinks

10. About _____ percent of Earth's land area is covered with permanent glacial ice. (p. 271)   10

11. An "iceberg" is made of frozen _____ (fresh/salt) water. (p. 271)   fresh

12. Lakes are especially common in regions that experienced erosion and deposition by _____ in the recent geologic past. (p. 274)   glaciers

13. The amount of water found beneath the land surface is _____ (greater/less) than that found on the land surface. (p. 280)   greater

14. An _____ is a layer of permeable rock or sediments separated by layers of impermeable rock called _____. (p. 281)   aquifer / aquicludes

15. The top of the zone of water saturation below the surface is called the _____ _____. (p. 281)   water table

16. With an _____ well, water rises to the surface without pumping. (p. 283)   artesian

SELF-TEST

1. Oceanic ice is made up of:
    (a) about 50% freshwater and 50% saltwater.
    (b) about 25% freshwater and 75% saltwater.
    (c) all saltwater.
    (d) all freshwater.

2.   The "water table" refers to:
      (a)   the uppermost layer of saturated rock or sediments below the surface.
      (b)   the layer of impermeable rock or sediments below a zone of groundwater.
      (c)   the layer of impermeable rock or sediments above a zone of groundwater.
      (d)   sea level.

3.   When water is taken from a well faster than it is replenished:
      (a)   the water table will rise toward the surface.
      (b)   the water table will sink around the well.
      (c)   the water will become less salty.
      (d)   surface runoff will decrease.

4.   Water flows to the surface without pumping in an artesian well because:
      (a)   surface tension of the water pulls it toward the surface.
      (b)   water expands when it freezes.
      (c)   confining pressure forces water to the surface.
      (d)   dissolved minerals make the water less dense.

5.   The most important sources of water that evaporates into the atmosphere are:
      (a)   the polar ice caps.
      (b)   freshwater lakes.
      (c)   the oceans.
      (d)   saltwater lakes.

6.   Permanently frozen subsoil is known as:
      (a)   permafrost.
      (b)   ice floe.
      (c)   ice pack.

7.   In the hydrologic cycle, what percentage of water is contained in the oceans?
      (a)   55%   (b)   63%
      (c)   82%   (d)   97%

8.   What percentage of the land surface of Earth is covered by ice?
      (a)   1%   (b)   2%
      (c)   10%   (d)   50%

9.   Transpiration involves the transfer of moisture to the atmosphere from:
      (a)   plants.
      (b)   glaciers.
      (c)   evaporation.
      (d)   the greenhouse effect.

10.   The salinity of the oceans is likely to be greatest:
        (a)   at the mouth of a large river in the tropics.
        (b)   at the mouth of a large river in the high latitudes.
        (c)   off the coast from a subtropical desert.
        (d)   below the Arctic ice cap.

11.   Tides are primarily caused by:
        (a)   the gravitational pull of the moon and Sun.
        (b)   ocean currents along the coast of a continent.
        (c)   ocean currents in the middle of the ocean.
        (d)   waves produced by storms at sea.

Answers to Self-Test:

1.	d	6.	a	11.	a
2.	a	7.	d		
3.	b	8.	c		
4.	c	9.	a		
5.	c	10.	c		

HINTS FOR TEXTBOOK STUDY QUESTIONS

1.   Review the textbook section beginning on page 161.

2.   Figure 9-2 (p. 128 of the Study Guide) may help.

3.   See Figure 9-2 (p. 128 of the Study Guide). You may also want to review page 147 in Chapter 6.

4.   Again, see Figure 9-2 (p. 128 of the Study Guide).

5.   Refer to the diagram of the hydrologic cycle (Figure 9-2, p. 128 of the Study Guide); look for the different kinds of water reservoirs.

6.   See "How Many Oceans" beginning on page 263.

7.   Size is just one characteristic.

8.   Consider what factors would tend to increase or decrease the concentration of dissolved salts in the ocean.

9.   See Figure 9-6 (p. 129 of the Study Guide).

10.   These terms are defined on page 267.

11.   See Figure 9-6 (p. 129 of the Study Guide) and the associated text material describing the monthly tidal cycle (pp. 267–268).

12.   Figure 9-9 (p. 270) is a photograph of a tidal bore; the related text material is found on page 268.

13.   Figure 9-10 (p. 270) is a good place to start when answering this question.

14.   This is discussed on page 272.

15.   Figure 9-15 (p. 274) shows the distribution of permafrost in the Northern Hemisphere.

16.   There are two main ways that lakes disappear. The textbook discusses this on page 274.

17.   See pages 275–278.

18.   Figure 9-22 (on page 130 of the Study Guide) may help.

19.   Again, see Figure 9-22 (on page 130 of the Study Guide).

20.   View the animation, *Groundwater Cone of Depression*.

21.   This is illustrated in Figure 9-24 (p. 282).

22.   This is discussed on page 283.

23.   Read the section "Groundwater Mining" beginning on page 283.

ADDITIONAL STUDY QUESTIONS

1. How long might it take for a water molecule to go through the hydrologic cycle?

2. Why is most of the volume of an iceberg below the water line?

Hints for Additional Study Questions:

1. See the section "Residence Times" on page 263.

2. Review the characteristics of water in Chapter 6 (p. 143).

CHAPTER 10

Cycles and Patterns in the Biosphere

OVERVIEW

In this chapter, the fundamental processes in the biosphere are presented. The chapter begins by looking at the different "biogeochemical" cycles of energy, water, and nutrients that link the biosphere with the atmosphere, the hydrosphere, and the lithosphere. The concept of food chains, factors influencing natural distributions of plants and animals, and an overview of basic environmental relationships are then presented.

When studying the biogeochemical cycles, look for the relationships between these cycles and other patterns and processes covered in previous chapters. For example, relate the energy cycle and the carbon cycle to the various components of Earth's solar radiation budget (Chapter 4), and examine the water cycle in the context of the material about the hydrosphere presented in Chapter 9. Especially note the important relationship between the distribution patterns of organisms and the distribution of climate.

KEY CONCEPTS

THE GEOGRAPHIC APPROACH TO THE STUDY OF ORGANISMS (p. 289):

Chapter 10 focuses on the various factors that influence the distribution of plants and animals around the world. Biogeographers look for the interrelationships between living organisms and the other components of the natural environment. (This approach will be developed further in Chapter 11.)

BIOGEOCHEMICAL CYCLES (p. 291):

One of the most fundamental concepts in the study of the biosphere is that life depends on an intricate network of interactions and interrelationships between different facets of the natural world. The most basic of these interrelationships can be presented as a series of *biogeochemical cycles* or "flows." This section describes the most important of these cycles. Keep in mind that these cycles are exceedingly complex, and are presented here in only superficial detail.

The Flow of Energy (p. 291): The most basic of all cycles is the flow of solar energy through the biosphere. This cycle is an extension of the solar radiation budget presented in Chapter 4. Note in **Figure 10-3** (shown below), that while only a very small amount of solar energy is "fixed" (stored) by green plants during the process of *photosynthesis*, this solar energy is cycled through the biosphere by the consumption of plants by animals, and by the decomposition of organic matter.

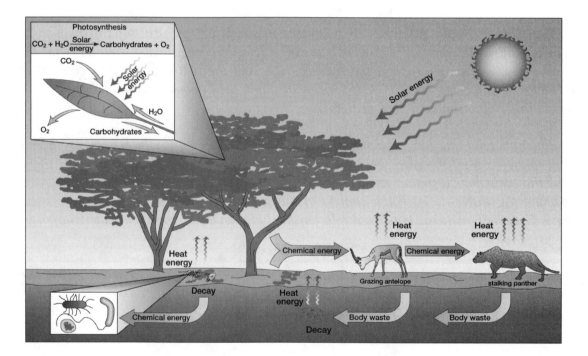

Figure 10-3: Energy flow in the terrestrial biosphere. Plants use and store solar energy as carbohydrates through the process of photosynthesis. Grazing animals then acquire that energy by eating plants. Other animals eat the grazers and thereby acquire some of this energy. Body wastes from the animals, the bodies of the animals once they die, and dead plant matter all return energy to the soil. As all this waste and dead matter decays, it gives off energy in the form of heat.

Note that *net primary productivity* refers to the *net photosynthesis* (the difference between the amount of carbohydrate produced by photosynthesis and the amount of carbohydrate lost through *plant respiration*) of a plant community over a period of a year—measured as the mass of fixed carbon per unit area.

The Hydrologic Cycle (p. 293): Water is found in the biosphere in two basic forms. *Water in residence* refers to water that is chemically part of living tissue. *Water in transit* is water that is moving in and out of the biosphere, primarily through photosynthesis.

The Carbon Cycle (p. 294): Carbon is fundamental to all forms of life, and so the carbon cycle is one of the most important biogeochemical cycles.

Notice in Figure 10-6 (p. 294) that carbon is introduced into the biosphere through photosynthesis. Carbon dioxide is fixed by green plants into *carbohydrates*. Carbohydrates then can be used for energy directly by the plant, or consumed by animals. As these carbohydrates are utilized by living organisms, carbon dioxide is released into the atmosphere through *respiration*. Note that the carbon cycle is intimately related to the energy cycle since sunlight provides the energy that is stored in carbohydrates through the process of photosynthesis.

See the animations *Net Primary Productivity* and ***Biological Productivity in Midlatitude Oceans*** for a description of the seasonal patterns of photosynthesis, temperature, as well as plankton growth in the ocean.

The Oxygen Cycle (p. 295): Oxygen is crucial for life in the biosphere. Oxygen is cycled into the biosphere through photosynthesis. (Note that in the process of photosynthesis, the energy from sunlight helps convert carbon dioxide and water into carbohydrates and oxygen.) However, as Figure 10-7 (p. 295) suggests, free oxygen gas cycles from the atmosphere through the biosphere in a variety of ways.

The Nitrogen Cycle (p. 295): As with oxygen and carbon, nitrogen is essential to all living organisms.   The key to understanding the nitrogen cycle (Figure 10-8, p. 296) is in recognizing that very few organisms can directly utilize nitrogen gas from the atmosphere. In most cases, nitrogen must be *fixed* into *nitrates*, a form of nitrogen that can be utilized by plants. Some nitrogen is fixed in the atmosphere, but most is fixed by microorganisms in the soil.

FOOD CHAINS (p. 297):

Energy and nutrients are cycled through the biosphere in *food chains* (Figure 10-9, p. 297), although the terms *food web* or *food pyramid* are perhaps more accurate. Figure 10-10 (p. 298) shows a food pyramid and illustrates an important concept. The transfer of energy from plants (the *producers*) at the bottom of the food pyramid to higher and higher levels of *consumers* is not very efficient. In other words, only a small portion of the energy stored in an organism can be passed on to the consumer of that organism. That is why it takes about 1000 kilograms of plankton to produce just 10 kilograms of fish.

NATURAL DISTRIBUTIONS (p. 299):

The fundamental factors that determine the distribution of organisms are presented in this section: the location where an organism first evolves, the migration patterns of that organism, the opportunity for successful reproduction, and the reduction in the range of a species through death of some (or all) of a population.

Plant Succession (p. 302): *Plant succession* is a key concept in biogeography. Succession represents a natural progression in which one plant community is replaced with another plant community over time. The example of the infilling of a lake bed (**Figure 10-17**, shown below) is a basic illustration of this process.

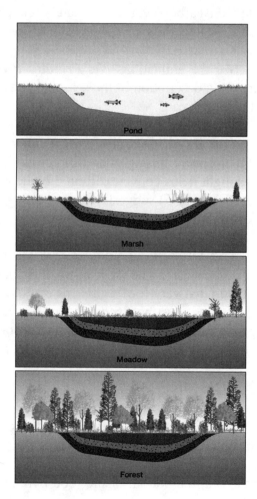

Figure 10-17: A simple example of plant succession: infilling of a small lake. Over time, successional colonization by different plant associations changes the area from pond to marsh to meadow to forest.

As the text cautions, do not confuse the replacement of plant species in succession with *extinction*. In the case of succession, during specific stages of environmental change, certain plants will be able to thrive. Later, as the environment continues to change, these species will be replaced by other species.

ENVIRONMENTAL RELATIONSHIPS (p. 303):

The Influence of Climate (p. 304): The importance of climate to the distribution of organisms is clearly shown in the map of major biomes of the world in Chapter 11 (Figure 11-25, pp. 330-331). Notice the similarities in patterns seen in the map of biomes with those in the map of climate types (Figure 8-4, pp. 214–215). In Chapters 3 through 8, patterns of the environmental factors mentioned in this section (light, moisture, temperature, and wind) were discussed.

Wildfire (p. 306): Of the many factors that influence the distribution of plants and animals in the biosphere, fire might seem to many people to be the most catastrophic or unusual, but this is not the case. *People and the Environment: Wildfires in Yellowstone* (p. 307) is an informative discussion of the importance of wildfire to many ecosystems, as well as a discussion of the difficulties of establishing wildfire control policies.

PROGRESSIVE CONTENT REVIEW

1. The binomial system of biological classification is primarily based on the _____ of an organism. (p. 289)

   morphology/ structure

2. Biota are subdivided into _____ or plants, and _____ or animals. (p. 291)

   flora; fauna

3. _____ is a term referring to the animals that swim freely in the ocean. (p. 291)

   Nekton

4. The _____ is the most basic energy source for nearly all life. (p. 291)

   Sun

5. Only about 0.1 percent of received solar energy is stored by plants through the process of _____. (p. 291)

   photosynthesis

6. The most abundant single substance in the biosphere is
   _____. (p. 293)   water

7. Water is found in the biosphere in two ways: first, in _____,   residence
   chemically bound into plant and animal tissues, and second,
   in _____ as part of the respiration and transpiration process.   transit
   (pp. 293–294)

8. The most important process in the carbon cycle is the fixation
   of carbon dioxide from the atmosphere into _____ through   carbohydrates
   the process of photosynthesis, and then the eventual
   conversion back to carbon dioxide. (p. 294)

9. Plant-eating animals consume carbohydrates and release
   carbon dioxide through the process of _____. (p. 294)   respiration

10. The largest "reservoir" of carbon on or near the surface of
    Earth is found in sedimentary deposits such as _____ and   coal/petroleum/
    _____. (p. 294)   carbonate rocks

11. Most oxygen gas in the atmosphere has been released during
    the process of _____. (p. 295)   photosynthesis

12. Most free nitrogen gas becomes available for use in the
    biosphere only after being converted into nitrates through the
    process of nitrogen _____. (p. 296)   fixation

13. Microorganisms are primarily responsible for the _____   denitrification
    process, in which useable nitrogen (nitrate) is converted back
    into _____ _____. (p. 296)   nitrogen gas

14. Energy and nutrients flow through the biosphere from one
    organism to another in _____ _____. (p. 297)   food chains/
                                                                        food pyramids

15. In the most basic food chain, plants are eaten by _____   primary
    consumers, which in turn can be eaten by _____ consumers.   secondary
    (p. 297)

16. _____ _____ is the natural replacement of one type of   Plant succession
    vegetation with another over time. (p. 302)

17.   _____ refers to the permanent elimination of a species on Earth. (p. 302)   Extinction

18.   The most important environmental constraints on organisms are usually _____ factors. (p. 304)   climatic

19.   Light is crucial to green plants because of their dependence on the process of _____. (p. 304)   photosynthesis

20.   _____ refers to an organism's response to the length of exposure to light. (p. 304)   Photoperiodism

21.   Edaphic factors relate to the characteristics of the _____. (pp. 305–306)   soil

22.   Some plant species scatter their seeds only after the heat from a _____ has opened their cones or seedpods. (p. 308)   wildfire

SELF-TEST

1.   What is the primary source of energy in the biosphere?
    (a)   Water.   (b)   Volcanoes.
    (c)   Gravity.   (d)   The Sun.

2.   What is the most abundant single substance in the biosphere?
    (a)   Carbon.   (b)   Water.
    (c)   Phosphorous   (d)   Calcium.

3.   How is solar energy "stored" in the biosphere?
    (a)   As heat in warm surface waters.
    (b)   Through latent heat in the atmosphere.
    (c)   In carbon dioxide produced by respiration.
    (d)   In carbohydrates produced by photosynthesis.

4. In the process of photosynthesis, carbon dioxide and water combine, in the presence of sunlight, to produce carbohydrates and:
    (a)   oxygen.   (b)   argon.
    (c)   nitrogen.   (d)   ozone.

5. What is the primary source of carbon for *active* use in the biosphere?
    (a)   Water vapor in the atmosphere.
    (b)   Carbon dioxide in the atmosphere.
    (c)   Carbon dissolved in the oceans.
    (d)   Fossil carbon, such as coal and petroleum.

6. What is the primary source of carbon that *humans* have added to the atmosphere?
    (a)   Water vapor in the atmosphere.
    (b)   Carbon dioxide in the atmosphere.
    (c)   Carbon dissolved in the oceans.
    (d)   The burning of "fossil" carbon, such as coal and petroleum.

7. Why is it difficult to integrate nitrogen gas from the atmosphere into the nitrogen cycle of the biosphere?
    (a)   Nitrogen is not very abundant in the atmosphere.
    (b)   Nitrogen gas in the atmosphere can only be directly utilized by a few organisms.
    (c)   Organic nitrogen compounds are not required for survival by most plants.
    (d)   Nitrogen gas is quickly absorbed by the oceans.

8. Plant succession involves:
    (a)   the extinction of plant species.
    (b)   the evolution of new plant species over time.
    (c)   the movement of plant seeds across an ocean.
    (d)   changes in species composition over time.

9. Most oxygen now in the atmosphere came from:
    (a)   volcanic activity.
    (b)   the evaporation of water.
    (c)   plants through the process of photosynthesis.
    (d)   oxidative weathering of rocks.

10. Animals that eat plants are known as:
    (a)   primary consumers.   (b)   secondary consumers.
    (c)   primary producers.   (d)   carnivores.

11. What is the main reason that trees in dense forests are likely to be tall with narrow tops?
    (a) Competition for light.
    (b) Lack of water.
    (c) Abundance of water.
    (d) Tall trees can be held up by neighboring trees.

Answers to Self-Test:

1.	d	6.	d	11.	a
2.	b	7.	b		
3.	d	8.	d		
4.	a	9.	c		
5.	b	10.	a		

HINTS FOR TEXTBOOK STUDY QUESTIONS

1. See Figure 10-3 (on page 138 of the Study Guide).

2. Again, it may help to review Figure 10-3 (on page 138 of the Study Guide).

3. This process is described on page 292.

4. This process is also described on page 292.

5. When answering this question, consider that plants engage in both photosynthesis and respiration during the year.

6. A discussion of this is found on page 292 in the textbook.

7. Figure 10-6 (p. 294) is a good place to start.

8. Consider forms of carbon that involve long-term storage.

9. See Figure 10-6 (p. 294).

10. Notice how many biogeochemical cycles involve the process of photosynthesis.

11. See the text beginning on page 295.

12.   This is discussed in the text beginning on page 296.

13.   Contrast Figures 10-9 and 10-10 (pp. 297–298).

14.   Figure 10-3 (p. 138 of the Study Guide) may help here.

15.   See Figure 10-9 (p. 297) and the associated text material.

16.   Consider the efficiency of energy transfer from one organism to another.

17.   Figure 10-14 (p. 302) illustrates one way.

18.   Figure 10-17 (p. 140 in the Study Guide) illustrates an example of this.

19.   This term is defined on page 304.

20.   A description of photoperiodism is found on page 304.

21.   Figure 10-18 (p. 305) is a starting point for understanding this.

22.   Reviewing the section *People and the Environment: Wildfires in Yellowstone* (p. 307).

ADDITIONAL STUDY QUESTIONS

1.   Compare the distribution of tropical rainforest (*selva*) shown in Figure 10-22 (p. 308) to that of global climate (Figure 8-4, pp. 214–215).   What general climate characteristics are associated with the locations of tropical rainforest?

2.   In what ways is wildfire *not* a catastrophic event in the biosphere?

Hints for Additional Study Questions:

1.   Especially consider the patterns of annual temperature and precipitation.

2.   Review the section *People and the Environment: Wildfires in Yellowstone.*

CHAPTER 11

Terrestrial Flora and Fauna

OVERVIEW

Chapter 11 continues our examination of the biosphere, moving beyond the introduction of biogeochemical cycles and environmental influences presented in Chapter 10, to a more specific look at the distribution patterns of plants and animals. The chapter highlights the most important characteristics and adaptations of plants and animals to constraints in the natural environment.

A key geographic relationship is well illustrated in the section on the major biomes of the world: the close relationship between climate and the distribution of various plant communities. As you study this chapter, look for the relationships between the pattern of biomes and climatic patterns we have studied, such as temperature and precipitation.

KEY CONCEPTS

ECOSYSTEMS AND BIOMES (p. 313):

Note the difference in meaning of the terms ecosystem and biome. An *ecosystem* is a "fundamental biological community" that is tied together by the flow of energy and nutrients through biogeochemical cycles. The problem with studying ecosystems is that they can be described at all scales, from the planetary scale to the microscopic world in a drop of water. For this reason, biogeographers most often describe distribution patterns of ecosystems in terms of biomes. A *biome* is a "large, recognizable assemblage of plants and animals in functional interaction with the environment."

TERRESTRIAL FLORA (p. 314):

This section covers the most important characteristics and adaptations of plants.

Floristic Terminology (p. 314): Note the distinctions between *gymnosperms* and *angiosperms*, between *evergreen* and *deciduous* trees, and between *broadleaf* and *needle-leaf* trees. The diagram contrasting the two basic types of trees (Figure 11-3, p. 315) may help clarify the distinction between angiosperms and gymnosperms.

Environmental Adaptations (p. 315): Two of the most important (and common) categories of environmental adaptations of plants concern moisture—either adapting to high amounts of moisture or to low amounts of moisture. *Xerophytic* adaptations refer to mechanisms for adjusting to prolonged dry conditions, while *hygrophytic* adaptations refer to mechanisms for adjusting to prolonged wet conditions.

Spatial Groupings of Plants (p. 317): The term *climax vegetation* refers to the stable community of plants that exists after plant succession. This can be thought of as the optimal group of plants for a given environment.

Identifying and Mapping Associations (p. 317): Figure 11-7 (p. 318) is a map showing the distribution of major natural climax vegetation associations around the world. Note that this map shows the distribution of plant communities assuming that there has been no human intervention. This theoretical distribution has been dramatically altered by humans in many parts of the world.

Vertical Zonation (p. 320): One of the most striking patterns seen in plant distributions is that of *vertical zonation*. As elevation increases in mountain areas, the dominant type of vegetation changes. As was discussed in the chapters on weather and climate, an increase in elevation is much like an increase in latitude. **Figure 11-10** (shown on the following page) illustrates the vertical zones of vegetation over the Sierra Nevada mountain range in California. Note that the western side of the Sierra receives much more precipitation than the eastern side.

Local Variations (p. 321): The exposure of a hill slope to sunlight is an important determinant of vegetation cover. *Adret slopes*, which receive the Sun's rays at a high angle, typically have a different vegetation composition from *ubac slopes*, which receive the Sun's rays at lower angles (**Figure 11-13**, on the following page).

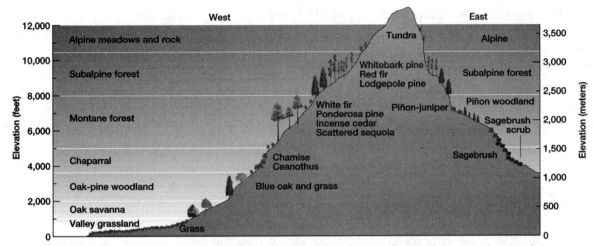

Figure 11-10: A west-east profile of California's Sierra Nevada, indicating the principal vegetation at different elevations on the western (wet) and eastern (dry) sides of the range.

TERRESTRIAL FAUNA (p. 322):

This section presents the most important characteristics and adaptations of animals.

Kinds of Animals (p. 322): The number of different species of *invertebrates* (animals without backbones), especially the arthropods, is far greater than the number of species of *vertebrates* (animals with backbones). Also note the difference between the *placental mammals* and the *marsupials*. Young placentals (such as humans) grow and develop inside the mother's body, while marsupials (such as kangaroos) have pouches where undeveloped young live for some time after birth.

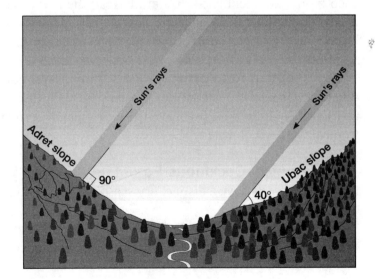

Figure 11-13: A typical adret-ubac situation.

Environmental Adaptations (p. 324): *Focus: Desert Adaptations of the Amazing Camel* (p. 326) is an interesting example of the anatomical and physiological adaptations of the camel to the desert environment.

Cooperation Among Animals (p. 327): Note the difference between mutualism and parasitism. *Mutualism* involves a relationship between two different species that is beneficial to both. In the case of *parasitism*, one species (the *parasite*) is nourished by attaching itself to another species (the "host"). Typically, the host species is weakened but not killed by the parasite.

ZOOGEOGRAPHIC REGIONS (p. 328):

While it is more difficult to explain the global distribution of animals than plants, we can recognize general *zoogeographic regions* of animals. Within these nine major regions (Figure 11-23, p. 329), characteristic and distinctive groups of animal species are found. The basic explanation of this distribution is that geographic isolation (produced by natural barriers of oceans, mountains, or deserts) has allowed animals to evolve differently.

THE MAJOR BIOMES (p. 331):

The 10 major biomes of the world are shown in Figure 11-25 (pp. 330-331). These biomes are primarily distinguished by the dominant type of vegetation, although each biome generally contains characteristic animals as well. The close relationship between vegetation and climate has already been mentioned.

In the following paragraphs only one or two important or distinguishing characteristics of each biome are mentioned. Carefully read the text description for a more complete explanation of each biome. Note that the text has a small map showing the general location of each of these biomes, as well as one or more photographs to illustrate these environments.

Tropical Rainforest (p. 332): Tropical rainforests are characterized by very high species diversity (many different species present, but with just a few individuals of each species in a given area), and by infertile soils. Note the close spatial correlation of the tropical rainforest biome to the tropical wet (Af) climate type.

Tropical Deciduous Forest (p. 333): Unlike the tropical rainforest biome, the tropical deciduous forests have a distinct dry season and many trees may shed their leaves during this period.

The usual transition between the humid tropical deciduous forest biome and the much drier deserts is either the tropical scrub or tropical savanna biome.

Tropical Scrub (p. 333): Tropical scrub areas are found in the drier areas of the tropical humid (Group A) climate, and typically contain thorny or spiny shrubs.

Tropical Savanna (p. 333): These tropical grasslands are often, but by no means always, found in the climatic region of tropical savanna (Aw). They typically contain a wide variety of tall grasses, interspersed with scattered trees.

Desert (p. 335): In the map showing the distribution of the desert biome (Figure 11-31b, p. 337) note that these areas generally correspond to the climatic regions of the subtropical deserts (BWh) or the midlatitude deserts (BWk). Since this biome includes both hot and relatively cool desert areas of the world, the appearance of the vegetation cover varies widely.

Mediterranean Woodland and Shrub (p. 336): Two major plant associations are found in the regions of mediterranean (Cs) climate around the world. The mediterranean woodland consists of open grassland with interspersed trees (such as the oak in California), while the mediterranean shrub (also known as *chaparral*) consists of low, dense stands of shrubs and small trees. Both plant associations are highly adapted to wildfire and a summer dry season.

Midlatitude Grassland (p. 339): These grasslands develop in regions too dry for forests, but too wet for deserts, such as in areas of midlatitude steppe climate (BSk). They include grasslands such as the *pampa* of Argentina and the *prairies* of North America.

Midlatitude Deciduous Forest (p. 340): These forests, consisting primarily of broadleaf trees, are found in humid areas in the midlatitudes with warm or hot summers but cold winters, such as in the northeastern United States.

Boreal Forest (p. 340): The boreal forest biome is closely associated with severe continental climates (such as subarctic, Dfc) and forms an almost unbroken belt across the whole of North America and Eurasia between about 50°–60° N latitude (Figure 11-36b, p. 341). This biome typically consists of forests composed of just a few species of evergreen conifers.

Tundra (p. 342): The tundra biome consists of treeless plains that occur under harsh, dry climates of very low average temperatures (such as the tundra climate, ET).

HUMAN MODIFICATION OF NATURAL DISTRIBUTION PATTERNS (p. 343):

For dramatic examples of the alteration of natural habitats by human activity, see *People and the Environment: Rainforest Loss in Brazil* (p. 346) and "Biotic Rearrangement: The Sad Case of Florida" (pp. 347–349).

PROGRESSIVE CONTENT REVIEW

1. An _____ is defined as a functional community of plants and animals (at many different scales). (p. 313)

    ecosystem

2. A _____ is a large, functional assemblage of plants and animals, usually named after the dominant type of _____. (p. 313)

    biome
    vegetation

3. _____ is the total weight of all organisms in an area. (p. 313)

    Biomass

4. Biomes merge with each other through transition zones called _____. (p. 314)

    ecotones

5. _____ are plants that survive throughout the year, while _____ die off in one season but leave seeds behind to germinate during the next favorable season. (p. 314)

    Perennials
    annuals

6. _____ are plants that hold their seeds in cones. (p. 315)

    Gymnosperms

7. _____ trees shed leaves throughout the year, but appear fully leaved at all times, while _____ trees shed their leaves during one season of the year. (p. 315)

    Evergreen
    deciduous

8. Xerophytic adaptations in plants allow survival in _____ (dry/wet) environments. (pp. 315–316)

    dry

9. Plants with fleshy stems that store moisture are called _____. (p. 316)

    succulents

10. _____ are plants that live in water-saturated soils, while _____ are plants that live permanently immersed in water. (p. 316)

    Hygrophytes
    hydrophytes

11. The stable community of plants that remains after plant succession is called the _____ vegetation. (p. 317)

    climax

12. Plant associations that are dominated by short woody plants are called _____. (p. 318)

    shrublands

13. A low latitude (tropical), tall grassland is the _____, while a midlatitude tall grassland is the _____. (p. 319)

savanna
prairie

14. The elevation of the upper treeline generally becomes _____ (higher/lower), moving from the equator toward the poles. (pp. 320–321)

lower

15. The Sun-facing _____ slope of a mountain is generally hotter and drier than the less Sun-exposed _____ slope. (p. 321)

adret
ubac

16. About _____ percent of all animal species have no backbone and are referred to as _____ (p. 323)

90
invertebrates

17. _____ mammals grow inside the mother's body until old enough to survive outside the womb. (p. 323)

Placental

18. Animals that maintain a constant body temperature regardless of the temperature of the air or water are known as _____ (p. 323)

endothermic

19. _____ refers to the state of an animal that is dormant during the winter, while _____ refers to the state of an animal that is dormant during a hot or dry period. (p. 325)

Hibernation
estivation

20. A relationship between two species that is mutually beneficial is called _____. (p. 327)

mutualism

21. The _____ zoogeographic region has the most distinctive fauna of any major region of the world. (p. 330)

Australian

22. Most nutrients in the tropical rainforest biome are held in the living _____ rather than in the soil. (p. 333)

vegetation

23. Recurrent wildfires are a typical occurrence in the tropical _____ biome. (pp. 334-335)

savanna

24. _____ refers to the dense, woody plant community of the mediterranean shrublands of North America. (p. 336)

Chaparral

25. Most tree species in midlatitude deciduous forests are _____ (broadleaf/needle-leaf) and deciduous. (p. 340)

broadleaf

26. Most trees in the boreal forest biome are needle-leaf _____ (deciduous/evergreen) trees. Typically in this biome, a _____ (large/small) number of different species is represented. (p. 341)

evergreen

small

27. Trees are unable to survive in the tundra biome because the summers are so short and _____ (warm/cool). (p. 342)

cool

28. Organisms that have been introduced into a new habitat by humans are known as _____ species. (p. 347)

exotic

SELF-TEST

1. Small waxy leaves are a likely plant adaptation to:
   (a) reduce the surface area on which frost can form.
   (b) reduce the amount of moisture loss through transpiration.
   (c) reduce the amount of water absorbed during a heavy rain.
   (d) increase the strength of leaves in a windy environment.

2. Deep taproots are a likely adaptation of plants in:
   (a) very cold regions.
   (b) areas of wet and soggy soil.
   (c) areas with little sunshine.
   (d) dry regions.

3. A wide, flared trunk near the ground is a likely adaptation of trees in:
   (a) very cold regions.
   (b) areas of wet and soggy soil.
   (c) areas with little sunshine.
   (d) dry regions.

4. Evergreen trees:
   (a) never lose their leaves.
   (b) drop all of their leaves at the same time.
   (c) never lose all of their leaves at the same time.
   (d) are always conifers.

5. Climax vegetation refers to:
   (a) the stable plant community remaining after succession.
   (b) the first plant community to develop after a wildfire.
   (c) the tallest trees in the tropical rainforest.
   (d) the tallest trees in a desert.

6. What is the most important way that an increase in elevation is similar to an increase in latitude?
   (a) It generally becomes more sunny.
   (b) Precipitation increases.
   (c) It generally becomes warmer.
   (d) It generally becomes colder.

7. In relationships between two species known as mutualism:
   (a) neither species benefits.
   (b) both species benefit.
   (c) one species benefits, while the other is not affected.
   (d) one species benefits, but the other is weakened.

8. In relationships between two species known as parasitism:
   (a) neither species benefits.
   (b) both species benefit.
   (c) one species benefits, while the other is not affected.
   (d) one species benefits, but the other is weakened.

9. Hibernating animals:
   (a) sleep during the day, and hunt at night.
   (b) hunt during the day, and sleep at night.
   (c) spend the winter underground in an active state.
   (d) spend the winter in an inactive state.

10. What is one factor that helps explain the collections of animals found in the various zoogeographical regions?
    (a) Physical barriers limited animal migration.
    (b) Different climates are found in each region.
    (c) Humans modified the distribution of animals.
    (d) Different patterns of soils.

11.   Tropical rainforests tend to have:
       (a)   a wide variety of plant and tree species growing in close conjunction.
       (b)   very few plant and tree species.
       (c)   very slow decomposition of plant litter.
       (d)   few arboreal animal species.

12.   Which environmental condition is *most closely* associated with the distribution of midlatitude grasslands?
       (a)   Rich soils.
       (b)   Poor soils.
       (c)   Moderate to low precipitation (steppe climates)
       (d)   High precipitation.

13.   Which of the following statements regarding tropical rainforests and boreal forests is true?
       (a)   Boreal forests have much lower species diversity than tropical rainforests.
       (b)   All trees in tropical rainforests are deciduous.
       (c)   Tropical rainforests have more fertile soils than boreal forests.
       (d)   Much more light reaches the floor of tropical rainforests than boreal forests.

14.   Refer to the biomes map in the text (Figure 11-25; pp. 330–331). The tropical rainforest biome generally corresponds to the distribution of which climatic type?
       (a)   Subtropical steppe (BSh)
       (b)   Humid subtropical (Cfa)
       (c)   Tropical savanna (Aw)
       (d)   Tropical wet (Af)

15.   Refer to the biomes map in the text (Figure 11-25; pp. 330-331). The boreal forest biome generally corresponds to the distribution of which climate type?
       (a)   Marine west coast (Cfb)
       (b)   Humid subtropical (Cfa)
       (c)   Subarctic (Dfc)
       (d)   Tundra (ET)

16.   The boundaries between biomes (ecotones) are *usually* seen as:
       (a)   gradual transition zones.
       (b)   abrupt changes in vegetation, but not of animals.
       (c)   abrupt changes in both vegetation and animals.
       (d)   distinct topographic barriers such as mountains and rivers.

Answers to Self-Test:

1.	b	6.	d	11.	a	16.	a
2.	d	7.	b	12.	c		
3.	b	8.	d	13.	a		
4.	c	9.	d	14.	d		
5.	a	10.	a	15.	c		

HINTS FOR TEXTBOOK STUDY QUESTIONS

1.   These concepts are discussed beginning on page 313.

2.   See Figure 11-2 (p. 314).

3.   These terms are defined on page. 314.

4.   If you are not clear on the distinctions between these different kinds of plants, see the section, "Floristic Terminology" (pp. 314–315), and Figure 11-3 (p. 315).

5.   This is also discussed in the section "Floristic Terminology" (pp. 314–315), and illustrated in Figure 11-3 (p. 315).

6.   Again, this is discussed in the section "Floristic Terminology" (pp. 314–315), and illustrated in Figure 11-3 (p. 315).

7.   Figure 11-4 (p. 316) illustrates several of these adaptations.

8.   The photographs in Figure 11-6 (p. 317) illustrate several of these adaptations.

9.   For a discussion of this concept, see the section "The Inevitability of Change" (p. 317).

10. Consider the internal distance that trees must transport fluid and nutrients compared with grasses.

11.   This distinction is described on page 318.

12.   These terms are defined on page. 319.

13.   See the section "Vertical Zonation" beginning on page 320.

14.   The photograph of the Sierra Nevada mountains (Figure 11-11, p. 320) helps illustrate this.

15.   See Figure 11-12 (p. 321).

16.   Figure 11-13 (p. 321) illustrates this difference.

17.   The photograph in Figure 11-14 (p. 322) shows one example of this.

18.   These fundamental differences are discussed on page 322.

19.   The term "vertebrate" is a reference to the bones of the spine; see Figure 11-15 (p. 323) for an example of an "invertebrate" animal.

20.   Some of these characteristics are discussed beginning on page 323.

21.   Consider the ability of animals to live in environments where the temperature is well below freezing.

22.   Examples of all of these adaptations are discussed beginning on page 324.

23.   For example, see *Focus: Desert Adaptations of the Amazing Camel* (p. 326).

24.   Figure 11-22 (p. 328) is a photograph showing one such relationship.

25.   These concepts are discussed beginning on page 327.

26.   See the map showing zoogeographic regions (Figure 11-23, p. 329) and the associated text material.

27.   Consider the role of geographic isolation.

28.   Compare the location of the tropical rainforest biome to that of climate distribution (Figure 11-26, p. 332).

29.   These biomes are discussed beginning on page 332.

30. This topic is covered beginning on page 333.

31. Figure 11-33 (p. 338) and the associated text is a good place to start.

32. Compare the biome and climate maps in Figure 11-30b (p. 336) and Figure 11-34b (p. 339).

33. See Figure 11-31 (p. 337).

34. This is well illustrated in Figures 11-35 and 11-36 (pp. 340–341).

35. Also see Figure 11-36b (p. 341).

36. This difference may be visible in the photographs of these biomes; also see the photograph in Figure 8-7a (p. 218).

37. The vegetation in the tundra biome is well shown in the photograph in Figure 11-38a (p. 342).

38. A discussion of this begins on page 343. Also see *People and the Environment: Rainforest Loss in Brazil* (p. 346).

39. See the section, "Artificial Translocation of Organisms" (p. 347).

40. The photographs in Figures 11-44 and 11-45 (pp. 348–349) are good examples of this.

ADDITIONAL STUDY QUESTIONS

1. What characteristics have allowed mammals to live in almost all parts of the world?

2. Why do geographers study plants more than they study animals?

Hints for Additional Study Questions:

1. For example, consider the advantages of being warm-blooded.

2. Some of the reasons for this are discussed on page 322.

CHAPTER 12

SOILS

OVERVIEW

    Chapter 12 discusses the characteristics, development, and distribution of soils around the world. The chapter describes soil-forming factors, soil components, soil properties, soil chemistry, and soil profiles. The section on pedogenic regimes relates the formation and characteristics of soil to differences in the environment, especially differences in climate. The chapter concludes with a description of soil classification and the distribution pattern of major soil types around the world.

    As you begin your study of soils, focus on how the various processes of soil formation influence the characteristics of soil. The pattern of soil distribution is complex, but by noting the close relationship between climate and many soil types, this pattern is more comprehensible.

KEY CONCEPTS

SOIL AND REGOLITH (p. 353):

    The soil found in an area represents the outcome of an ever-continuing set of soil-forming processes. A soil should not be thought of as a final product, but rather, as a stage in an ongoing evolution.

SOIL-FORMING FACTORS (p. 355):

    This section presents the most important factors that influence soil development.

The Geologic Factor (p. 355): In addition to the chemical composition of the bedrock, the texture that results as rock disintegrates also influences the characteristics of soil.

The Climatic Factor (p. 355): In general, high temperatures and ample moisture tend to increase chemical and biological processes and generally will produce deeper soil horizons.

The Topographic Factor (p. 355): Note that soil generally becomes deeper in flat areas since soil formed on steep slopes tends to be removed by erosion (Figure 12-4, p. 355).

The Biological Factor (p. 356): Even though only a small portion of soil typically consists of organic material, this small fraction is extremely important. Biological factors in soil development include both the burrowing activity of animals such as earthworms (see *Focus: Earthworms in the Soil*, p. 358), as well as the decomposing effects of microorganisms that produce *humus*, a dark, organic material.

The Chronological Factor (p. 357): Since all soils are in various stages of ongoing evolution, time becomes a key factor in determining soil characteristics. Keep in mind that the soil-forming processes being described in this section usually require long periods of time to operate.

SOIL COMPONENTS (p. 359):

Notice in Figure 12-9 (p. 360), that a typical soil will contain about half mineral matter (disintegrated rock), one quarter pore space filled with air, one quarter pore space filled with water, and a small amount of organic matter.

Soil Water (p. 360): Note the importance of *leaching*, a process in which water flushes nutrients out of the upper layers of soil. Mineral matter in general may be carried to deeper soil layers by percolating ground water in the process of *eluviation*. These soil particles are then deposited in deeper soil layers in the process of *illuviation* (Figure 12-13, p. 362).

The *soil–water balance* refers to the balance between the water that infiltrates the soil from the surface and the moisture that leaves through evaporation and plant transpiration (*evapo-transpiration*). Figure 12-14 (p. 363) illustrates a soil–water budget, relating the amount of precipitation to the amount of evapotranspiration during a year. In the summer months, when moisture loss is greatest, the soil is depleted of moisture and the *wilting point* is reached.

SOIL PROPERTIES (p. 362):

Texture (p. 364): Figure 12-16 (p. 364) illustrates the different sizes of soil particles (or *separates*). Figure 12-17 (p. 364) shows the standard classification scheme for soil texture based on the combination of *clay-*, *silt-*, and *sand-*sized particles. A *loam* is the soil texture in which there is a fairly even mix of all three separate sizes.

Structure (p. 364): Two soil structure factors are especially important with regard to soil moisture. *Porosity* is the amount of pore space in a soil that can hold water. *Permeability* describes how easily water can move through the soil.

SOIL CHEMISTRY (p. 365):

The ability of a soil to provide nutrients to plants partially depends upon the chemical characteristics of its components. Key components of soils are *colloids*. Colloids are microscopic soil particles that can mix with water and provide nutrients to plants. These tiny colloidal particles are suspended in water and can attract and hold nutrient chemicals that plants utilize.

The attraction of chemicals to colloids is the result of different electrical charges. Colloids usually have a strong negative electrical charge that attracts the positive electrical charge of the nutrient chemicals. Many of the most important mineral nutrients produce positively charged atoms or molecules called *cations*. The strength of the attraction of cations to the colloids suspended in water varies. If the bonds are too strong, the plants will be unable to absorb the nutrients; but if the bonds are too weak, the nutrients will be easily flushed away.

SOIL PROFILES (p. 367):

Figure 12-21 (shown on the following page) illustrates the four processes that age and deepen soils: "addition," "loss," "translocation," and "transformation."

Figure 12-22 (shown on page 165 of the Study Guide) shows the different vertical zones or *horizons* that can develop in soil. The *O horizon* (if present) consists of decaying organic matter. The *A horizon* or "topsoil" contains both mineral and organic material. The *E horizon* is an eluvial layer from which minerals have been removed. The *B horizon* or "subsoil" is a layer of illuviation where material from the E horizon above has been deposited. The *C horizon* is a layer of unconsolidated parent rock. Soil classification is largely based on the extent of development and characteristics of the horizons in a soil's *profile*.

PEDOGENIC REGIMES (p. 368):

Pedogenic regimes refer to environmental settings that produce characteristic soil types.

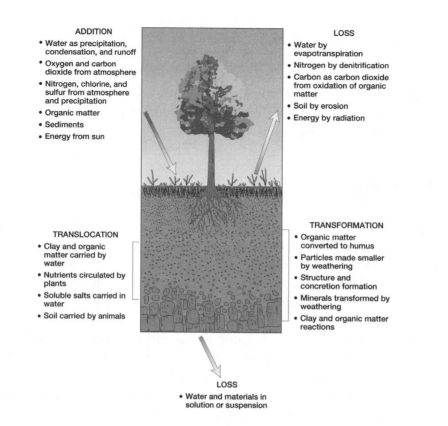

ADDITION
- Water as precipitation, condensation, and runoff
- Oxygen and carbon dioxide from atmosphere
- Nitrogen, chlorine, and sulfur from atmosphere and precipitation
- Organic matter
- Sediments
- Energy from sun

LOSS
- Water by evapotranspiration
- Nitrogen by denitrification
- Carbon as carbon dioxide from oxidation of organic matter
- Soil by erosion
- Energy by radiation

TRANSLOCATION
- Clay and organic matter carried by water
- Nutrients circulated by plants
- Soluble salts carried in water
- Soil carried by animals

TRANSFORMATION
- Organic matter converted to humus
- Particles made smaller by weathering
- Structure and concretion formation
- Minerals transformed by weathering
- Clay and organic matter reactions

LOSS
- Water and materials in solution or suspension

Figure 12-21: The four soil-forming processes: addition, loss, translocation, transformation. Geologic, climatic, topographic, biological, and chronological soil-forming factors influence the rate at which these four processes occur and therefore the rate at which soil is formed.

Laterization (p. 368): *Laterization* occurs in hot and humid areas and is characterized by the leaching of most minerals.

Podzolization (p. 369): *Podzolization* occurs in cool but fairly humid areas, is characterized by chemical leaching, and is especially common in coniferous forests where the soil is acidic.

Gleization (p. 370): *Gleization* is prominent in cool, waterlogged regions and tends to produce slowly decomposing, acidic soils.

Calcification (p. 371): *Calcification* occurs in arid or semiarid climates where chemical compounds such as calcium carbonate are concentrated in the B horizon.

Salinization (p. 371): *Salinization* also occurs in arid areas (especially in areas of high water tables) and is characterized by the accumulation of salts on the surface due to high evaporation.

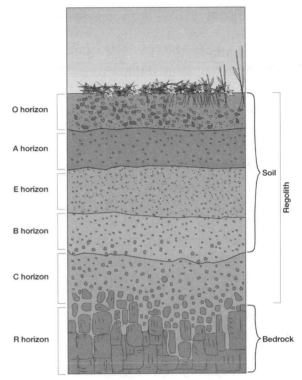

O horizon

A horizon

E horizon

B horizon

C horizon

R horizon

Soil

Regolith

Bedrock

Figure 12-22: Idealized soil profile. The O horizon consists mostly of organic matter. The A horizon, or "topsoil," contains both mineral and organic matter. The E horizon is primarily where eluviation takes place. The B horizon, or subsoil, is a layer of illuviation. The C horizon is unconsolidated but weathered parent material. The R horizon is bedrock. The true soil, or solum, consists of the O, A, E, and B horizons.

SOIL CLASSIFICATION (p. 372):

The Soil Taxonomy (p. 372): The system of soil classification used in the text divides all soil types into 12 major groups (called *soil orders*). This soil taxonomy system is based on the observable characteristics of soils, rather than the conditions that produce these soils. Table 12-2 (p. 374) describes the name derivations of the soil orders—many of the names are quite descriptive, and so it may be helpful to review the origins of these words. Figure 12-26 (p. 375) outlines the relationships among soil orders with regard to the amount of weathering, soil profile development, and the broad environmental conditions under which they develop.

The Mapping Question (p. 373): It is important to recognize the difficulties in mapping the distribution of soils. The Soils of the World map (Figure 12-25, pp. 372–373) is based on the most prevalent soil type, but by no means the only soil type, found in an area.

GLOBAL DISTRIBUTION OF MAJOR SOILS (p. 374):

For each of the 12 major soil orders, look at the generalized world distribution map (Figure 12-25; pp. 372–373), the small distribution map for each soil, as well as the photograph of a typical soil profile. For example, for Entisols, see Figure 12-27 (p. 376).

Entisols (p. 374) are young soils without well-developed soil horizons.

Inceptisols (p. 374) are immature soils that exhibit eluviation, but little illuviation; they generally lack diagnostic soil horizons.

Andisols (p. 375) develop from recent deposits of volcanic ash and exhibit minimal profile development.

Gelisols (p. 375) develop in areas of *permafrost*; "frost churning" or *cryoturbation* from the freeze–thaw cycle is commonly seen.

Histosols (p. 376) are soils consisting largely of water-logged organic material.

Aridisols (p. 377) are found in arid regions; they often have thinly developed, sandy profiles and lack extensive organic material.

Vertisols (p. 378) contain clay in large quantities; these soils swell when wet, then contract and crack when dry.

Mollisols (p. 379) are common in midlatitude grasslands; they contain a mineral surface layer that is dark and rich with organic material known as *humus*.

Alfisols (p. 379) are extensive mature soils that contain a subsurface clay horizon.

Ultisols (p. 380) are similar to the Alfisols, but are generally more deeply weathered and leached of nutrients.

Spodosols (p. 381) are common in areas of coniferous forests and regions of subarctic climate; the upper layers are heavily leached and often acidic.

Oxisols (p. 382) are the most thoroughly leached and weathered of the soils; they develop from the processes of laterization in warm, moist climates.

PROGRESSIVE CONTENT REVIEW

1. _____ is a layer of loose, weathered rock below the surface. Regolith
    (p. 354)

2. In general, soil-forming processes are most active in areas of _____ (high/low) temperature and _____ (high/low) moisture. (p. 355)   high; high

3. Soil tends to be deepest where the slope of the land is _____. (p. 355)   gentle/flat

4. _____ decompose organic matter into soil humus. (p. 357)   Microorganisms

5. Dead plant parts often accumulate at the surface to form a layer of _____. (p. 359)   litter

6. About _____ percent of the average soil consists of pore spaces. (p. 360)   50

7. Water can be pulled upward through a soil by _____ action. (pp. 360–361)   capillary

8. Dissolved nutrients are carried down through a soil in solution in a process called _____. (p. 362)   leaching

9. A soil is said to be at _____ _____ when most pore spaces are filled with water. (p. 362)   field capacity

10. A _____ is a soil texture in which there is an even mixture of clay, sand, and silt. (p. 364)   loam

11. Porosity is a measure of a soil's ability to hold _____ and _____. (p. 365)   air water

12. _____ are chemically active microscopic soil particles that are able to hold _____ and soil nutrients. (p. 366)   Colloids water

13. The _____ horizon is the uppermost soil layer, and contains mostly _____ matter. (p. 367)   O organic

14. Most seeds germinate in the ___ horizon. (p. 367)   A

15. The E horizon is an eluvial layer, consisting mostly of resistant materials such as _____. (p. 367)   sand

16. The _____ horizon is the zone where clay, iron, and aluminum accumulate. (p. 367)   B

17. The _____ horizon consists of regolith and generally lacks organic matter. (p. 367)   C

18. Laterization processes are common in regions of the world with _____ temperatures and _____ rainfall. (p. 368)   warm; high

19. A laterization regime typically results in the leaching away of _____, leaving primarily _____ and _____ oxides. (pp. 368–369)   silica;
          iron & aluminum

20. Podzolization normally takes place in regions of _____ (warm/cool) temperatures and _____ precipitation, such as the boreal forest biome. (pp. 369–370)   cool
          moderate

21. Gleization occurs in waterlogged areas in _____ (warm/cool) climates. (p. 370)   cool

22. The speed of decomposition of organic matter in gley soils is generally _____. (p. 370)   slow

23. In calcification regimes, _____ _____ often concentrates in the B horizon to form a _____. (p. 371)   calcium carbonate
          hardpan

24. Salinization takes place in arid regions where intense evaporation concentrates _____ near the surface of the soil. (p. 371)   salts

25. The Soil Taxonomy system is organized around the _____ characteristics of the soil rather than the environment or genesis of the soil. (p. 372)   observable

26. _____ have the least-developed horizons of any soil order. (p. 374)   Entisols

27. _____ are common in tundra and mountain areas. (p. 375)   Inceptisols

28. _____ are soils that have developed out of volcanic ash. (p. 375)   Andisols

29. _____ are soils that develop in regions of permafrost. (p. 375)   Gelisols

30. _____ are composed mostly of undecayed organic materials. (pp. 376-377)   Histosols

31. _____ are the most extensive of all soil orders, and are found predominantly in dry regions. (p. 377)   Aridisols

32. _____ are soils with a large proportion of clay, and are characterized by cracks on the surface. (p. 378)   Vertisols

33. _____ are the most fertile of all soil orders. (p. 379)   Mollisols

34. _____ have a horizon of clay below the surface, and are quite productive agriculturally. (p. 380)   Alfisols

35. _____ are highly leached, reddish (oxidized) soils with relatively low fertility. (p. 380)   Ultisols

36. _____ common in areas of coniferous forest and have a dark, reddish illuvial layer, with highly-leached upper layers. (pp. 383-382)   Spodosols

37. _____ are extremely leached and weathered soils, found primarily in old landscapes of the humid tropics. (p. 382)   Oxisols

SELF-TEST

1. Soils tend to be deepest in a region that is:
   (a)   cold and dry.
   (b)   cold and wet.
   (c)   warm and dry.
   (d)   warm and wet.

2.   Which factor is usually *most* important in determining soil characteristics?
        (a)   The climate.
        (b)   The type of bedrock (parent-material).
        (c)   The vegetation cover.
        (d)   The animal life present.

3.   Why do soils tend to be thin on steep slopes?
        (a)   Steep slopes tend to be cooler than gentle slopes.
        (b)   Steep slopes tend to be warmer than gentle slopes.
        (c)   More plants grow on steep slopes than gentle slopes.
        (d)   On steep slopes soil erosion is faster than soil formation.

4.   The smallest soil particles are:
        (a)   sand.
        (b)   clay.
        (c)   silt.
        (d)   gravel.

5.   Soil air tends to be:
        (a)   rich in carbon dioxide and poor in oxygen.
        (b)   rich in both carbon dioxide and oxygen.
        (c)   poor in carbon dioxide and rich in oxygen.
        (d)   poor in both carbon dioxide and oxygen.

6.   Leaching is the process in which:
        (a)   calcium carbonate accumulates at the surface of the soil.
        (b)   dissolved nutrients are carried downward.
        (c)   nutrients are concentrated in the A horizon.
        (d)   humus accumulates at the surface of the soil.

7.   What conditions would cause the soil to reach the "wilting point?"
        (a)   When there is too much moisture available for plants.
        (b)   When the annual evapotranspiration is less than the annual precipitation.
        (c)   When the average daily temperature range is the same as the average annual temperature range.
        (d)   When there is no more available moisture for plants.

8.   Reddish soils in tropical areas are caused by:
        (a)   minerals leaching away, leaving iron oxide stains.
        (b)   an abundance of organic material in the soil.
        (c)   an abundance of decomposing vegetation above the soil.
        (d)   the lack of iron oxides in the soil.

9.   Loam is:
        (a)   a soil consisting mostly of silt.
        (b)   a soil consisting mostly of clay.
        (c)   a soil with fairly even proportions of sand, silt, and clay.
        (d)   a sandy soil.

10.   Acidic soils:
        (a)   are inefficient in dissolving minerals.
        (b)   easily leach dissolved nutrients away.
        (c)   dry out faster than alkaline soils.
        (d)   hold water in layers of clay.

11.   Which factor would most severely inhibit the development of a soil profile?
        (a)   A long period of time to develop.
        (b)   An abundance of water.
        (c)   A lack of water.
        (d)   An abundance of decomposing vegetation.

12.   The B horizon tends to collect:
        (a)   minerals from above.
        (b)   large amounts of organic matter.
        (c)   silica sand.
        (d)   plant seeds.

13.   In warm, rainy areas:
        (a)   laterization produces deep but poor soils.
        (b)   podzolization produces shallow, acidic soils.
        (c)   gleization produces dark, organic, and oxygen-poor soils.
        (d)   salinization produces deposits of salts on the surface.

14.   In cool, waterlogged areas:
        (a)   laterization produces deep but poor soils.
        (b)   podzolization produces shallow, acidic soils.
        (c)   gleization produces dark, organic, and oxygen-poor soils.
        (d)   salinization produces deposits of salts on the surface.

15.   In the cool regions of boreal forests:
        (a)   laterization produces deep but poor soils.
        (b)   podzolization produces shallow, acidic soils.
        (c)   gleization produces dark, organic, and oxygen-poor soils.
        (d)   salinization produces deposits of salts on the surface.

16. In arid areas:
    (a) laterization produces deep but poor soils.
    (b) podzolization produces shallow, acidic soils.
    (c) gleization produces dark, organic, and oxygen-poor soils.
    (d) salinization produces deposits of salts on the surface.

17. Deserts are most likely to have:
    (a) Aridisols.
    (b) Spodosols.
    (c) Oxisols.
    (d) Histosols.

18. Coniferous forests are most likely to have:
    (a) Aridisols.
    (b) Spodosols.
    (c) Oxisols.
    (d) Histosols.

19. Areas with permafrost are most likely to have:
    (a) Aridisols.
    (b) Oxisols.
    (c) Andisols.
    (d) Gelisols.

Answers to Self-Test:

1.	d	6.	b	11.	c	16.	d
2.	a	7.	d	12.	a	17.	a
3.	d	8.	a	13.	a	18.	b
4.	b	9.	c	14.	c	19.	d
5.	a	10.	b	15.	b		

HINTS FOR TEXTBOOK STUDY QUESTIONS

1. Consider how regolith forms.

2. See Figure 12-2 (p. 354).

3. A description of these five factors begins on page 355.

4. Consider both the chemical composition and texture of the resulting soil.

5. See Figure 12-5 (p. 356).

6. Consider both the action of burrowing animals and waste decomposition. Also see the section, "The Biological Factor" (p. 356).

7. Consider the role that earthworms play in the development of soils. See *Focus: Earthworms in the Soil* (p. 358).

8. This topic is discussed on page 357.

9. See Figure 12-8 (p. 359) for one aspect of this.

10. These terms are discussed on pages 359–360.

11. See Figure 12-12 and the associated text material beginning on page 360.

12. Figure 12-13 (p. 362) illustrates these processes.

13. See the section, "Soil–Water Budget" (p. 362).

14. This is covered on page 362.

15. Remember the concept of "moisture deficit" used in determining dry climates. Figure 12-14 (p. 363) may also help with this concept.

16. Consider what black/dark brown, reddish/yellowish, and gray/bluish colors often indicate about the soil. This is discussed beginning on page 363.

17. See Figures 12-16 and 12-17 (p. 364).

18.   Figure 12-17 (p. 364) may help here.

19.   This was discussed in Chapter 9 (p. 280). A brief description in Chapter 12 is on page 365.

20.   See the section, "Cation Exchange" (p. 366).

21.   See Figure 12-22 (on page 165 in the Study Guide).

22.   A description of soil horizons is found on page 367.

23.   If you're not sure clear about these regimes, it is worth some time reviewing this section in the textbook, beginning on page 368.

24.   Remember the effects of high precipitation and high temperatures on soil formation.

25.   The Soil Taxonomy is described on pages 372-373.

26.   This is discussed beginning on page 373.

27.   Once you have determined a likely soil order found in your area, review the text and soil profile photograph found on pages 374–383.

28.   You may want to compare the global map of soil distribution (Figure 12-25, pp. 372–373) to that of climate (Figure 8-4, pp. 214–215) and biomes (Figure 11-25, pp. 330–331).

ADDITIONAL STUDY QUESTION

1.   Describe the distribution and characteristics of a soil order not found near where you live.

Hint for Additional Study Question:

1.   Once you have chosen a soil order to describe, take advantage of the maps and soil profile photographs found on pages 374–383.

Introduction to Landform Study

OVERVIEW

The remaining chapters of the textbook concentrate on the study of landforms. Chapter 13 provides a general introduction to this topic by discussing the overall structure of Earth, the basic types of rocks, the key concepts of geologic time and uniformitarianism, and the various scales of landform analysis.

Several sections of this chapter deserve special attention. The general introduction to the structure of Earth is important because terms and concepts first presented here will be utilized when we discuss plate tectonics in Chapter 14. Similarly, references to various types of rocks are also found in subsequent chapters. One of the most important concepts to consider in Chapter 13 is "geologic time." Unless we can expand our perspective of time to include periods of millions of years, the processes described in the remainder of the text will have little meaning.

KEY CONCEPTS

THE STRUCTURE OF EARTH (p. 387):

The overall vertical structure of Earth (**Figure 13-1**, shown on the following page) is simple to describe: a thin outer *crust*, the dense *mantle* below, the liquid *outer core*, and solid *inner core*.

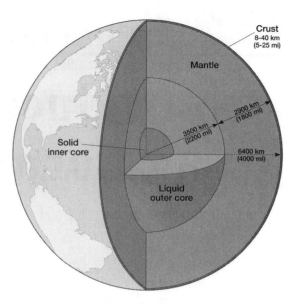

Figure 13-1: The presumed vertical structure of Earth's interior.

However, in order to understand *plate tectonics* and the dynamics of Earth's surface to be presented in Chapter 14, we need to think in terms of functional layers of Earth. **Figure 13-2** (shown on the following page) shows the uppermost several hundred kilometers of Earth. The thin crust of Earth (which includes both the ocean floors and the continents) together with the rigid upper mantle is called the *lithosphere*. The lithosphere is broken into large sections commonly called *plates*. These plates "float" and move around over the hot, mobile layer of the mantle called the *asthenosphere* (this will be discussed in greater detail in Chapter 14).

THE COMPOSITION OF EARTH (p. 389):

This section begins with a description of *minerals*—the solid elements and compounds from which *rocks* are made.

It is important to have a general understanding of the origin and overall characteristics of the three basic classes of rocks: *igneous*, *sedimentary*, and *metamorphic* (Figure 13-6, p. 392). Table 13-2 (p. 393) describes some of the common rocks that are mentioned in the remaining chapters of the text.

Igneous Rocks (p. 391): Igneous rocks form from the cooling and solidification of molten rock (*magma*). As you see in the photographs and descriptions in Figure 13-7 (p. 394), there are two subcategories of igneous rocks.

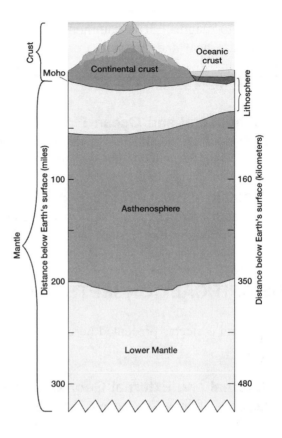

Figure 13-2: Idealized cross section through Earth's crust and part of the mantle. The crust and uppermost mantle are rigid, and together are called the lithosphere. The asthenosphere is part of the mantle and is hot and easily deformed.

Plutonic (Intrusive) Rocks (p. 392): Plutonic igneous rocks develop from magma that cools below the surface. *Granite* is the most widespread plutonic igneous rock. Since plutonic rocks, such as granite, cool slowly beneath the surface, they have larger mineral crystals than volcanic rocks that form from lava flows cooling quickly on the surface (Figure 13-8, p. 394).

Volcanic (Extrusive) Rocks (p. 392): Volcanic igneous rocks develop from the cooling of *lava* (molten rock on the surface of Earth), or from the accumulation of pyroclastic material such as volcanic ash or cinders. *Basalt* is the most widespread volcanic igneous rock (Figure 13-9, p. 395).

Sedimentary Rocks (p. 394): Sedimentary rocks form from the bonded fragments of other rocks, from the chemical precipitation of soluble materials such as calcium carbonate, or from the accumulation of organic matter. The bonding process that forms most sedimentary rocks usually consists of pressure and/or the cementing action of various chemicals. Also, note that most sedimentary rocks are laid down in horizontal layers (called *strata*). Later, these layers may be tilted or folded.

Metamorphic Rocks (p. 398): Metamorphic rocks are rocks that have been altered, primarily by heat and/or pressure, but the heating has not been great enough to completely melt the rock back into magma. It is common to see metamorphic rocks around the margins of plutonic intrusions—the heat and pressure from the magma alter the surrounding rocks through *contact metamorphism*. The animation ***Metamorphic Rock Foliation*** describes the way that some metamorphic rocks develop banded layers.

Continental and Ocean Floor Rocks (p. 400): The distinction between the basaltic crust of the ocean floor and the generally less dense granitic crustal rocks of the continents will become important for us when we discuss plate tectonics in Chapter 14.

Isostasy (p. 400): The addition of significant amounts of weight on Earth's surface (such as a thick continental ice sheet) can cause the crust to sink, while the removal of this weight will allow the crust to rise again (Figure 13-21, p. 402). Also see the animation ***Isostasy***.

SOME CRITICAL CONCEPTS (p. 403):

Several concepts presented here are fundamental to an understanding of the development of landforms.

Internal and External Geomorphic Processes (p. 404): This section describes two basic categories of processes that are shaping the surface of Earth. *Internal processes* originate from within Earth and result in various kinds of crustal movement. *External processes* originate on or above the surface of Earth, and generally serve to wear down the landscape. Both internal and external processes can operate at the same time in a landscape. The landscape we see today represents the temporary balance between these two opposing sets of processes. In the following chapters, we will discuss the many different kinds of internal and external processes.

Uniformitarianism (p. 404): The concept that "the present is the key to the past" is a foundation for the study of landforms. This means that we can understand how landforms developed in the past by looking at the processes that are shaping landforms today.

Geologic Time (p. 405): If we are to understand the various processes shaping landforms presented in subsequent chapters of the textbook, we must expand our thinking to include incredibly long periods of time. In order for most geomorphic processes to significantly alter the landscape, many thousands, if not millions, of years are required.

PROGRESSIVE CONTENT REVIEW

1. The oceanic crust of Earth is about _____ kilometers (miles) thick. (p. 387)

   5 km (3 mi.)

2. The _____ is the abrupt change of rock composition and density at the base of the crust. (p. 387)

   Moho/
   Mohorovičić
   discontinuity

3. The uppermost mantle is rigid and extends down to a depth of about _____ to _____ kilometers (miles). (p. 388)

   65–100 km
   (40-60 mi.)

4. Together, the crust and the rigid upper mantle are referred to as the _____. (p. 388)

   lithosphere

5. The lithosphere rests on a hot, mobile layer of the mantle called the _____ which extends down to about _____ kilometers (miles). (p. 388)

   asthenosphere;
      350 km (200 mi.)

6. The _____ core of Earth is thought to be molten, while the layer below, the _____ core, is believed to be solid. (p. 388)

   outer
   inner

7. _____ are solid substances found in the crust, and have a specific crystal structure and chemical composition. (p. 389)

   Minerals

8. About _____ different minerals make up more than 95 percent of all rocks in the crust of Earth. (p. 391)

   20

9. Magma is _____ rock material. (p. 391)

   molten

10. Igneous rocks are formed from the cooling and solidification of _____. (p. 391)

    magma

11. Igneous rocks that cool below the surface tend to have relatively _____ (large/small) mineral crystals, while igneous rocks that cool from lava on the surface have relatively _____ crystals. (p. 391)

    large

    small

12. Igneous rocks that cool below the surface are called _____ or _____ igneous rocks. The most common rock of this type is _____. (p. 392)

    plutonic
    intrusive
    granite

179

13. Igneous rocks that form on the surface are called _____   volcanic (extrusive)
igneous rocks. The most common rock of this type is _____.   basalt
(p. 392)

14. Sediments can be bonded into sedimentary rocks by _____   pressure
and _____ cementation. (p. 394)   chemical

15. Most sedimentary rocks are deposited in horizontal layers
called _____. (pp. 394-396)   strata

16. Limestone is composed of the chemical _____ _____ that is   calcium carbonate
often derived from the skeletal remains of coral and sea
shells. (p. 396)

17. Metamorphic rocks form from preexisting rocks that have
been altered by _____ and _____, generally under the surface   heat; pressure
over long periods of time. (p. 398)

18. When metamorphosed, limestone typically turns into _____.   marble
(p. 399)

19. Because of isostasy, adding a great amount of weight to
Earth's crust will cause it to _____, while removing a great   sink
amount of weight will cause it to _____. (p. 400)   rise

20. An individual topographic feature is called a _____. (p. 402)   landform

21. The _____ of a landform refers to the nature and arrangement   structure
of its rocks. (p. 402)

22. The difference in elevation between the highest and lowest
points in an area is termed the local _____. (p. 403)   relief

23. _____ processes tend to increase the relief of the landscape,   Internal
while _____ processes tend to diminish the relief. (p. 404)   external

24. The doctrine of _____ holds that "the present is the key to the   uniformitarianism
past." (p. 404)

SELF-TEST

1. The Mohorovičić discontinuity refers to:
   (a) the top of the inner core of Earth.
   (b) the change in rock composition and density between the crust and the mantle.
   (c) the change of rock density between the lithosphere and the asthenosphere.
   (d) the change in rock density between the ocean floors and the continents.

2. The rocks of the asthenosphere are:
   (a) hot and easily deformed.
   (b) cold and easily deformed.
   (c) hot and rigid.
   (d) cold and rigid.

3. The lithosphere:
   (a) consists only of the continents.
   (b) consists only of the ocean floors.
   (c) is the upper layer of the mantle.
   (d) consists of the crust and part of the upper mantle.

4. Compared to the mantle below, the crust is relatively:
   (a) flexible.
   (b) rigid.
   (c) thick.

5. The inner core of Earth is believed to be:
   (a) solid.
   (b) molten.
   (c) composed mostly of granite.
   (d) composed mostly of basalt.

6. The thickness of oceanic crust is about:
   (a) 1.6 km (1 mile).
   (b) 5 km (3 miles).
   (c) 24 km (15 miles).
   (d) 160 km (100 miles).

7.	Intrusive (plutonic) igneous rocks have larger mineral crystals than extrusive (volcanic) igneous rocks that form from the cooling of lava flows because:
	(a)	intrusive rocks cool faster.
	(b)	intrusive rocks cool more slowly.
	(c)	oxygen in the atmosphere inhibits crystal growth.
	(d)	nitrogen in the atmosphere inhibits crystal growth.

8.	The most common volcanic (extrusive) igneous rock is:
	(a)	basalt		(b)	granite		(c)	sandstone		(d)	gneiss

9.	The most common plutonic (intrusive) igneous rock is:
	(a)	basalt		(b)	granite		(c)	sandstone		(d)	gneiss

10.	Sediments are bonded into sedimentary rocks primarily through:
	(a)	contact with magma.
	(b)	heat.
	(c)	the capillary action of water.
	(d)	pressure and chemical cementation.

11.	Limestone is composed primarily of:
	(a)	pieces of granite.
	(b)	pieces of basalt.
	(c)	silica.
	(d)	calcium carbonate.

12.	Metamorphic rocks develop from:
	(a)	magma under the surface.
	(b)	other kinds of rocks.
	(c)	sediments when they become saturated with water.
	(d)	lava that has cooled on the ocean floor.

13.	Local relief is the:
	(a)	highest point in a landscape.
	(b)	lowest point in a landscape.
	(c)	the difference between the highest and lowest points in a landscape.
	(d)	the steepest slope in a landscape.

14.	When a great load, such as a continental ice sheet, is removed from a portion of Earth's crust:
	(a)	the crust will slowly sink.
	(b)	the crust will slowly rise.
	(c)	the level of the crust will remain the same.

Answers to Self-Test:

1.	b	6.	b	11.	d
2.	a	7.	b	12.	b
3.	d	8.	a	13.	c
4.	b	9.	b	14.	b
5.	a	10.	d		

HINTS FOR TEXTBOOK STUDY QUESTIONS

1.   See Figure 13-1 (p. 176 of the Study Guide).

2.   This is an important distinction. See Figure 13-2 (p. 177 of the Study Guide).

3.   The Moho is shown in Figure 13-2 and described on page 387.

4.   This distinction is discussed at the beginning of the section, "The Composition of Earth" (p. 389).

5.   Figure 13-6 (p. 392) is a good starting point, but you should read the associated text and look at the photographs of the various kinds of rocks mentioned in this chapter.

6.   Figure 13-6a (p. 392) illustrates the basic difference.

7.   This is an important concept. See Figure 13-7 (p. 394) and the associated text section for a discussion of this.

8.   The general difference in overall color and texture of granite and basalt are clues; see page 392 and Figures 13-7, 13-8, and 13-9 (pp. 394–395) for a discussion of this.

9.   See Figure 13-6b (p. 392) and the associated text section.

10.   Again, see Figure 13-6c (p. 392) and the associated text section.

11.   Figure 13-18 (p. 400) illustrates several of the possibilities.

12. Consider the source of material for sedimentary rocks.

13. This is an important distinction; see page 400.

14. See Figure 13-21 (p. 402).

15. These terms are introduced on pages 401–402.

16. See the photograph in Figure 13-13 (p. 397); you may also want to review the text on page 402.

17. Relief is defined on page 403.

18. These conceptual categories are discussed on page 404 and conceptually illustrated in Figure 13-24 (p. 404).

19. This simple-sounding concept is a key to understanding geomorphology. Consider how processes we observe today can help us understand what has happened in the past.

20. Here we are less interested in the names of the various eras and periods of geologic time shown in Figure 13-25 (p. 406) than in the vast expanse of time involved in the history of Earth.

21. This is a key to understanding geomorphology. Without long periods of time very slow internal and external processes usually cannot produce much change.

22. The reason for this is discussed beginning on page 407.

ADDITIONAL STUDY QUESTION

1. How have scientists learned about the structure and characteristics of the interior of Earth?

Hint for Additional Study Question:

1. This is discussed on page 387.

CHAPTER 14

The Internal Processes

OVERVIEW

This chapter introduces a wide range of important concepts in geomorphology. It begins with a discussion of the theory of plate tectonics and the broadest-scale movements of the surface of Earth. The second major section of the chapter focuses on vulcanism, including both the consequences of volcanic activity, as well as the movement of magma beneath the surface. The final section looks at diastrophism, the deformation of Earth's crust through folding and faulting.

After studying the section on plate tectonics, you should be familiar with the kinds of major topographic features and tectonic activity associated with the three different types of plate boundaries, as well as the modifications to the basic plate tectonic model, such as terranes and mantle plumes. Also, pay attention to the historical development of this theory and the lines of evidence that have helped verify it.

The sections in the chapter on vulcanism and diastrophism focus mainly on the development of landforms. However, note the general relationship of these different kinds of processes to plate tectonics and plate boundaries.

KEY CONCEPTS

FROM RIGID EARTH TO PLATE TECTONICS (p. 413):

This section deals with the history, evidence, and results of crustal movement as explained by the theory of plate tectonics. However, as the text points out, there are still many details left to be worked out in our understanding of the movements of Earth's surface.

Wegener's Continental Drift (p. 413): This section primarily looks at the history of plate tectonic theory, or *continental drift* as it was first called. Alfred Wegener, and others, noticed the "jigsaw puzzle" fit of continental coastlines, geologic structures, and mountain ranges that began on one continent and continued on another (Figure 14-2, p. 414), and the evolutionary fossil record that was hard to explain if the continents had always been in their present configuration (Figure 14-3, p. 415). The main obstacles to the early acceptance of continental drift as proposed by Wegener were the lack of a plausible mechanism, as well as an incomplete understanding of the ocean floors.

PLATE TECTONICS (p. 415):

The slowly moving convection of heated material within the mantle now seems the best (although perhaps incomplete) explanation of the driving force behind plate tectonics.

The Evidence (p. 415): One of the first steps toward the formulation of modern plate tectonic theory came with the mapping of the ocean floors in the late 1950s. In Figure 14-5 (p. 416), note the symmetry of the Mid-Atlantic Ridge to the shapes of the continental margins on either side.

In the early 1960s, the theory of *seafloor spreading* suggested that new ocean floor is introduced at the *midocean ridges* by rising convection currents, and that old lithosphere is "recycled" back down into the mantle through *subduction* near the *deep oceanic trenches* (**Figure 14-7**, shown on the following page).

Verification that new ocean floor was indeed being introduced into the midocean ridges came when magnetic maps of the ridges were made. Over millions of years, reversals of Earth's magnetic field have been recorded in the volcanic rock of the ocean floor. As magma rises and solidifies into new ocean floor at a ridge, the magnetic polarity of the time is retained in the rocks. As this ocean floor in turn splits and spreads apart, the newer ocean floor rocks will also record the magnetic polarity of the time. Polarity reversals have been preserved as a series of magnetic "stripes" on the ocean floor—alternating between normal and reverse polarity—spreading away from the ridge in both directions in a symmetrical pattern (Figure 14-8, p. 418).

Further, ocean core samples showed that seafloor sediments were youngest and thinnest at a ridge, becoming older and thicker moving away from the ridge in both directions. The observed magnetic and ocean core patterns can be easily explained if new ocean floor is indeed being added to the middle of oceanic ridges (Figure 14-9, p. 418).

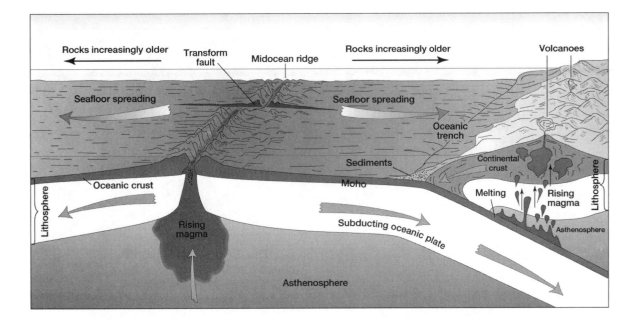

Figure 14-7: Magma rises from the asthenosphere to form new ocean floor at a midocean ridge. Ocean floor spreads in both directions from the ridge. Where dense ocean floor converges with less-dense continental crust, the ocean crust is subducted. The magma produced by this subduction rises to form a series of volcanoes.

Plate Boundaries (p. 420): There are three basic types of boundaries between plates: divergent, convergent, and transform (Figure 14-11, p. 420).

1. **Divergent Boundaries** (p. 420): Plates move apart at *divergent boundaries* (sometimes called *spreading centers* or "constructive" plate boundaries) where new crustal material is introduced from the asthenosphere. The most common kind of divergent plate boundary is the midocean ridge, where new basaltic ocean floor is being created (**Figure 14-7**, above).

   In a few places, spreading has taken place within a continent, producing *continental rift valleys*, such as the Great Rift Valley of East Africa (Figure 14-13, p. 421).

2. **Convergent Boundaries** (p. 420): Plates come together at *convergent boundaries* (sometimes referred to as "destructive" plate boundaries). The three kinds of convergent boundaries are shown in **Figure 14-14** (shown on the following page).

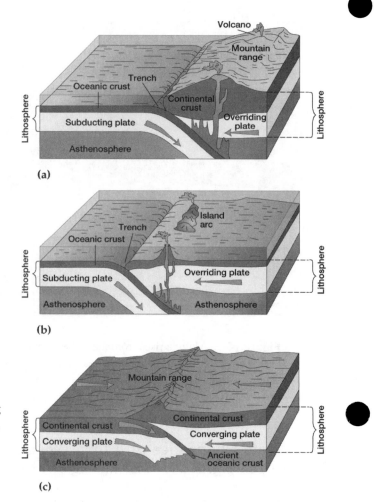

Figure 14-14: Idealized portrayals of convergent plate boundaries. (a) Where an oceanic plate meets a continental plate, the oceanic plate is subducted, forming an oceanic trench and coastal mountains with volcanoes. (b) Where an oceanic plate meets another oceanic plate, subduction occurs, forming an oceanic trench and a volcanic island arc. (c) Where a continental plate meets another continental plate, mountains are thrust upward.

Note that the first two cases, oceanic plate to continental plate convergence and oceanic plate to oceanic plate convergence, result in subduction. Very deep earthquakes (as deep as 600 kilometers [375 miles] below the surface) are possible in these subduction zones as the lithospheric plate descends into the mantle (see Figure 14-15, p. 423). As the plate descends, water driven out of the subducting lithosphere lowers the melting temperature of the mantle rocks above, generating magma, and so volcanic activity is also associated with subduction.

(a)   Oceanic plate to continental plate subduction typically produces a deep oceanic trench, with mountain building and volcanic activity just inland (such as the Andes along the west coast of South America; Figure 14-14a).

(b)   Oceanic plate to oceanic plate subduction typically produces a deep oceanic trench, and a chain of volcanic islands known as an *island arc* (such as the Aleutian Islands in Alaska; Figure 14-14b).

(c)   The third variation of convergent boundary is shown in Figure 14-14c. When continental crust meets continental crust, there is no subduction, but the uplift of mountains results (for example, the Himalayas).

3.   **Transform Boundaries** (p. 422): Plates slide past each other along *transform boundaries*. The San Andreas Fault system of California is the best-known example of a transform boundary within a continent. In this case, the portion of California west of the fault is attached to the Pacific Plate and is moving northwest relative to the rest of California, which is part of the North American Plate (Figure 14-16, p. 424).

Maps showing the present boundaries and general direction of movement of the major lithospheric plates are seen in Figure 14-10 (p. 419). Several animations will enhance your understanding of plate tectonics: ***Plate Boundaries***, ***Seafloor Spreading***, ***Divergent Boundaries***, ***Subduction Zones***, ***Transform Faults and Boundaries***, and ***Collision of India with Eurasia***—all of these animations will help you visualize the dynamics of plate movement.

Additions to the Basic Plate Tectonic Theory (p. 426): Two important modifications to the basic plate tectonic model are mentioned in this section.

Mantle Plumes (p. 426): One important addition to plate tectonic theory is the recognition of *mantle plumes* (or *hot spots*). A mantle plume is a narrow plume of magma rising from the mantle through a plate to the surface (Figure 14-19, p. 426). While the locations of mantle plumes, such as the one underneath the Hawaiian Islands, cannot yet be explained easily with the theory of plate tectonics, the pattern of volcanic activity on a plate moving over a hot spot does help verify the speed and direction of plate movement.

In the case of the Hawaiian chain, the currently active volcanoes on the Big Island of Hawaii are thought to be over the hot spot. The ongoing movement of the Pacific Plate has carried older volcanoes off the hot spot, at which point they become extinct. The age pattern of volcanic rocks in Hawaii verifies this (Figure 14-20, p. 426). Review the animation ***Mantle Plumes*** to see the formation of such a hot spot "trail."

Accreted Terranes (p. 427): A *terrane* is a slice of lithosphere (often ocean floor rock) that has been attached to the edge of another plate, usually at the edge of a continent. This process is illustrated in Figure 14-21 (p. 427), showing an old island arc being added to the edge of a continent—the old island arc is too buoyant to be subducted, so this additional lithosphere extends the margin of the continent. A map showing the major terranes in western North America is also provided. The animation ***Terrane Formation*** clearly illustrates how this process works.

VULCANISM (p. 428):

This section describes the processes and features of both *extrusive vulcanism* ("volcanism") and *intrusive vulcanism* (shallow intrusive vulcanism and deep "plutonic" activity).

Volcano Distribution (p. 429): Note that most volcanic activity around the world (but not all) is associated with plate boundaries. Most known volcanoes are associated with the Pacific "Ring of Fire" (Figure 14-18, p. 425 and Figure 14-24, p. 430) produced by the subduction zones and other plate boundaries around the margins of the Pacific Ocean. Most of the volcanoes around the rim of the Pacific are andesitic volcanoes. These volcanoes are typically steep-sided composite volcanoes.

Magma Chemistry and Styles of Eruption (p. 430): The character of a volcano's eruption largely depends on the kind of magma (the "chemistry" of the magma). Magma with relatively little silica (such as the magma that produces basalt) tends to be very hot and fluid, and generally produces quiet eruptions of flowing *lava* (such as the volcanoes in Hawaii). In contrast, magma with relatively high amounts of silica (such as the magmas that produce the volcanic rocks rhyolite and andesite), tends to be more viscous (thick and pasty) and contains more trapped gas. Such viscous, high-silica magmas typically produce rather explosive eruptions of *pyroclastic material* such as volcanic ash and cinders. The eruptions of Mount St. Helens were of this explosive type. The animation ***Formation of Crater Lake*** illustrates one of the occasional consequences of a major explosive eruption.

Volcanic Peaks (p. 433): The shape of a volcanic mountain is largely determined by the chemistry of the magma and the style of eruption. The four major kinds of volcanic peaks are shown in **Figure 14-29** (shown on the following page) and described in Table 14-1 (p. 434).

Shield Volcanoes: The quiet, fluid eruptions typical of volcanoes emitting basaltic lava tend to produce mountains with gently sloping sides called *shield volcanoes* (Figure 14-29b). The large Hawaiian volcanoes are of this type.

Composite Volcanoes: The explosive eruptions common with volcanoes emitting lava that is higher in silica than basalt, such as andesite, will tend to produce mountains with steeper sides, developed by the buildup of alternating layers of ejected pyroclastics and lava flows—the pyroclastics produce steep slopes, while the lava flows hold the loose pyroclastics together. This eruptive pattern produces tall, symmetrical volcanic cones called *composite volcanoes* or *stratovolcanoes* (Figure 14-29d).

Lava Domes: *Lava domes* (or *plug domes*) develop from very viscous lava that bulges up from a vent (Figure 14-29c).

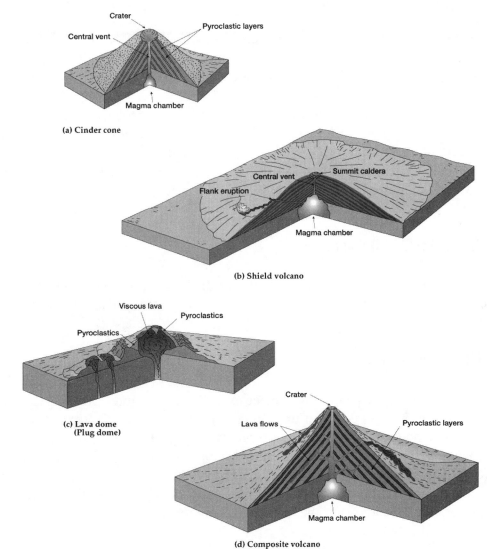

Figure 14-29: The four principal types of volcanic cones.

Cinder Cones: Cinder cones are small cone-shaped peaks that develop almost entirely from ejected pyroclastic material (Figure 14-29a).

The animation *Volcanoes* illustrates the formation of different types of volcanoes. Also look at Figure 14-30 (p. 436) to see examples of volcano profiles drawn at the same scale—the shield volcanoes of Hawaii are enormous compared with even large composite volcanoes such as Mt. Rainier in Washington.

Volcanic Hazards (p. 439): This section primarily describes the hazards associated with composite volcanoes (although some of these hazards may develop with other kinds of volcanoes as well). Loose pyroclastic material on the slopes of a volcano may be remobilized by rainwater or melting snow and produce a wet, rapidly moving mixture of mud and debris known as a *volcanic mudflow* or *lahar*. An explosive eruption may produce a *pyroclastic flow*—a hot, dense avalanche of gas, ash, and rock that can rush off a volcano, burning and burying everything in its path.

Igneous Features (p. 442): When magma cools beneath the surface, it produces a mass of intrusive igneous rock. Figure 14-42 (p. 443) illustrates some of these intrusions. Note that the largest of these intrusions (batholiths, stocks, and laccoliths) are sometimes simply referred to as *plutons*. View the animation *Igneous Features* to see the development and subsequent exposure of a variety of intrusive igneous features.

DIASTROPHISM (p. 444):

Diastrophism—such as folding and faulting—is crustal deformation that may or may not be directly related to the movements associated with plate tectonics.

FOLDING (p. 445):

Folding generally takes place when rock structures are subjected to great compressional stresses over long periods of time (Figure 14-45, p. 445). Note the structural relationship between different kinds of folds and the surface topography. Figure 14-46 (p. 446) shows the basic kinds of folds and the simplest structural relationships in which the upfolded anticlines form ridges and the downfolded synclines form valleys. Figure 14-47 (p. 446) shows a more complex structural relationship. In this case, because of erosion, parts of some synclines have remained as topographic ridges, while parts of some anticlines have become valleys. See the animation *Folding* for additional details.

FAULTING (p. 447):

Figure 14-50 (p. 448) describes the most important features and terminology associated with *faulting*. By definition, faulting entails the breaking and displacement of a rock structure. Notice in this diagram that one side of the fault (called the *downthrown block*) has slipped down the fault plane relative to the other side of the fault (the *upthrown block*).

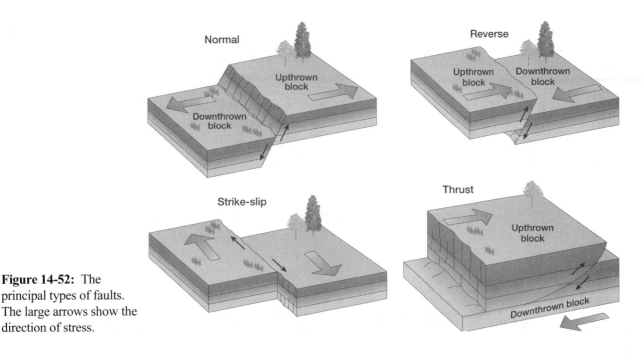

Figure 14-52: The principal types of faults. The large arrows show the direction of stress.

Types of Faults (p. 448): Note the different kinds of stress that produce the four principal types of faults (**Figure 14-52**, shown above). *Normal faulting* results from tension ("extension"—being pulled apart). Both *reverse* and *thrust faults* result from compression (pushing together). *Strike-slip faults* are produced by shearing (force is directed so that neither side of the fault goes up over the other side, but rather, one side slips past the other horizontally). See the animation ***Faulting*** to see the patterns of movement associated with normal faults, reverse faults, and strike-slip faults.

Landforms Associated with Normal Faulting (p. 449): Normal faulting produces a number of common landforms. Figure 14-54 (p. 449) shows the Sierra Nevada, a *fault-block mountain* (sometimes called a *tilted fault-block mountain*)—uplift along the east side produced a very steep eastern slope and a gentle western slope. Figure 14-55 (p. 450) illustrates the sets of parallel faults necessary to produce an uplifted *horst* mountain or a down-dropped trough known as a *graben*.

Landforms Associated with Strike-Slip Faulting (p. 450): The common landforms produced by strike-slip faults are shown in Figure 14-56 (p. 450). *Linear fault troughs* and *sag ponds* commonly develop within the zone of crushed rock along the surface trace of the fault, while *offset streams* develop where a stream's course is displaced by lateral fault movement.

Earthquakes (p. 450): The *magnitude* of an earthquake, such as the *Richter Scale* and *moment magnitude*, describe the size of an earthquake (in other words, the relative amount of energy released during an earthquake). Magnitude scales are logarithmic—for each additional magnitude, the amount of energy released increases by about 32 times. For example, a magnitude 6 earthquake releases about 32 times the energy of a magnitude 5 quake, while a magnitude 7 earthquake releases 1,000 times more energy than a magnitude 5 quake.

The *intensity* of an earthquake refers to the violence of the local ground shaking. Every earthquake can be assigned a single magnitude to describe its size, but each earthquake will produced a range of shaking intensities—the local intensity depends on the magnitude of the earthquake, the distance from the epicenter, and the local geology. Earthquake intensity is commonly described with the *Modified Mercalli Intensity Scale* (Table 14-3 p. 452).

The animations ***Earthquake Waves*** and ***Seismographs*** illustrate the movement of different kinds of earthquake waves, and how these waves are recorded by a seismograph.

PROGRESSIVE CONTENT REVIEW

1. All of the present continents were unified in a supercontinent called _____ about _____ million years ago. (p. 413)   Pangaea; 250

2. Reversals of Earth's _____ field are recorded in the volcanic rock of the ocean floor in a pattern of symmetrical stripes on both sides of a midocean ridge. (p. 416)   magnetic

3. Ocean sediments become thicker and _____ (younger/older) away from midocean ridges. (p. 419)   older

4. A "plate" (the lithosphere) moves slowly over the less rigid ("plastic") _____ below. (p. 419)   asthenosphere

5. The mechanism of plate movement is thought to be the result of slow _____ of heated rocks within the mantle. (p. 420)   convection

6. Because of the continual recycling of ocean crust, continental crust is almost always _____ (younger/older) than oceanic crust. (pp. 383–384)   older

7. At _____ boundaries two plates move apart in opposite directions and new crust is added. (p. 420)   divergent

8. _____ _____ are the most common type of divergent boundary and are places where new ocean floor is being produced by volcanic activity. These boundaries are often associated with _____ (deep/shallow) earthquakes. (p. 420)

Midocean ridges

shallow

9. At _____ boundaries two plates collide together and so crust may be "removed." (p. 420)

convergent

10. Old ocean floor descends back into the mantle near oceanic _____ in a process called _____. (p. 420)

trenches; subduction

11. When an oceanic plate collides with a continental plate, there is subduction, forming an oceanic trench and chains of _____ inland from the continental edge. These boundaries are associated with both _____-focus and _____-focus earthquakes. The _____ Mountains of South America are associated with this kind of plate boundary. (pp. 421–422)

volcanoes

shallow; deep
Andes

12. When an oceanic plate collides with an oceanic plate, there is subduction, forming a deep oceanic _____ and a volcanic island arc. The _____ Islands of Alaska are an example of this. (p. 422)

trench
Aleutian

13. When two continental plates collide there is no subduction, but _____ building and _____-focus earthquakes are common. (p. 422)

mountain; shallow

14. At a _____ boundary, two plates slide past each other laterally. The _____ _____ Fault system of California is an example of this kind of boundary. (p. 422)

transform
San Andreas

15. The Hawaiian Islands are a chain of islands that formed as the Pacific Plate moves over a _____ _____. Volcanoes become _____ as they move away from the hot spot atop the moving plate. (pp. 426–427)

mantle plume (hot spot); extinct

16. A _____ is a piece of lithosphere that has been "accreted" onto the edge of another plate, typically a continental margin. (p. 427)

terrane

17. Magma that cools on the surface of Earth is called _____.
    _____ material includes solid rock, ash, and dust ejected from
    a volcano. (p. 429)

    lava
    Pyroclastic

18. Magma that is _____ (low/high) in silica, such as basalt,
    tends to produce fluid lava and quiet eruptions. (p. 430)

    low

19. Typically, volcanoes erupting lava that is fairly high in silica
    (such as andesite) will produce relatively _____-sided
    volcanic peaks known as _____ volcanoes, while volcanoes
    erupting low-silica lava (basalt) will produced _____ slopes
    and peaks known as _____ volcanoes. (pp. 433–434)

    steep
    composite
    gentle
    shield

20. A caldera develops when a volcano _____ or _____. (p. 437)

    explodes; collapses

21. A _____ _____ is high-speed avalanche of hot gases, ash and
    rock fragments that rushes down the slopes of a volcano. A
    _____ _____ is a rapidly moving mixture of water and
    pyroclastic material that flows off a volcano. (pp. 440–442)

    pyroclastic flow

    volcanic mudflow
     (lahar)

22. A _____ is the largest type of igneous intrusion, often
    forming the core of a large mountain range. A _____ is
    formed when viscous magma is forced between layers of
    rock. (p. 443)

    batholith
    laccolith

23. A _____ is a narrow vertical sheet of intrusive rock. (p. 444)

    dike

24. A simple upfold is called an _____, while a simple downfold
    is called a _____. (p. 446)

    anticline
    syncline

25. Faulting occurs when rock is forcefully broken and _____.
    (p. 447)

    displaced

26. A _____ fault results from tension stresses. (p. 449)

    normal

27. Reverse and thrust faults result from _____ stresses. (p. 449)

    compression

28. The movement along a _____-_____ fault is horizontal.
    (p. 449)

    strike-slip

29. When a block of crust is upthrown along one side, a _____
    _____-_____ mountain is produced. (p. 449)

    tilted fault-block

30. A _____ is produced when a block of crust is upthrown between two parallel faults, while a _____ is formed when a valley is downdropped between two parallel faults. (p. 449)

horst
graben

31. A magnitude 5 earthquake releases about _____ times as much energy as a magnitude 4 earthquake (p. 451)

32

SELF-TEST

1. The Mid-Atlantic ridge is a plate boundary where:
   (a) plates are sliding past each other.
   (b) ocean floor is being subducted.
   (c) ocean floor is colliding with ocean floor to produce a range of mountains.
   (d) new ocean floor is being made.

2. In general, the thinnest and youngest sediments on the ocean floor will be found:
   (a) in an oceanic trench.
   (b) halfway between a midocean ridge and a trench.
   (c) at a midocean ridge.
   (d) in a random pattern around the oceans.

3. Paleomagnetic records indicate that:
   (a) new ocean floor is being made at midocean ridges.
   (b) ocean floor is being consumed at midocean ridges.
   (c) the north and south magnetic poles have never reversed.
   (d) the north and south magnetic poles have reversed only twice in the last 100 million years.

4. Which of the following is *not* evidence that South America and Africa were once joined?
   (a) Similar fossil records on both land masses.
   (b) Large amounts of granite are found on both continents.
   (c) Mountain ranges begin on one continent and finish on the other.
   (d) The shape of their Atlantic coastlines is similar.

5.   Oceanic plate to oceanic plate subduction produces:
     (a)   a midocean ridge.
     (b)   a deep oceanic trench and continental mountains.
     (c)   a transform boundary such as the San Andreas fault system.
     (d)   a deep oceanic trench and a volcanic island arc.

6.   When a continental plate collides with a continental plate, which of the following is the *most* likely consequence?
     (a)   Widespread volcanic activity.
     (b)   A transform boundary will form.
     (c)   Mountain building will take place.
     (d)   A rift valley will form.

7.   The Himalayan Mountains were primarily formed by:
     (a)   oceanic plate to oceanic plate subduction.
     (b)   oceanic plate to continental plate subduction.
     (c)   continental plate to continental plate collision.
     (d)   transform plate motion.

8.   A terrane is:
     (a)   a slice of lithosphere accreted on a midocean ridge.
     (b)   a slice of lithosphere accreted on the edge of a continent.
     (c)   formed when a plate passes over a hot spot.
     (d)   a volcanic island next to a subduction zone.

9.   A mantle plume is:
     (a)   a narrow plume of magma rising through a plate to the surface.
     (b)   a slice of crust accreted on the edge of a midocean ridge.
     (c)   a volcanic island next to an oceanic trench.
     (d)   a continental volcano next to an oceanic trench.

10. Lava that is relatively low in silica (such as basalt) is likely to be associated with:
     (a)   explosive eruptions of pyroclastics.
     (b)   relatively quiet eruptions of fluid lava.
     (c)   very thick, viscous lava.
     (d)   lots of gas.

11. Lava that is relatively high in silica (such as andesite) is likely to be associated with:
     (a)   low-lying shield volcanoes.
     (b)   flood basalts.
     (c)   steep-sided composite volcanoes.
     (d)   very fluid lava.

12.   The Pacific "Ring of Fire" is mostly the result of:
        (a)   transform boundaries.
        (b)   mantle plumes.
        (c)   terranes.
        (d)   subduction zones.

13.   A batholith is most likely to be composed of which kind of rock?
        (a)   andesite   (b)   basalt
        (c)   sandstone   (d)   granite

14.   A thrust fault is the result of:
        (a)   compression.
        (b)   tension (pulling apart).
        (c)   shearing (lateral movement).
        (d)   the introduction of magma.

15.   A normal fault is the result of:
        (a)   compression.
        (b)   tension (pulling apart).
        (c)   shearing (lateral movement).
        (d)   the introduction of magma.

16.   A magnitude 8 earthquake releases how much more energy than a magnitude 6 earthquake?
        (a)   4x   (b)   10x
        (c)   32x   (d)   1000x

17.   A syncline is:
        (a)   a valley formed between two parallel faults.
        (b)   a mountain range formed between two parallel faults.
        (c)   a structural downfold.
        (d)   a structural upfold.

18.   A graben is:
        (a)   a valley formed between two parallel faults.
        (b)   a mountain range formed between two parallel faults.
        (c)   a structural downfold.
        (d)   a structural upfold.

Answers to Self-Test:

1.	d	6.	c	11.	c	16.	d
2.	c	7.	c	12.	d	17.	c
3.	a	8.	b	13.	d	18.	a
4.	b	9.	a	14.	a		
5.	d	10.	b	15.	b		

HINTS FOR TEXTBOOK STUDY QUESTIONS

1. See Figures 14-2 and 14-4 (pp. 414–415).

2. He had lots of good evidence. What *didn't* he have?

3. See Figures 14-8 and 14-9 (p. 418) and the associated text material.

4. Notice the relationship between the patterns of earthquakes shown in Figure 14-6 (p. 417) and the map of plate boundaries (Figure 14-10, p. 419).

5. Review the animation *Convection and Plate Tectonics*.

6. A general description of this is found on page 420 and shown in Figure 14-11 (p. 420).

7. See Figures 14-12 and 14-13 (p. 421) and the associated text material.

8. Diagrams of these convergent boundaries are shown in Figure 14-14 (on page 188 of the Study Guide), but you should also review the animation *Subduction Zones*.

9. Consider the difference in density of oceanic lithosphere and continental lithosphere.

10. Figure 14-16 (p. 424) may help here.

11. Review the animations *Seafloor Spreading* and *Subduction Zones*—consider where plate movement is taking place.

12. Compare the map showing the Pacific Ring of Fire (Figure 14-18, p. 425) to the map of plate boundaries (Figure 14-10, p. 419).

13.   See Figure 14-19 (p. 426) and the associated text material.

14.   Consider the location of Hawaii relative to plate boundaries.

15.   Look at the age pattern of volcanic rocks in Hawaii (Figure 14-20, p. 427).

16.   Review the animation **Terrane Formation**.

17.   These terms are discussed on page 429.

18.   See the section "Magma Chemistry and Styles of Eruption" beginning on page 430.

19.   See Figure 14-29 (on page 191 of the Study Guide) and Table 14-1 (p. 434). You may also want to review the animation **Volcanoes**.

20.   The animation **Formation of Crater Lake** illustrates this process quite well.

21.   This is discussed beginning on page 440 of the textbook.

22.   See Figure 14-42 (p. 443) and the associated text.

23.   These folds are illustrated in Figure 14-46 (p. 446).

24.   See Figure 14-47 (p. 446).

25.   Figure 14-52 (on page 193 of the Study Guide) illustrates this, but you should also review the animation **Faulting**.

26.   See Figures 14-54 and 14-55 (pp. 449–450) and the associated text material.

27.   These are shown in Figure 14-56 (p. 450), but the formation of an offset stream is also well illustrated in the animation **Faulting**.

28.   See Figure 14-57 (p. 451).

29.   See the discussion of "Earthquake Magnitude" on page 451.

30.   See the animation **Earthquake Waves**.

31.   See Figure 14-58 (p. 454) and the text material on "Earthquake Hazards" beginning on page 452.

ADDITIONAL STUDY QUESTIONS

1.   Why are earthquakes rare in Chicago, Illinois, but not in Los Angeles, California?

2.   What is the evidence that the Atlantic Ocean has been becoming wider over the last few tens of millions of years?

Hints for Additional Study Questions:

1.   Note the relationship between earthquakes and the different kinds of plate boundaries.

2.   See the hint for Study Question 3 above.

Preliminaries to Erosion: Weathering and Mass Wasting

OVERVIEW

In this chapter, we begin the discussion of the "external" processes that are shaping the landscape. The wearing away of rock and surface features involves three basic types of activities: weathering, mass wasting, and erosion (collectively called "denudation"). Chapter 15 focuses on the first two of these processes. First, the disintegration of rock material ("weathering") is discussed. Second, the short distance, downslope movement of weathered rock ("mass wasting") is examined.

In this chapter, you should note the basic difference between the processes of "mechanical" and "chemical" weathering, as well as the importance of joints and other kinds of rock openings to weathering. While there are many different types of mass wasting, the text classifies all forms of mass wasting into just four categories, based on similarities in the dominant processes involved. You should also note the varying roles of water in both weathering and mass wasting.

KEY CONCEPTS

WEATHERING AND ROCK OPENINGS (p. 459):

Weathering is most active along openings in rocks. Any size opening, even a microscopic open space, increases the surface area exposed to the action of weathering.

This is an important section. *Joints* are cracks that develop within rocks as a result of stress. As **Figure 15-4** (shown below) illustrates, joints are simply cracks in the rock structure, while *faults* (discussed in Chapter 14) form when rock on one side has moved relative to the other side. Joints are an important variable in the weathering process since they are so common, and because they may allow weathering to take place some distance below the surface (**Figure 15-3**, shown on the following page).

The distance between joints also influences the landscape. Compare the highly dissected landscape shown in the photograph of Bryce Canyon (Figure 15-5, p. 462), where closely spaced joints are found, to the landscape of Zion National Park (Figure 15-6, p. 462), where joints are more widely spaced.

WEATHERING AGENTS (p. 461):

Mechanical Weathering (p. 462): *Mechanical weathering* involves the physical disintegration of rock into smaller pieces.

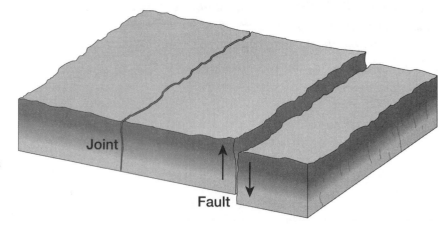

Figure 15-4: The essential difference between joints and faults is that joints exhibit no displacement along either side of the crack.

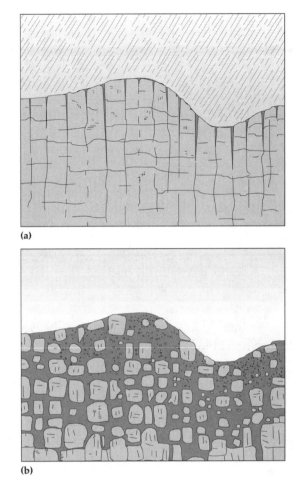

Figure 15-3: How deep weathering develops in bedrock containing many joints and cracks. (a) Before weathering. (b) After weathering.

Frost Wedging (p. 462): Perhaps the most important process of mechanical weathering is *frost wedging*. As **Figure 15-7** (shown on the following page) illustrates, water seeps into a crack in the rock. When the water freezes it expands as ice forms, further opening the crack. After the ice melts, water can now seep deeper into the rock than before. When this cycle is repeated many times, frost wedging is capable of breaking apart even very strong rock (see the photograph in Figure 15-8, p. 463). Also see the animation ***Mechanical Weathering***.

Exfoliation (p. 464): *Exfoliation* is another significant weathering process. Exfoliation involves the peeling off of curved layers of rock—in some cases, layers of rock several meters thick (Figure 15-11, p. 465). Exfoliation at this scale tends to produce a rounded landscape, including landforms known as *exfoliation domes* (see Figure 15-12, p. 465). This kind of exfoliation is most common in plutonic rocks such as granite. Although the exact mechanism for exfoliation is not completely understood, it probably involves the release of pressure from formerly buried rocks—this unloading of pressure allows the rock to expand slightly, causing the outer layer to peel off.

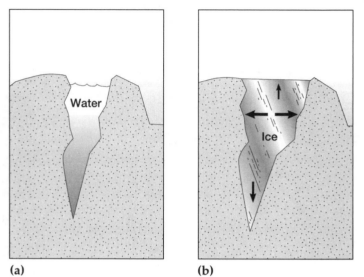

Figure 15-7: Frost wedging. When water in a crack freezes, the ice expansion exerts a force that can deepen and widen the crack.   **(a)**   **(b)**

Another kind of exfoliation causes very thin layers of rock to peel off—this kind of exfoliation most likely involves chemical weathering (see Figure 15-13, p. 466).

Chemical Weathering (p. 466):   In contrast to mechanical weathering, *chemical weathering* involves the decomposition of rock through chemical processes that weaken the mineral structure. Water is involved in almost all kinds of chemical weathering, and high temperatures tend to make these chemical reactions more rapid. As a result, chemical weathering is most pronounced in humid areas, especially warm and humid regions.

MASS WASTING (p. 469):

Mass wasting is the short distance, downslope movement of weathered rock material under the influence of gravity. Mass wasting does not always occur, but when it does, it happens after weathering has taken place and before erosion carries the material farther away. Figure 15-1 (p. 459) illustrates this general sequence.

Since gravity is the prime force behind mass wasting, the steepness of a slope exerts strong influence over the kind of mass wasting that will take place. Two other factors commonly influence mass wasting as well. Water can make weathered rock material heavier (and so more likely so slip downslope) and can also act to reduce the friction between particles, and so make them more susceptible to movement. Clay is another important variable in mass wasting since it often becomes slippery when wet.

The textbook groups all types of mass wasting into four general categories: *fall*, *slide*, *flow*, and *creep*. Within each category, there may be several distinct variations of mass wasting. The speed and moisture relationships of various kinds of mass wasting are shown in **Figure 15-19** (shown below). Be sure to review the animation ***Mass Wasting*** when you study this section.

Fall (p. 471):   In the process of *fall* (or *rockfall*), loose weathered rock simply falls down a steep slope or cliff and collects at the bottom (see Figures 15-20 and 15-21, p. 471). The angular, jagged rock that falls in this fashion is called *talus* or *scree*. The accumulated rock at the base of the slope often forms a *talus cone*.

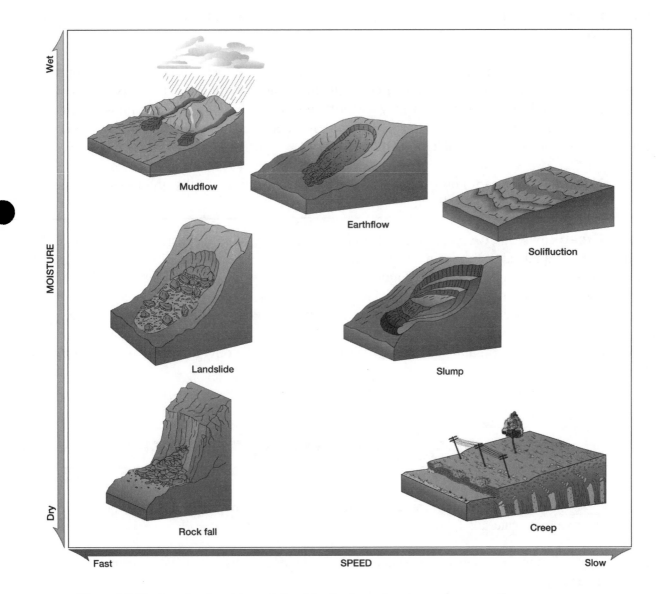

Figure 15-19: Speed and moisture relationships for the various types of mass wasting.

Slide (p. 472):   With a *slide*, a mass of weathered rock slides down a slope as a unit. Although the presence of water may be important in a *landslide* (especially by adding weight to the rock mass), a slide does not involve the flow of rock in a mixture of water. In all forms of slides, a prominent "scar" can be found where the slide originated, as well as an irregular jumble of material where the slide comes to rest.

A *slump* is a common variety of slide in which a unit of weathered rock and soil rotates out of a hillside and slides downslope a short distance (notice the curved arrow in Figure 15-23, p. 474).

Flow (p. 474):   The several varieties of *flow* involve the flowing movement of weathered rock material as a waterlogged mass. The speed and style of flow varies with the amount of water and the type of slope.

Earthflow is the often slow movement of saturated surface material down the side of a hill (Figure 15-24, p. 474). In contrast, a *mudflow* results from the rapid movement of very wet mud and debris that has collected in a stream valley. Mudflows are common after heavy rains in arid and semi-arid mountainous areas. The term *debris flow* is often used instead of mudflow, especially when the flow contains large boulders and other debris (see Figure 15-25, p. 475).

Note that while earthflows usually take place on the sides of hills, mudflows and debris flows take place within stream valleys.

Creep (p. 475):   *Creep* (or *soil creep*) entails the very slow downslope movement of the surface layer of a hillside. The main mechanism of creep seems to involve the freeze/thaw cycle (or simply a cycle of wetting and drying). Figure 15-26 (p. 476) shows a greatly magnified view of soil particle movement down a slope. As the surface expands (due to the freezing of water, or simply the swelling of the soil surface) particles are pushed outward. When the surface thaws, the particles drop straight down the slope due to gravity. In this way, particle by particle, the surface of a slope slowly moves downhill. Figure 15-27 (p. 477) shows some of the obvious signs of soil creep on a hillside.

PROGRESSIVE CONTENT REVIEW

1. _____ is the collection of processes that wear away and remove rock material. (p. 459)   Denudation

2. _____ is the first step in the shaping of the landscape by external processes. (p. 459)   Weathering

3. _____ are cracks in rocks that develop due to stress, while _____ are formed when rock is forcibly broken and displaced. (p. 460)

Joints
faults

4. Long sets of _____ _____ often form planes of weakness that extend for great distances. These planes of weakness become more susceptible to the processes of _____ and _____ than the surrounding rock. (p. 461)

master joints

weathering;
  erosion

5. From a chemical standpoint, the three most important atmospheric components of weathering are _____, _____ _____, and _____ _____, although liquid water is probably the most important agent overall. (p. 461)

oxygen
carbon dioxide;
  water vapor

6. _____ weathering involves the disintegration of rock without a change in its chemical composition. (p. 462)

Mechanical

7. When water freezes, it _____ (contracts/expands). When this process occurs in rock openings, the process of _____ _____ can shatter even strong rock. (p. 462)

expands
frost wedging

8. When water is drawn into rock cracks in arid climates, the crystallization of minerals can break apart rock in the process of _____ _____. (p. 463)

salt wedging

9. _____ is the process in which the surface of a rock peels off in concentric curved layers. The _____ of pressure from formerly buried rock is thought to play a part in this process. (p. 464)

Exfoliation
unloading

10. Usually, mechanical weathering is accompanied by _____ weathering in which the chemical composition of the rock is altered and weakened. (p. 466)

chemical

11. Almost all chemical weathering processes require the presence of _____. (p. 467)

moisture

12. The process of _____ occurs when oxygen that has been dissolved in water reacts with certain _____ elements to form a new substance, such as rust. (p. 467)

oxidation
metallic

13.	Hydrolysis is the joining of _____ with other substances to form weaker products. (p. 467) water

14.	In the process of carbonation, _____ _____ dissolved in water produces carbonic acid that is capable of producing very soluble products. (p. 468) carbon dioxide

15.	Biotic processes, such as the growth of plant _____, also contribute to mechanical weathering. (p. 468) roots

16.	Chemical weathering tends to be greatest in environments with _____ (high/low) temperatures and _____ (high/low) levels of precipitation. (p. 468) high; high

17.	The most important propelling force behind all kinds of mass wasting is _____. (p. 469) gravity

18.	The _____ of _____ is the steepest slope that loose particles can maintain without moving downslope. (p. 469) angle of repose

19.	Water often adds _____ to weathered materials, and may also act as a _____, making them slip more easily. (pp. 469-470) weight
lubricant

20.	Clay tends to become _____ when wet. (p. 470) slippery

21.	_____ is a form of mass wasting in which weathered rock drops to the foot of a steep slope, often accumulating material in _____ cones. (p. 471) Fall

talus

22.	A _____ involves the downslope movement of mostly unconsolidated regolith, often assisted by the presence of _____ which makes the mass of rock heavier. (p. 472) landslide

water

23.	A _____ is a type of slide in which a portion of a hillside rotates and/or slips downslope a short distance. (p. 474) slump

24.	An _____ results when a section of hillside becomes saturated and flows downslope a short distance. (p. 474) earthflow

25.	Mudflows take place in _____ and involve the accumulation of mud and debris during a heavy rain. (pp. 474-475) valleys

26.   _____ is a very slow type of mass wasting in which just the   Creep
surface layer of soil moves downhill. (p. 475)

27.   _____ is a type of soil creep that usually takes place in   Solifluction
regions of tundra climate. (pp. 476–478)

SELF-TEST

1.   Which of the following is *not* an example of a process of mechanical weathering?
      (a)   Hydrolysis.
      (b)   Salt wedging.
      (c)   Frost wedging.
      (d)   Temperature changes.

2.   Which of the following characteristics is the *same* for both earthflows and mudflows?
      (a)   Both take place in stream valleys.
      (b)   Both take place on hillsides.
      (c)   Both are very slow processes.
      (d)   Both involve the flow of water-saturated rock material.

3.   Why is talus that accumulates at the base of cliffs usually angular and unsorted (of all different sizes)?
      (a)   Rock has simply broken off and fallen to the bottom of the cliff.
      (b)   It was moved by running water.
      (c)   The rock slowly slid down the cliff to the bottom.
      (d)   Chemical weathering always produces angular pieces of rock.

4.   Which conditions will likely result in the greatest chemical weathering?
      (a)   Cool and dry climates.
      (b)   Cool and wet climates.
      (c)   Warm and dry climates.
      (d)   Warm and wet climates.

5.   Which of the following allows frost wedging to occur?
      (a)   Water expands when frozen.
      (b)   Water contracts when frozen.
      (c)   Granite becomes soft when frozen.
      (d)   Chemical weathering is fastest when the temperature is below freezing.

6.   What is exfoliation?
        (a)   Normal faulting in granite.
        (b)   Reverse faulting in granite.
        (c)   Soil creep in granite hillsides.
        (d)   The peeling off of curved layers of rock.

7.   What is the difference between a joint and a fault?
        (a)   Joints are always longer than faults.
        (b)   Faults show displacement of the rock structure; joints do not.
        (c)   Joints show displacement of the rock structure; faults do not.
        (d)   Joints are horizontal cracks, while faults are vertical cracks.

8.   Which of the following is *not* generally associated with soil creep?
        (a)   Very slow downslope movement of the top layer of soil.
        (b)   The freeze–thaw cycle slowly moves particles downhill.
        (c)   Blocks of weathered rock slide downhill on a layer of clay.
        (d)   Over many years, fence posts and telephone poles begin to tilt downhill.

9.   Which of the following is a common property of clay?
        (a)   It becomes heavy and slippery when wet.
        (b)   It repels water.
        (c)   It becomes sticky when wet.
        (d)   It becomes slippery when dry.

10.   Which factor is important in all forms of mass wasting?
        (a)   Running water.   (b)   Clay.
        (c)   Thick soil cover.   (d)   Gravity.

11.   Solifluction most commonly takes place:
        (a)   in deserts.
        (b)   in areas of permafrost.
        (c)   in wet, warm climates.
        (d)   on cliffs of granite.

12.   Which kind of mass wasting typically takes place on the steepest slopes?
        (a)   rockfall.   (b)   creep.
        (c)   landslide.   (d)   earthflow.

Answers to Self-Test:

1.	a	6.	d	11.	b
2.	d	7.	b	12.	a
3.	a	8.	c		
4.	d	9.	a		
5.	a	10.	d		

HINTS FOR TEXTBOOK STUDY QUESTIONS

1.   These terms are defined on page 459.

2.   See Figure 15-4 (on page 204 of the Study Guide).

3.   See Figures 15-5 and 15-6 (p. 462) for some examples of this.

4.   Figure 15-3 (on page 205 of the Study Guide) illustrates how this can happen.

5.   See the section "Weathering Agents" on page 461.

6.   Frost wedging is a result of a special characteristic of water; see Figure 15-7 (on page 206 of the Study Guide).

7.   See Figure 15-11a (p. 465) and the associated text material.

8.   What was rust before it was rust? What caused this change? See page 467 in the textbook.

9.   Figure 15-16 (p. 468) may give you some ideas.

10.   Review the processes of chemical weathering. They all have one common characteristic or component.

11.   All of the different styles of mass wasting have one thing in common.

12.   The angle of repose is defined on page 469.

13.   Some of these roles are discussed on page 470.

14.   Consider each of the four main categories of mass wasting. Water may play different roles in each.

15.   Figure 15-20 (p. 471) is a photograph showing the outcome of rockfall.

16.   See Figure 15-21 (p. 471).

17.   Consider the ways in which the addition of water might increase the chance that a slope will fail and begin to slide.

18.   Notice the arrow showing the pattern of slippage in Figure 15-23 (p. 474).

19.   Consider where each develops, as well as the general differences between "slide" and "flow."

20.   Consider where each takes place, as well as the circumstances that tend to initiate these mass wasting events.

21.   You should discuss why creep takes place, as well as the visible evidence of soil creep in the landscape.

22.   Solufluction is discussed beginning on page 477.

ADDITIONAL STUDY QUESTION

1.   In what ways is water a key to both mechanical and chemical weathering?

Hint for Additional Study Question:

1.   Review the various processes of mechanical and chemical weathering.

CHAPTER 16

The Fluvial Processes

OVERVIEW

The work of running water is the most important external process shaping the landscape. Chapter 16 introduces the fundamental principles of these "fluvial processes." The chapter discusses the basics of stream erosion and deposition, patterns of stream channels and drainage systems, the shaping of stream valleys, and the most common landforms produced by running water.

This chapter begins by discussing a series of different fluvial processes. By understanding these processes (for example, the shaping of stream valleys through valley deepening, valley widening, and valley lengthening), you will have a clearer understanding of how fluvial landforms develop in general.

Several topics are worth special attention. You should note that most fluvial erosion takes place in valleys, and that the greatest amount of stream erosion occurs when a stream is flooding. As you read the sections on the shaping of valleys, note that just a few key processes are at work here—downcutting, lateral erosion, and headward erosion—and that deposition can take place whenever and wherever the speed of the water decreases.

You should note the variety of drainage patterns. In some locations the underlying structure has exerted strong control over the pattern of streams, while in other locations there is little structural control. Finally, note the imprint that stream rejuvenation leaves on the landscape.

KEY CONCEPTS

STREAMS AND STREAM SYSTEMS (p. 481):

The concepts and definitions presented in this section are keys to understanding the development of fluvial landscapes.

Valleys and Interfluves (p. 481): In the simplest terms, a *valley* refers to the part of the landscape where there is a clearly established drainage system (where running water is channeled into streams). There is no clear drainage system over an *interfluve*—the water flows overland and is not concentrated in channels (see **Figure 16-2**, shown below).

A problem with these terms is that we can recognize valleys and interfluves at many different scales. These different scales of drainage systems are illustrated in Figure 16-3 (p. 483), showing the hierarchy of drainage systems associated with the Mississippi River.

Stream Orders (p. 482): This section examines the various patterns that develop as small streams join to form larger streams. The lowest order streams (first-order) represent the smallest tributaries of a river system. When two first-order streams join, a second-order stream is formed; when two second-order streams join, a third-order stream is formed, and so on (Figure 16-4, p. 483). As a generalization, lower order streams tend to be shorter, steeper, and more numerous than higher order streams.

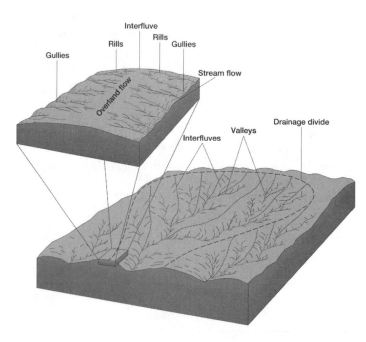

Figure 16-2: Valleys and interfluves. Valleys normally have clear-cut drainage systems, interfluves do not.

Fluvial Erosion and Deposition (p. 483): It is important to note that while *overland flow* does accomplish some erosion, the greatest erosion takes place within valleys by *streamflow*. Also note the factors that influence the power of erosion: the speed and volume of water (and the turbulence), the abrasive "tools" carried by the stream, the chemical action of the water (*corrosion*), as well as the resistance of the bedrock channel.

Transportation (p. 485): Perhaps the most important point to remember here is that the amount of material a stream can carry (the *load*) varies tremendously, depending on the volume and speed of the water. During times of flood flow, even a small stream is capable of moving great quantities of material, including very large rocks.

Deposition (p. 485): Whenever the speed of a stream decreases, its *capacity* to carry a load also decreases and deposition will take place. Streams typically "sort" *alluvium* (stream deposits) by size. As the velocity of a stream starts to decrease, the heaviest (usually the largest) pieces of rock can no longer be moved by the stream. As the speed drops still more, progressively smaller pieces of alluvium will be deposited, until the finest particles (such as suspended silt) settle out in quiet water.

The Role of Floods (p. 486): Even small streams can accomplish a great deal of erosion over long periods of geologic time, especially given the periods of high erosion that occur during times of flood flow.

STREAM CHANNELS (p. 486):

Stream Channel Patterns (p. 487): Few streams have straight courses over great distances—even apparently straight stream channels will have sinuosity in the actual flow of water (Figure 16-10a, p. 488). A *meandering stream* exhibits a very sinuous course (Figure 16-10b, p. 488). Meandering streams are especially common where a stream is flowing down a gentle slope. A *braided stream* has many interconnected channels, and the pattern of these channels tends to change often. Braided streams develop in situations where a stream is choked with a very heavy load that can't be easily carried by the stream during normal flow (see Figure 16-13, p. 489).

STRUCTURAL RELATIONSHIPS (p. 489):

The underlying structure of a landscape (such as patterns of rock resistance) may exert a strong influence over the paths taken by individual streams and over the geometry of stream networks. For example, *consequent streams* simply flow down the initial slope of the land, while *subsequent streams* develop along structural weaknesses in the landscape. Note two circumstances in which a stream seems to "defy" the structure by flowing through a ridge: an *antecedent stream* develops when a stream maintains its course and cuts through a slowly rising ridge (Figure 16-14, p.

490), while a *superimposed stream* has eroded down into an old structure that bears no structural relation to the present surface.

Stream Drainage Patterns (p. 491): The drainage pattern of stream systems is often strongly influenced by the underlying topographic and geologic structure. The common branching *dendritic drainage pattern* indicates that the underlying structure is not exerting much influence on the paths of streams. In other words, all of the rock is equally resistant to erosion (**Figure 16-15**, shown below).

In the *trellis drainage pattern*, the paths of streams are largely controlled by a pattern of alternating parallel ridges and valleys. In a trellis drainage network, tributaries usually flow parallel to each other down the valleys until one can cut across a low spot in the separating ridge to join another (**Figure 16-16**, shown below). Note in the map of West Virginia (Figure 16-17, p. 492), that the drainage pattern changes from dendritic in the west, to trellis in the eastern folded ridges and valleys of the Appalachian Mountains.

THE SHAPING AND RESHAPING OF VALLEYS (p. 492):

This section focuses on the four general ways that a stream can change its valley shape: through valley deepening, valley widening, valley lengthening, and deposition in valleys.

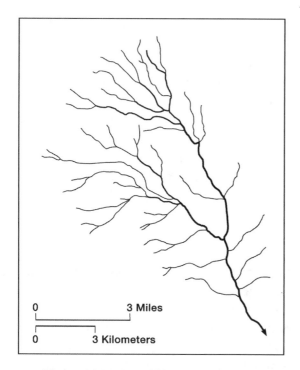

Figure 16-15: Dendritic drainage pattern.

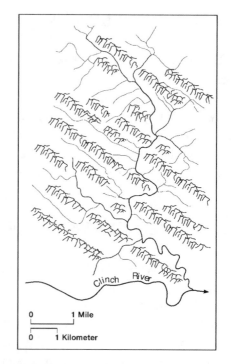

Figure 16-16: Trellis drainage pattern.

Valley Deepening (p. 493): If a stream has either high velocity or a large volume of water, *downcutting* tends to be the dominant activity. Downcutting produces a "V-shaped" stream cross section. This is very common in the upper reaches of a river system where the gradients of the streams are steep.

Knickpoint Migration (p. 494): *Knickpoints*, such as rapids and waterfalls, are also common in the upper reaches of a river system where downcutting is prominent. Greater turbulence and faster flow concentrates the erosive power of water at a knickpoint, and so these stream irregularities tend to wear down and retreat upstream with time (**Figure 16-23**, shown below). This process is known as *knickpoint migration*. Read *Focus: Niagara Falls* (p. 495) for a dramatic illustration of knickpoint migration.

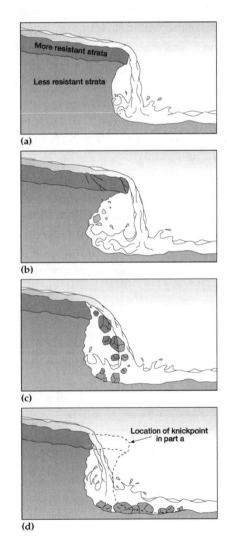

Figure 16-23: (a) Knickpoint formed where a stream flows over a resistant layer of rock. (b) The water flow undercuts the lip and (c) causes it to collapse. (d) Position of knickpoint has migrated upstream.

Valley Widening (p. 496): In places where a stream has developed a gentle profile (a gentle slope), the energy of a stream is diverted from downcutting to *lateral erosion*. Erosion is concentrated on the outside bank of a meandering stream channel (since the water is moving fastest there). At the same time, deposition is taking place on the inside bank (since the water velocity is slowest there). See **Figure 16-24** (shown below).

Through lateral erosion, the channel of a meandering stream tends to swing back and forth across the floodplain. Where it reaches the edge of the valley floor, it cuts into the valley walls and widens the valley (see Figure 16-25, p. 496). Mass wasting also contributes to valley widening.

Valley Lengthening (p. 496): Streams can increase the length of their courses through two processes: *headward erosion* and *delta* formation.

Headward Erosion (p. 496): *Headward erosion* is a key concept in geomorphology. At the top of a valley where water flows over the lip of an interfluve, the water velocity increases as it falls into the valley. This concentrates the erosive power of the water at the lip of the interfluve and so the stream cuts higher and higher into the interfluve, thereby slowly increasing the length of its valley (Figure 16-26, p. 497). The photograph in Figure 16-27 (p. 498) illustrates the results of this process.

Stream Capture (p. 497): *Stream Capture* is an example of the power of headward erosion (see Figure 16-29, p. 499).

Delta Formation (p. 498): *Delta formation* is the other way in which a stream can lengthen its course (Figure 16-32, p. 501). Note that deltas can only form where a stream enters a quiet body of water. For example, the Amazon River does not develop a delta because of the active ocean conditions near its mouth. See *People and the Environment: The Bird's-foot of the Mississippi* for a description of the processes associated with the changing Mississippi River delta.

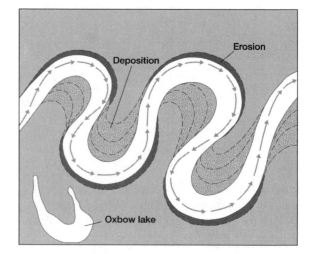

Figure 16-24: Erosion occurs on the outside of meander bends, whereas deposition is common on the inside. If the neck of a meander is cut through by the stream, an oxbow lake is formed. (After Shelden Judson, Marvin E. Kauffman, and L. Don Leet, *Physical Geology*, 7th ed. Englewood Cliffs, NJ: Prentice Hall, 1987, p. 264.)

Deposition in Valleys (p. 499):   A cross section of a stream channel is illustrated in Figure 16-33 (p. 501). In times of flood flow, the channel is made deeper through scouring, while in periods of lower flow, the channel fills up again due to deposition.

FLOODPLAINS (p. 501):

The *floodplain* of a river is largely a depositional landform (although its width may be due, at least in part, to lateral erosion). Figure 16-36 (p. 504) and **Figure 16-37** (shown below) illustrate common features of floodplains.

Natural levees develop over the years as alluvium is deposited along the banks of a stream during floods. When one meander cuts into another, an isolated section of river channel remains that can become an *oxbow lake* (see Figure 16-35, p. 503). The photograph in Figure 16-12 (p. 489) shows the meandering path of a river on a floodplain. Review the animations *Meandering Streams* and *Floods and Natural Levee Formation* to see the development of these landforms as well as the processes associated with flooding.

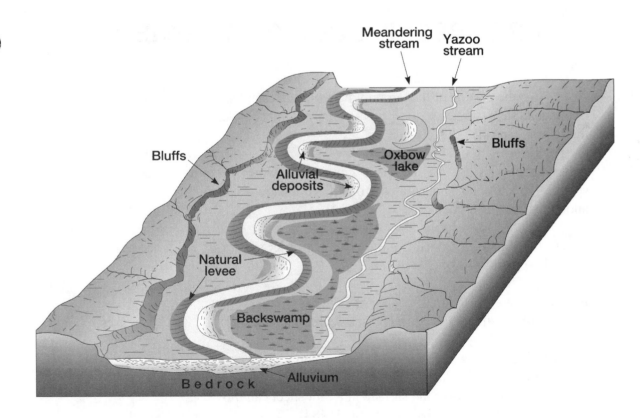

Figure 16-37: Typical landforms in a floodplain.

STREAM REJUVENATION (p. 506):

The presence of *stream terraces* (Figure 16-40, p. 507) and *entrenched meanders* (Figure 16-41, p. 508) indicate that a stream has undergone renewed downcutting. This *rejuvenation* is often the result of tectonic uplift of the landscape. For example, stream terraces represent old valley floors—during rejuvenation, a stream may begin downcutting into its old valley floor, leaving a pair of terraces above the present stream level. Review the animation **Stream Rejuvenation** if these processes are not clear to you.

THEORIES OF LANDFORM DEVELOPMENT (p. 507):

Note that the Davisian "geomorphic cycle" has been largely discounted as a general theory that explains how a fluvial landscape should develop over time. However, the language of Davis (characterizing landscapes as "youthful," "mature," or "old age") is sometimes used to describe the regional topography of stream valleys.

PROGRESSIVE CONTENT REVIEW

---

1. A _____ is the portion of the terrain with a clearly established drainage system, while an _____ is the area of land "between the rivers." (pp. 481–482)

    valley
    interfluve

2. A drainage _____ is an area that contributes water to a specific stream, and is separated from the drainage area of another stream by a drainage _____. (p. 482)

    basin

    divide

3. Where two first-order streams unite, a _____-order stream is formed. (pp. 482–483)

    second

4. In general, as the order of a stream increases, the average gradient of the stream _____ (increases/decreases). (p. 483)

    decreases

5. Small particles on a hill can be moved a short distance by falling drops of rain through the process of _____ erosion, while water flowing over the surface in a thin sheet can move material through _____ erosion. (pp. 483–484)

    splash

    sheet

6. The greatest erosion takes place when water is channeled into a _____. (p. 484)   stream

7. The hydraulic power of the water is usually aided by the _____ "tools" carried in a stream. (p. 484)   abrasive

8. The chemical action of water also helps a stream erode through the process of _____. (p. 484)   corrosion

9. The erosive power of a stream is largely determined by the velocity of the water, which is dependent on the _____ of the   gradient
stream, and by the _____ of flow. (pp. 484–485)   volume

10. The _____ load of a stream includes salts carried in solution,   dissolved
while the _____ load of fine particles is carried along in the   suspended
flow of water. (p. 485)

11. The bedload of a stream consists of larger rock fragments,
such as _____ and _____, that are bounced along the stream   sand; gravel
bottom by the process of _____, or rolled along through the   saltation
process of _____. (p. 485)   traction

12. The _____ of a stream refers to the largest size particle that   competence
can be carried by the water flow. (p. 485)

13. The _____ of a stream refers to the amount of solid material   capacity
that can be carried by a stream at a given time. (p. 485)

14. Whenever the speed (and/or volume) of a stream decreases,
_____ can take place. (p. 485)   deposition

15. _____ is a term for stream-deposited material. (p. 485)   Alluvium

16. Most streams exhibit great variation in their volume of flow
or "_____." (p. 486)   discharge

17. Most stream erosion takes place during times of _____ flow.   flood
(p. 486)

18. A _____ stream carries water all year, while an _____ stream   perennial; ephemeral
only carries water immediately after a rain. (p. 86)

19. Because of _____ along the bottom and sides of a stream channel, the water tends to move _____ (slowest/fastest) at the center of a channel. (p. 487)

friction
fastest

20. _____ (slow/fast) moving streams tend to be fairly turbulent, and this can _____ (increase/decrease) the amount of erosion possible. (p. 487)

Fast
increase

21. The line connecting the deepest parts of a stream channel is called the _____. This line rarely forms a _____ (straight/curving) line. (p. 488)

thalweg; straight

22. A _____ stream has many interconnected shallow channels. (p. 489)

braided

23. In _____ drainage patterns, geologic structures do not control the evolution of the drainage pattern. (p. 491)

dendritic

24. A _____ drainage pattern often develops in areas with alternating parallel ridges and valleys. (p. 491)

trellis

25. A _____ drainage pattern develops around a steep, round mountain such as a volcano. (p. 491)

radial

26. Valley deepening typically takes place when the velocity of the water is _____ (low/high) or there is a relatively _____ (small/large) volume of water. (p. 493)

high; large

27. When streams are downcutting rapidly, a steep-sided _____-shaped valley cross section usually is present. (p. 493)

V

28. The ultimate _____ level represents the lowest possible elevation to which a stream can downcut. (p. 493)

base

29. Knickpoints typically migrate _____ (upstream/downstream) and disappear. (p. 494)

upstream

30. When a stream flows down a gentle slope, energy will be diverted from downcutting, and _____ erosion will predominate through stream meandering. (p. 496)

lateral

31. Erosion in a meandering stream channel takes place on the _____ (inside/outside) banks of the channel, while deposition takes place along the _____ banks. (p. 496)

outside

inside

32. Valleys are lengthened through _____ erosion near their upper end, and by _____ formation at their lower end. (p. 496)

headward

delta

33. _____ _____ results when one stream cuts into the course of another stream and "steals" its water. (p. 497)

Stream capture (Stream piracy)

34. Deltas will form only where rivers flow into _____ bodies of water. (p. 498)

quiet

35. During periods of low water flow, streams tend to _____ (fill/scour) their channel bottoms, while during periods of high water flow, the stream bottom is usually _____. (pp. 499–500)

fill

scoured

36. When a stream accumulates a great thickness of alluvium after a period of flooding, the level of the stream bed may be raised through the process of _____. (p. 500)

aggradation

37. When one meander of a stream cuts into another meander, a section of old stream channel may be left as an _____ lake. (p. 502)

oxbow

38. A _____ stream may run parallel to a large river when it cannot flow directly into the main channel because of large _____ _____. (p. 502)

yazoo

natural levees

39. Stream terraces indicate that stream _____ has taken place. (p. 507)

rejuvenation

40. When a meandering stream is uplifted slowly, _____ meanders may result. (p. 507)

entrenched

41. _____ _____ suggests that slope forms in a landscape are adjusted so that there is a balance of energy. (pp. 510–511)

Equilibrium theory

SELF-TEST

1. A stream will downcut most rapidly if:
    (a)   it has a low velocity and a heavy load.
    (b)   it has a low velocity and a light load.
    (c)   it has a high velocity.
    (d)   it is flowing over resistant rock.

2. Waterfalls tend to migrate upstream *primarily* due to:
    (a)   delta formation.
    (b)   deposition.
    (c)   lateral erosion.
    (d)   undercutting and erosion due to the higher stream velocity at the knickpoint.

3. A V-shaped valley suggests that a stream is:
    (a)   downcutting rapidly.
    (b)   depositing a great deal of alluvium in the bottom of its channel.
    (c)   depositing a great deal of alluvium along the sides of its valley.
    (d)   mostly eroding through lateral erosion.

4. Why do streams erode mostly along the outside banks of a meander?
    (a)   Sand deposits reduce the erosion along the inside banks.
    (b)   The water is moving fastest near the outside bank.
    (c)   The water is moving slowest near the outside bank.

5. What would prevent a delta from forming where a large river enters the ocean?
    (a)   Calm ocean conditions.
    (b)   The river is carrying a heavy load of alluvium.
    (c)   A shallow coastal shelf.
    (d)   Active ocean currents along the coast.

6. An oxbow lake is most likely to form:
    (a)   when a cutoff meander develops in a floodplain.
    (b)   where a river crosses a knickpoint.
    (c)   near an interfluve.
    (d)   in a steep V-shaped valley.

7.   A yazoo stream is prevented from joining a major river because:
       (a)   it is blocked by high natural levees.
       (b)   it is blocked by swamps.
       (c)   it is blocked by a knickpoint.
       (d)   it flows in the opposite direction from the main river.

8.   Entrenched meanders are formed by:
       (a)   deposition on a floodplain.
       (b)   headward erosion.
       (c)   stream rejuvenation.
       (d)   deposition on the bottom of a stream channel.

9.   Stream terraces are formed by:
       (a)   deposition on a floodplain.
       (b)   headward erosion.
       (c)   stream rejuvenation.
       (d)   deposition on the bottom of a stream channel.

10.   Which type of drainage pattern is mostly likely to develop in areas of alternating parallel ridges and valleys?
       (a)   Dendritic.   (b)   Radial.
       (c)   Centripetal.   (d)   Trellis.

11.   Which type of drainage pattern is mostly likely to develop where the underlying structure has little influence on the drainage?
       (a)   Dendritic.   (b)   Radial.
       (c)   Centripetal.   (d)   Trellis.

12.   Which type of drainage pattern is mostly likely to develop around a volcanic peak?
       (a)   Dendritic.   (b)   Radial.
       (c)   Centripetal.   (d)   Trellis.

13.   Natural levees form when:
       (a)   a river is meandering over resistant rock.
       (b)   alluvium is deposited on the bottom of a stream channel during normal flow.
       (c)   alluvium is deposited when water spills over the banks of a channel during flood flow.
       (d)   alluvium is deposited below the lip of an interfluve.

14. The process of headward erosion *primarily* occurs because:
    (a) water falls onto softer rock.
    (b) water falls onto more resistant rock.
    (c) alluvium is deposited at the lip of an interfluve.
    (d) the velocity of water increases as it falls off the lip of an interfluve into a valley.

15. The size of alluvium a stream is able to carry primarily depends on:
    (a) the temperature of the water.
    (b) the velocity and volume of the water.
    (c) the depth of the stream channel.
    (d) the width of the stream channel.

16. Perennial streams:
    (a) carry water only immediately after a rain.
    (b) carry water all year.
    (c) carry water only during the wet season.
    (d) never have water.

17. Ephemeral streams:
    (a) carry water only immediately after a rain.
    (b) carry water all year.
    (c) carry water only during the wet season.
    (d) never have water.

18. A floodplain is primarily:
    (a) an erosional feature.
    (b) a consequence of stream rejuvenation.
    (c) a depositional feature.
    (d) found on an interfluve.

19. A meandering river is most likely to be found flowing:
    (a) over a gentle slope.
    (b) down a steep slope.
    (c) over resistant rock.
    (d) over an interfluve.

Answers to Self-Test:

1.	c	6.	a	11.	a	16.	b
2.	d	7.	a	12.	b	17.	a
3.	a	8.	c	13.	c	18.	c
4.	b	9.	c	14.	d	19.	a
5.	d	10.	d	15.	b		

HINTS FOR TEXTBOOK STUDY QUESTIONS

1.   See Figure 16-2 (on page 216 of the Study Guide).

2.   Again, see Figure 16-2 (on page 216 of the Study Guide).

3.   These features are also illustrated in Figure 16-2 (on page 216 of the Study Guide).

4.   Consider which factors influence the hydraulic power of a stream, as well as the abrasive power of a stream.

5.   What does a stream transport that can help the water scour material from the streambed?

6.   See Figure 16-7 (p. 485) and the animation *Stream Sediment Movement*.

7.   These terms are discussed on page 485.

8.   Again, see page 485.

9.   Consider what would change the "competence" of a stream.

10.   Consider the process of stream abrasion and the role of floods.

11.   Compare the photograph of alluvium (Figure 16-6, p. 484) to that of talus (Figure 15-20, p. 471).

12.   Consider the relationship of a stream's discharge to its competence and capacity.

13.   For one factor influencing this, compare the photograph of a stream with a sinuous channel pattern (Figure 16-11, p. 488) with that of a stream with a meandering channel pattern (Figure 16-12, p. 489).

14.   Look at the stream bed in the photograph of a braided channel pattern (Figure 16-13, p. 489).

15.   See Figure 16-14 (p. 490).

16.   Consider the differences in topography and underlying structure that might account for the drainage patterns shown in Figure 16-17 (p. 492).

17.   Figure 16-18 (p. 492) provides one example of this.

18.   Think about some of the factors that explain the formation of the V-shaped valley shown in Figure 16-21 (p. 493).

19.   This concept is illustrated in Figure 16-22 (p. 494).

20.   Consider what happens to a stream's downcutting ability as its gradient is reduced.

21.   What stream conditions are required for a stream to downcut? Is deposition likely under those circumstances?

22.   This process is well illustrated in Figure 16-23 (p. 494).

23.   Figure 16-25 (p. 496) is a conceptual diagram that may help you visualize this process.

24.   Figure 16-26 (p. 497) does a good job of illustrating this process.

25.   Think of the role of headward erosion in stream capture as you review the sequence of diagrams in Figure 16-28 (p. 498).

26.   Figure 16-32 (p. 501) shows a sequence of delta formation.

27.   What conditions would prevent the accumulation of sediment at the mouth of a river?

28.   The animation *Floods and Natural Levee Formation* may help here.

29.   Recall the process that produces cutoff meanders and oxbow lakes.

30. Think about the importance of lateral erosion as you review Figure 16-35 (p. 503) and the animation *Meandering Streams*.

31. Look at Figure 16-36 (p. 504) and imagine a tributary stream trying to enter the main river channel.

32. This process is shown in the animation *Stream Rejuvenation* and in Figure 16-40 (p. 507).

33. See Figure 16-41 (p. 508).

34. See the section "Penck's Theory of Crustal Change and Slope Development" (p. 509). Penck's work developed in part as a critique of Davis' theory.

35. For example, equilibrium theory suggests that the angles of slopes in a landscape vary depending on the resistance of the rock and the geomorphic processes involved. How is this different from the geomorphic cycle of Davis?

ADDITIONAL STUDY QUESTIONS

1. Is it ever possible for a stream to erode below sea level? Explain.

2. Why is stream flow generally unsystematic and irregular?

3. Discuss some of the relationships between stream order and other characteristics of streams.

Hints for Additional Study Questions:

1. Are there any places on the continents (other than the bottoms of bodies of water) that have elevations below sea level?

2. You can answer this question in two ways: in terms of variations in the amount of water in a stream over time, or in terms of the flow pattern of water within the stream channel.

3.   For example, consider what generally happens to gradients and the amount of water as stream order increases.

CHAPTER 17

Solution Processes and Karst Topography

OVERVIEW

Chapter 17 introduces the work of water beneath the ground. This chapter begins with a discussion of the solution activity of underground water, then discusses both the underground features and surface "karst" topography that can result from these processes. The chapter concludes with a discussion of hydrothermal features such as hot springs and geysers.

Although this is a brief chapter, it is an important one. Relatively large areas of Earth's surface consist of limestone or other easily soluble rock, and so karst landforms are quite widespread. It is important to note that underground solution processes involve both the dissolution of rock and the subsequent precipitation and redeposition of this material. Also, note the set of conditions that are necessary for hydrothermal features to develop.

KEY CONCEPTS

THE IMPACT OF SOLUTION PROCESSES ON THE LANDSCAPE (p. 515):

The key point of this chapter is that in areas of soluble rock such as limestone, the chemical activity of water below the surface can be more important in shaping the surface topography than the action of running water on the surface.

SOLUTION AND PRECIPITATION (p. 515):

The first part of this chapter is primarily concerned with the chemical action of water on limestone (and similar rocks). In the discussion of chemical weathering in Chapter 15, we noted that carbon dioxide is easily dissolved in water, forming *carbonic acid*. Calcium carbonate (the main chemical component of limestone, sea shells, and coral) is decomposed by carbonic acid into a much softer material (calcium bicarbonate) that is easily dissolved and carried away by water.

Figure 17-1 (p. 515) compares the relative ease with which water dissolves various common elements. Starting off with equal amounts of each mineral, the dark area in each container represents the amount of each mineral left undissolved. This shows that both sodium (a key component of salts) and calcium (a key component of limestone) are easily dissolved, while substances such as iron and aluminum are not easily dissolved.

Also note that due to the structure of limestone, the joints and bedding planes provide the openings along which water can seep down and remove rock in solution.

CAVERNS AND RELATED FEATURES (p. 516):

Caverns tend to develop along the weaknesses provided by the joints and bedding planes in limestone. The depositional features in caverns (such as *stalactites* and *stalagmites*) form very slowly as minerals carried in solution are precipitated by water dripping into cave openings (see Figure 17-4, and the photograph in Figure 17-3, p. 517).

KARST TOPOGRAPHY (p. 517):

Figure 17-7 (shown on the following page) illustrates the variety of landforms that can develop in limestone areas. For example, solution activity at joint intersections can lead to the development of *sinkholes*. As caverns or other openings just below the surface collapse, depressions such as *collapse dolines* develop on the surface. A series of collapse dolines can coalesce, producing a karst valley known as an *uvala*. In general, the surface topography in karst regions is very irregular, with many small hills and depressions.

Another important characteristic of karst topography is the lack of surface streams. This is common because most water on the surface seeps down into the rock structure through joints or *swallow holes* before surface streams can flow very far.

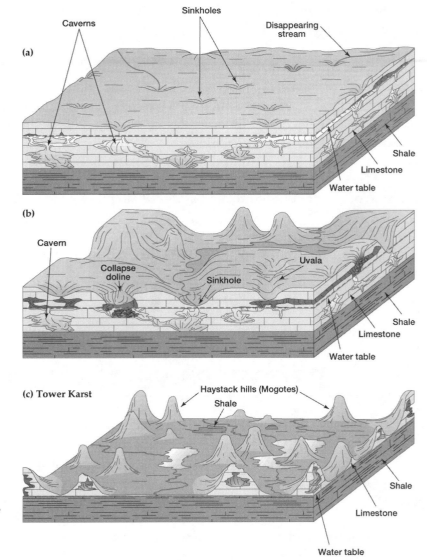

Figure 17-7: Examples of karst topography. (a) "Sinkhole karst" landscapes are characterized by many sinkholes and disappearing streams. (b) Over time, more extensive depressions such as uvalas may develop through the collapse of sinkholes. (c) In tower karst landscapes, steep-sided limestone hills, sometimes called "haystack hills" or *mogotes*, remain after long periods of weathering and solution activity.

HYDROTHERMAL FEATURES (p. 521):

Hydrothermal features are really a separate topic from karst features, although underground water is obviously important in both cases.

Hydrothermal features, such as *hot springs* and *geysers*, are formed when water comes in contact with hot rocks, or directly in contact with magma under the surface. This often requires a source of magma fairly close to the surface. In the case of the Yellowstone Park area, it is thought that the heat source is only about 1.6 kilometers (one mile) below the surface. For hydrothermal features to develop, two other conditions must also be met. First, ample water must be available to seep down and become heated. Finally, the bedrock must be fractured so that heated water or steam can move back to the surface through joints or other structural weaknesses.

Hot Springs (p. 521): Figure 17-9 (p. 521) shows a simplified diagram of a hot spring, but the diagram of Jupiter Terrace in Yellowstone (Figure 17-16, p. 525) presents a more complete diagram of how a large hot spring structure has developed. Also note the variety of depositional features, such as travertine terraces, that result from hot springs (see the photograph of Mammoth Hot Springs, Figure 17-17, p. 526).

Geysers (p. 522): The eruption of geysers seems to involve the buildup of a critical pressure of steam in underground passages that initiates the abrupt venting of the heated water and steam.

Hydrothermal Features in Yellowstone (p. 523): Yellowstone National Park offers a good case study of hydrothermal features.

PROGRESSIVE CONTENT REVIEW

---

1.   The _____ (mechanical/chemical) action of underground   chemical
        water in regions of limestone bedrock is much more
        important as a sculptor of topography than _____ action.   mechanical
        (p. 515)

2.   Underground water functions as a weak solution of _____   carbonic
        acid that is produced when _____ _____ is dissolved in   carbon dioxide
        water. This weak acid is especially effective in dissolving a
        rock such as _____. (p. 515)   limestone

3.   Groundwater usually is able to penetrate underground rock
        most easily through _____ and bedding planes. (p. 516)   joints

4.   Limestone can be deposited in cave openings when the _____   precipitation
         of the dissolved calcium carbonate takes place. (p. 516)

5.   The orange and green colors of mineral deposits around hot
        springs and geysers are often due to _____. (p. 516)   algae

6. The largest openings of caverns are usually developed horizontally along the _____ _____ in the limestone. (p. 516) — bedding planes

7. _____ are precipitated deposits of minerals in a cavern, and can include structures hanging from the ceiling called _____ and structures built up from the floor called _____. (p. 517) — Speleothems / stalactites / stalagmites

8. Although karst topography is most common in areas of massive limestone bedrock, it may also occur in other soluble rocks such as _____, _____, or _____. (p. 518) — dolomite; gypsum; halite (salt)

9. A _____ is a depression resulting from the dissolution of surface rocks, while a _____ _____ results from the collapse of a subsurface cave. (p. 518) — sinkhole / collapse doline

10. _____ _____ refers to landscapes where tall limestone towers with nearly vertical walls are found. (p. 520) — Tower karst

11. Most karst areas lack a well-defined system of _____ drainage. (p. 520) — surface

12. A _____ _____ forms when underground water comes in contact with heated rocks or magma below the surface. (p. 521) — hot spring

13. _____ is a common massive calcium carbonate deposit produced by a hot spring. (p. 522) — Travertine

14. An intermittent hot spring that sporadically emits hot water or steam is called a _____. (p. 522) — geyser

15. A _____ is a surface crack that is connected with an underground heat source, but the limited supply of water only produces the venting of _____ at the surface. (p. 523) — fumarole / steam

16. Hydrothermal activity usually requires an intrusion of _____ at a relatively shallow depth below the surface, an abundance of _____ that can seep down and become heated, and broken or weak surface rocks to allow the _____ to move up and down easily. (p. 524) — magma / water / water

237

SELF-TEST

1. Which factor is most important in allowing solution activity to occur in limestone under the surface?
   (a) High water temperatures.
   (b) Joints and bedding planes.
   (c) Cold air temperatures.
   (d) Dry climatic conditions.

2. Which substance is most easily dissolved by water?
   (a) Iron.   (b) Silicon.
   (c) Magnesium.   (d) Calcium.

3. Which of the following features is usually *not* prominent on the surface in areas of limestone karst topography?
   (a) Sinkholes.
   (b) Collapsed dolines.
   (c) Irregular surface topography.
   (d) Well-established surface drainage.

4. Which of the following is a depositional feature?
   (a) Stalactite.   (b) Sinkhole.
   (c) Uvala.   (d) Swallow hole.

5. Which characteristic is *not* necessary for hot springs to develop?
   (a) A heat source below the surface.
   (b) An abundance of water.
   (c) Steeply sloping surface topography.
   (d) Weak or broken surface rocks.

6. Geysers typically will erupt:
   (a) as soon as water trickles down and touches the hot rocks.
   (b) when a critical pressure of steam builds up in an underground passageway.
   (c) every hour.
   (d) when travertine plugs the geyser opening.

7.   A weak acid (carbonic acid) results when:
     (a)   carbon dioxide is dissolved in water.
     (b)   water contains no impurities.
     (c)   nitrogen is dissolved in water.
     (d)   ozone is dissolved in water.

8.   Most openings in caverns have developed along:
     (a)   faults.   (b)   joints and bedding planes.
     (c)   dikes.   (d)   beds of metamorphic rock.

9.   A common rock deposited around hot springs is:
     (a)   basalt.   (b)   andesite.
     (c)   travertine.   (d)   sandstone.

10. "Tower" karst refers to:
     (a)   stalactites and stalagmites inside caverns.
     (b)   waterfalls in karst regions.
     (c)   a deep, collapsed doline.
     (d)   tall, steep-sided hills of limestone.

11. A fumarole develops:
     (a)   when a small amount of water drains down to an underground heat source and is converted to steam.
     (b)   where water is heated and rises into pools just below the surface.
     (c)   when a hot spring has a great supply of water.
     (d)   where limestone is dissolved in water.

Answers to Self-Test:

1.	b	6.	b	11.	a
2.	d	7.	a		
3.	d	8.	b		
4.	a	9.	c		
5.	c	10.	d		

HINTS FOR TEXTBOOK STUDY QUESTIONS

1. Consider what kinds of rock are most susceptible to chemical weathering.

2. Review the section "Solution and Precipitation" (pp. 515–516).

3. Consider the ways that water moves around underground.

4. Figure 17-4 (p. 517) and the associated text describe this process.

5. Especially consider where sinkholes tend to develop in relationship to the structure of the limestone.

6. See Figure 17-2 (p. 516).

7. Again, see Figure 17-2 (p. 516).

8. These features are discussed beginning on page 521.

9. This is described on page 522.

10. These conditions are well met in Yellowstone National Park. See page 524.

11. See the section "Hydrothermal Features in Yellowstone" beginning on page 523.

ADDITIONAL STUDY QUESTION

1. How might the pumping of groundwater accelerate the process of sinkhole formation in a region of karst topography?

Hint for Additional Study Question:

1. See *People and the Environment: Sinkholes in Florida* for one example of this circumstance.

CHAPTER 18

The Topography of Arid Lands

OVERVIEW

Chapter 18 focuses on the development of landforms in deserts and other arid regions of the world. Dry regions exhibit a great variety of landscapes. This chapter emphasizes the processes that are shaping landforms in deserts, and does not attempt to describe the full range of desert landforms that can be found around the world. The chapter first looks at the specialized environmental conditions that shape desert landforms, followed by a discussion of the erosional and depositional processes of running water in arid lands, the work of wind, and finally, a look at the collections of landforms found in two common desert environments in North America.

Perhaps the most important concept in this chapter is also the most striking: running water is by far the most important process of erosion and deposition in deserts. In order to understand why this is true, pay close attention to the sections discussing the specialized environmental characteristics of deserts and desert hydrography. You'll notice that in many ways this chapter is an extension of Chapter 16 (The Fluvial Processes), since much of the discussion here also concerns fluvial processes—in this case those fluvial processes operating in the specialized conditions of the desert.

The discussion of "Basin-and-Range" and "Mesa-and-Scarp" desert landforms demands a close look. These American desert landform assemblages illustrate the results of the specialized conditions and processes that are responsible for landform development in deserts everywhere.

KEY CONCEPTS

A SPECIALIZED ENVIRONMENT (p. 529):

Read this section carefully. The 10 special characteristics of arid lands presented here contribute to the distinctive landscapes of deserts.

1. **Weathering** (p. 529): With less available moisture, mechanical weathering is more important than chemical weathering, although even mechanical weathering tends to operate rather slowly.

2. **Soil and Regolith** (p. 529): Desert landscapes often look rather stark since there is usually little soil or regolith cover (Figure 18-1, p. 529). This exposes the bedrock directly to weathering and erosional processes. The lack of soil cover, in part, compensates for the lack of water, since the rock is not protected from weathering and erosion by a mantle of soil.

3. **Soil Creep** (p. 529): With little soil and little water, soil creep is not an important factor in shaping desert landscapes.

4. **Impermeable Surfaces** (p. 529): This is an important characteristic of deserts, since this, too, in part, compensates for the lack of water. When it rains, little soaks into the ground at first, producing high runoff that is capable of significant erosion. There are many causes of impermeable surfaces in deserts. In some cases, the exposed bedrock doesn't allow water to soak in. But even in areas where soil or regolith are present, the surface may have developed a hard, impermeable layer such as from the accumulation of calcium carbonate or the presence of desert pavement (discussed below in "Characteristic Desert Surfaces").

5. **Sand** (p. 529): Note that most deserts are not "seas of sand." However, since sand can be easily moved around by wind and heavy rains, sand accumulations are found in parts of many deserts.

6. **Rainfall** (p. 529): This is another key concept in the chapter. Rainfall in deserts is often intense (such as from thunderstorms), although short-lived. This combines with the impermeable surfaces to produce high runoff and flash floods for short periods of time.

7. **Fluvial Deposition** (p. 529): Most desert streams do not flow all year (they are *ephemeral*). This characteristic, and the tendency of desert rainfall to be intense, means that desert streams are characterized by either flood flow, or no flow. There are two consequences of this combination of conditions. First, desert streams can accomplish a great deal of erosion

during their brief flood flows. Second, since the streams are not flowing continuously for very long periods of time, alluvium is usually not carried very far. The result of this is that deserts typically contain significant depositional features.

8. **Wind** (p. 530): Wind generally is not a significant erosional agent in deserts, although it does move around loose material such as sand.

9. **Basins of Interior Drainage** (p. 530): *Interior drainage* is another factor that contributes to the large number of depositional features in arid lands. Large portions of the American desert Southwest consist of basins of interior drainage—watersheds that do not eventually drain into the sea (see Figure 18-3, p. 530).

10. **Vegetation** (p. 530): The typical lack of a lush cover of vegetation in deserts leaves the landscape more directly exposed to the processes of weathering and erosion.

RUNNING WATER IN WATERLESS REGIONS (p. 530):

This is the key section of the chapter. Because of the special characteristics of deserts, such as impermeable surfaces, intense but short-lived rainfall, and the lack of vegetation and soil cover, running water is the most important agent of erosion and deposition in deserts.

Surface Water in the Desert (p. 531): While *exotic rivers* may flow through deserts (having obtained their water in more humid areas), almost all streams in deserts are *ephemeral* (see the photograph in Figure 18-13, p. 535). Ephemeral streams are usually dry, but the periodic, intense rainfall along with the high runoff characteristic of many desert surfaces means that these streams will be able to accomplish a great deal of erosion during their short periods of flood flow.

The dry lake beds found in deserts are typically covered with a crust of salt. These dry lake beds or *playas* develop in basins of interior drainage. Dissolved salts, carried by ephemeral streams flowing into the basin, eventually accumulate in a playa after the water evaporates.

In the western United States and other arid regions, such as the interior of Australia, there are many dry lake beds and a few remnant salt lakes that reflect the wetter conditions during former glacial periods (see Figure 18-7, p. 532, and Figure 19-2, p. 558).

Fluvial Erosion in Arid Lands (p. 532): A key concept in geomorphology is the notion of *differential erosion*—all rocks do not weather and erode easily. Resistant rocks tend to remain in the landscape as steep-sided landforms, while softer rocks wear away into more gently sloping landforms. Differential erosion tends to stand out clearly in deserts, since there is rarely a protective layer of soil or regolith (Figure 18-9, p. 534).

Fluvial Deposition in Arid Lands (p. 536): Because of the characteristics of desert hydrography, flowing streams tend not to carry alluvium very far at one time. This means that many desert landscapes are dominated by landforms produced by fluvial deposition.

The term *piedmont* refers to the "foot of the mountains," where the steep-sided desert mountains meet the valley bottoms. The abrupt change in slope slows streamflow coming out of the mountains, and so the piedmont zone becomes an area of deposition.

CHARACTERISTIC DESERT SURFACES— ERGS, REGS, AND HAMADAS (p. 536):

In this section, several general types of desert landscapes are presented. Although a "sea of sand" (*erg*) is popularly thought of as the typical desert landscape, most desert areas are not covered with sand. A coarse gravel surface or "stony" desert (*reg*) is often covered with a dark *desert varnish* of iron and manganese oxides. A third variety of desert landscape is the *hamada*, a flat, barren surface with little loose material.

THE WORK OF WIND (p. 538):

Most of the work accomplished by wind in deserts is the shifting around of sand or other loose material. As a consequence, the most important *aeolian* (wind produced) landscapes are depositional.

Aeolian Transportation (p. 497): Note that similar principles apply to the movement of particles by both wind and water. Wherever the speed of the wind decreases, deposition can take place.

Aeolian Deposition (p. 540): The type of sand dunes found in a desert relate to the supply of sand, the persistence of the wind, and the presence of vegetation to anchor dunes (**Figure 18-21**, shown on the following page).

Desert Sand Dunes (p. 540): Crescent-shaped *barchan* dunes move over nonsandy surfaces with their cusps pointing in the direction of movement (downwind). *Transverse* dunes are crescent-shaped ridges of sand that occur in areas with a greater supply of sand than with barchans. Both barchan and transverse dunes are characterized by a gentle windward slope and a steep *slip face*, or leeward slope (**Figure 18-20**, shown on the following page). *Seif* or "longitudinal" dunes are long ridges of sand that tend to form in areas with two different dominant wind directions during the year. You should also review the animation ***Desert Sand Dunes***.

Figure 18-20: Sand dunes migrate downwind as sand grains move up the gentle windward slope and are deposited on the steep slip face.

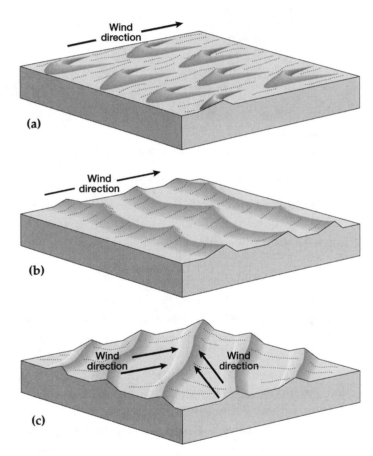

Figure 18-21: Common desert sand dune types: (a) barchan; (b) transverse; (c) seif.

TWO CHARACTERISTIC DESERT LANDFORM ASSEMBLAGES (p. 544):

The two landform assemblages presented in this section are not intended to be representative of all deserts. Rather, the landforms in these two desert environments illustrate the results of the erosional and depositional processes that are typical in deserts. Figure 18-27 (p. 544) is a map showing the locations of these two desert regions of North America.

245

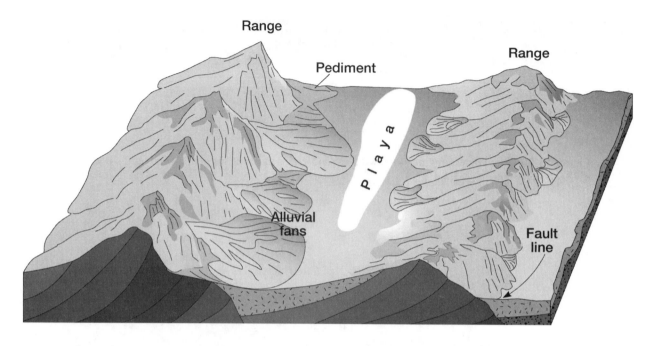

Figure 18-28: A typical basin-and-range landscape with alluvial fans and a playa.

Basin-and-Range Terrain (p. 544): The Basin-and-Range province of the United States is a region of basins of interior drainage, rugged fault-block mountains, and flat basin floors (**Figure 18-28**, shown above).

Note the significance of the piedmont zone. The foot of the mountains becomes the location of deposition by streams coming out of the steep mountain canyons. In the piedmont zone, stream and mudflow deposits accumulate at the mouths of canyons in gently sloping *alluvial fans* (Figure 18-29, p. 545). These alluvial fans may eventually coalesce into a *bajada*.

Note the difference between the "piedmont" zone (the foot of the mountains) and a landform called a *pediment* (a gently sloping erosional platform) shown in Figure 18-14 (p. 436).

Death Valley: A Primer of Basin-and-Range Terrain (p. 547): This section discusses a spectacular example of a Basin-and-Range landscape.

Mesa-and-Scarp Terrain (p. 548): Mesa-and-scarp topography clearly illustrates the principle of differential erosion. Notice in Figure 18-35 (p. 549) that the resistant layers of rock form the steep slopes, while the softer, less-resistant layers form the gentle slopes.

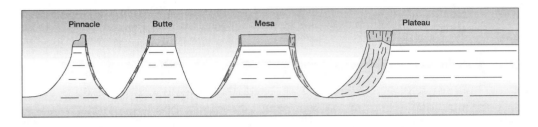

Figure 18-36: Typical development of residual landforms in horizontal sedimentary strata with a hard caprock. With the passage of time, larger features are eroded into smaller features.

Figure 18-36 (shown above) shows the prominent landforms that develop as a *plateau* gradually wears back into a *mesa*, then a *butte*, and finally into a *pinnacle* or *pillar*. These flat-topped landforms erode back through undercutting of the *caprock*. The less-resistant rock below is worn way, gradually undercutting the resistant caprock above until it collapses. In this way, the walls of these landforms retreat, until the flat tops are completely worn away.

PROGRESSIVE CONTENT REVIEW

1. In arid areas _____ (mechanical/chemical) weathering is dominant. (p. 529)

    mechanical

2. Deserts often do not have a layer of _____ and _____ over the bedrock. (p. 529)

    soil and regolith

3. _____ is one size of material that is easily moved around by wind in deserts. (p. 529)

    Sand

4. Rainfall in deserts is typically _____ but brief, and so when streams are flowing, they are usually at _____ flow. (p. 529)

    intense
    flood

5. Most streams in deserts are _____, carrying water only after a rain. (p. 529)

    ephemeral

6. _____ tends not to be a powerful erosional force in deserts. (p. 530)

    Wind

7. A basin of interior drainage has no outlet for water to flow to the _____. (p. 530)

    ocean

8.   Deserts typically have _____ (extensive/sparse) vegetation cover. (p. 530)

    sparse

9.   A dry lake bed, or _____, forms in the lowest part of a basin floor. These dry lake beds are called _____ if they contain a high concentration of salts in the sediments of the lake bed. (p. 532)

    playa
    salinas

10.   Most large lakes in deserts are the remnants of larger lakes that formed during a time of _____ (drier/wetter) climate. (p. 532)

    wetter

11.   In general, resistant rock layers will form _____ (gentle/steep) slopes, while softer layers of rock will form _____ slopes. (p. 533)

    steep
    gentle

12.   Isolated steep-sided mountains or hills rising up in the middle of deserts are often called _____, or _____ if they have rounded or domed shapes. (p. 533)

    inselbergs; bornhardts

13.   A _____ is a gently sloping bedrock surface in the piedmont zone of a mountain front. (p. 533)

    pediment

14.   Most deposition in deserts takes place in the _____ zone of a mountain. Deposition takes place here because the speed of the streams coming out of the mountains _____ (increases/decreases) when they reach the flatter valley floors. (p. 536)

    piedmont

    decreases

15.   _____-sized rock fragments rarely are deposited in the middle of flat basins since the flow of water into these areas is limited. (p. 536)

    Large

16.   Sandy desert landscapes are called an _____, while stony deserts are called a _____. (p. 536)

    erg
    reg

17.   _____ _____ is a dark and shiny coating on desert rocks. (p. 538)

    Desert varnish

18.   _____ processes are those relating to the action of wind. (p. 539)

    Aeolian

19.   _____ is the process of shifting loose particles around, and can take place by blowing them into the air, or _____ them along the ground. (p. 539)

Deflation
rolling

20.   Shallow depressions formed by wind action are called _____ or _____ _____. (p. 539)

blowouts
deflation hollows

21.   Particles carried by wind can be deposited when the speed of the wind _____. (p. 540)

decreases

22.   Sand moves up the _____ (gentle/steep) slope of the windward side of a sand dune, and down the _____ slope of the leeward side. (p. 540)

gentle
steep (slip face)

23.   A _____ dune is an isolated crescent-shaped dune moving across a mostly _____ (sandy/nonsandy) surface. (p. 541)

barchan
nonsandy

24.   _____ dunes are long ridges of sand that commonly form in regions with two different _____ directions. (p. 541)

Seif
wind

25.   _____ is wind-deposited silt that is not associated with dry lands. (p. 542)

Loess

26.   Most mountains in the Basin-and-Range province of North America were formed through _____. (p. 544)

faulting

27.   _____ fans develop in the piedmont zone of the mountains, and over time may coalesce into a _____. (p. 545)

Alluvial
bajada

28.   The accumulation of _____ is common in the playas on basin floors. (p. 546)

salt

29.   The _____ that supports the steep scarps in the mesa-and-scarp region of the United States typically consists of a resistant layer of _____ rock. (p. 549)

caprock

sedimentary

30.   The edge of the mesa escarpments is gradually worn back by undermining the _____, often through the process of groundwater _____. (p. 550)

caprock
sapping

31. With time, mesas are gradually worn back to a _____, which   butte
     in time will be worn back to a _____, a final spire held up by   pillar
     the caprock. (p. 550)

32. Poorly consolidated sedimentary strata can be worn down
     into a highly gullied landscape known as _____. (p. 550)   badlands

---

SELF-TEST

1. Why is mechanical weathering generally more important than chemical weathering in deserts?
    (a) Sand accumulation limits chemical weathering.
    (b) The lack of water limits chemical weathering.
    (c) Desert varnish increases the speed of mechanical weathering.
    (d) The heating of rocks by the sun is a rapid process of mechanical weathering.

2. Which kind of mass wasting is *least* likely in deserts?
    (a) Mudflow.   (b) Debris flow.
    (c) Rockfall.   (d) Soil creep.

3. Most desert streams are:
    (a) exotic.
    (b) ephemeral.
    (c) perennial.
    (d) remnants of a wetter climate.

4. Wind in deserts:
    (a) mainly moves around loose material.
    (b) is the primary force of erosion.
    (c) is rare.
    (d) produces alluvial fans.

5. A playa is a:
    (a) flat erosional surface in desert basins.
    (b) dry lake bed.
    (c) flat-topped desert mountain.
    (d) steep river gorge.

6. A pediment is a:
   (a) gently sloping bedrock platform.
   (b) depositional feature consisting of sand.
   (c) depositional feature consisting of evaporated salts.
   (d) crescent shaped sand dune.

7. Most deposition in the Basin-and-Range desert takes place in:
   (a) a playa.
   (b) a salina.
   (c) steep stream canyons.
   (d) the piedmont zone.

8. Barchan sand dunes:
   (a) are crescent-shaped.
   (b) are long ridges of sand.
   (c) form where the wind changes direction several times during the year.
   (d) form when there is an unlimited supply of new sand.

9. The "horns" of a barchan dune:
   (a) may orient either into or away from the wind.
   (b) point into the wind.
   (c) point away from the wind.

10. Which is *not* a characteristic of alluvial fans?
    (a) Consist of alluvium deposited by ephemeral streams.
    (b) Develop in the piedmont zone.
    (c) Commonly have very large boulders at their bases.
    (d) May coalesce with other fans to form a bajada.

11. With time, a butte will most likely become a:
    (a) plateau.
    (b) mesa.
    (c) pillar or pinnacle.
    (d) playa.

12. Badlands are primarily the result of:
    (a) fluvial deposition.
    (b) fluvial erosion.
    (c) aeolian deposition.
    (d) aeolian erosion.

13.   Sand dunes are primarily the result of:
        (a)   fluvial deposition.
        (b)   fluvial erosion.
        (c)   aeolian deposition.
        (d)   aeolian erosion.

14.   Bajadas are primarily the result of:
        (a)   fluvial deposition.
        (b)   fluvial erosion.
        (c)   aeolian deposition.
        (d)   aeolian erosion.

15.   "Blowouts" are primarily the result of:
        (a)   fluvial deposition.
        (b)   fluvial erosion.
        (c)   aeolian deposition.
        (d)   aeolian erosion.

16.   Mesas are primarily the result of:
        (a)   fluvial deposition.
        (b)   fluvial erosion.
        (c)   aeolian deposition.
        (d)   aeolian erosion.

Answers to Self-Test:

1.	b	6.	a	11.	c	16.	b
2.	d	7.	d	12.	b		
3.	b	8.	a	13.	c		
4.	a	9.	c	14.	a		
5.	b	10.	c	15.	d		

HINTS FOR TEXTBOOK STUDY QUESTIONS

1.   Consider factors such as the weathering of rock and the factors that influence fluvial erosion and deposition.

2. This topic is discussed briefly on page 529.

3. "Interior" refers to the ultimate destination of the water.

4. Why would basins of interior drainage disappear faster in humid regions than in arid regions?

5. Figure 18-5 (p. 531) is a map of a prominent exotic stream, while Figure 18-13 (p. 535) is a photograph of a typical ephemeral stream.

6. This is an important question. Review the section "Special Conditions in Deserts" (p. 529) and the section "Fluvial Erosion in Arid Lands" (p. 532).

7. Review questions 3 and 4 above.

8. These are defined on page 532 in the textbook.

9. What eventually happens to the fine sediment that is carried to the middle of a desert basin by ephemeral streams?

10. See the photograph in Figure 18-9 (p. 534).

11. Figure 18-12 (p. 535) illustrates this process.

12. These two terms sound alike and are often confused. See Figure 18-14 (p. 536) and the associated text material. Figure 18-12 (p. 535) shows the development of a pediment.

13. Consider the nature of the streams and the prominence of basins of interior drainage in deserts.

14. These types of deserts are discussed beginning on page 536 in the textbook.

15. See the photograph in Figure 18-16 (p. 538) and the associated text material.

16. These aeolian processes are discussed on page 539 in the textbook.

17. This question refers to erosion—not the transportation or deposition of sand. Consider the work of wind in removing loose sand, as well as wind erosion of bedrock.

18. Review Figure 18-20 (on page 245 of the Study Guide).

19. See question 18 above and then review the text material on page 541. Also, review the animation *Desert Sand Dunes*.

20. These dunes are illustrated in Figure 18-21 (on page 245 of the Study Guide) and described in the textbook on page 541. Note the role of wind direction in shaping these different dunes.

21. Consider how loess was deposited.

22. See Figure 18-29 (p. 545) and the associated text material. What is the ultimate destination of both water and alluvium in the basin-and-range region?

23. Consider where each kind of landform develops, as well as the general shape and slope of each. You might also consider in what ways deltas and alluvial fans are similar.

24. The difference is discussed on page 546.

25. A good description of this is found on page 546.

26. Consider the conditions that would have to be met for deep stream channels to form across flat areas in deserts.

27. See Figure 18-36 (on page 247 of the Study Guide).

28. Figure 18-36 (on page 247 of the Study Guide) illustrates this sequence.

29. See Figure 18-38 (p. 551).

ADDITIONAL STUDY QUESTION

1. Characterize the surface water found in a typical desert.

Hint for Additional Study Question:

1. This is a broad question. Focus especially on the characteristics of streams in deserts—consider the factors that influence desert hydrography. Also, describe the types of lakes typically found in deserts.

CHAPTER 19

Glacial Modification of Terrain

OVERVIEW

This chapter discusses the impact of glaciers on the landscape. It begins by describing the extent and effects of the most recent episode of glacial activity, the Pleistocene epoch, commonly known as the "Ice Age," and contrasts this to the greatly reduced extent of glacial activity today. The chapter then focuses on the formation and movement of glaciers, and the erosional and depositional processes involved with glaciation. The chapter concludes with a description of the erosional and depositional landforms left by both continental and mountain glaciers.

Several key concepts deserve special attention in this chapter. It is important to recognize the great extent of Pleistocene glaciation, and the many consequences of this time in Earth's history. These consequences include not only the direct effects of the ice, but also the indirect effects such as variations in sea level and increased precipitation in some areas that were not glaciated.

As with other chapters in the textbook, Chapter 19 begins by focusing on the processes involved. In the case of glacial landforms, these processes include glacial erosion, transportation, and deposition, as well as glaciofluvial action. It is important to understand that glaciers can continue to erode and transport debris in their ice even when they are diminishing in size during a retreating phase. Finally, note that landforms develop from both the direct action of the ice and from the action of glacial meltwater.

KEY CONCEPTS

GLACIATIONS PAST AND PRESENT (p. 555):

This section contrasts the great extent of glaciation during the Pleistocene with contemporary glaciation. Note that much of the evidence of earlier glaciations has been erased by the extensive glaciation that took place during the Pleistocene.

Pleistocene Glaciation (p. 555): The *Pleistocene epoch*, popularly known as the "Ice Age," began at least 1.8 million years ago, and ended less than 10,000 years ago. (There is evidence that these glacial episodes actually began well more than 2 million years ago.) Note, however, that during the Pleistocene there were *interglacial periods* when glaciers melted back, followed by periods when the glaciers grew and advanced again. Even within these major glacial advances (as many as 18 major advances during the Pleistocene have been recognized), there was a great deal of fluctuation in the ice sheets. These fluctuations become important when we begin to consider the patterns of depositional landforms left by glaciers (discussed later in this chapter).

Because this last glacial episode ended only about 10,000 years ago, some geologists have suggested that today we are simply in an interglacial period, and that the ice could return. This topic is raised again at the end of the chapter in the section, "Are We Still in an Ice Age?" (p. 586).

Figure 19-1 (p. 556) shows the maximum extent of Pleistocene glaciation around the world, and in North America and Europe. Notice that most of the world's land area was not covered by ice. This suggests that while the climate of the world became somewhat colder (and probably wetter, at least in the high latitude areas) during the Pleistocene, Earth was not completely dominated by an icy climate. Also note that much of Alaska was not glaciated, perhaps due to inadequate precipitation in that region.

Four other important consequences of the Pleistocene are mentioned in this section (p. 557):

1. **Periglacial Processes**: In fringing regions outside the area of glacial ice (called *periglacial zones*), the glacial episodes left their mark on the landscape with meltwater erosion and deposition, and with the weathering and mass wasting processes intensified by the cold conditions. Periglacial processes are discussed in more detail beginning on page 583.

2. **Sea-level Changes**: During the Pleistocene, so much water was frozen as glacial ice that the level of the oceans dropped as much as 130 meters (430 feet). This allowed streams to cut below current sea level, and when sea level rose again after the Pleistocene, these former stream valleys became flooded.

3. **Crustal Depression**: The weight of massive glacial ice sheets depressed the continental crust by as much as 1200 meters (4000 feet), and the rising ("rebound") of the crust continues today in some places. Figure 13-21 (p. 402) in Chapter 13 shows this *isostatic adjustment* of the crust after glaciation.

4. **Pluvial (increased rain) Developments**: *Pluvial developments* refer to the wetter conditions that resulted during the Pleistocene. Even in regions that were not glaciated, the increased amount of water produced many lakes. Figure 19-2 (p. 558) shows the location of the former lakes in the western United States that developed due to the greater availability of water during the Pleistocene. The remnants of some of these Pleistocene lakes are still visible today (for example, the Great Salt Lake in Utah is the much-reduced remnant of Pleistocene "Lake Bonneville").

Contemporary Glaciation (p. 557): Figure 19-3 (p. 558) shows the present extent of glaciation around the world. Outside of Greenland and Antarctica, only limited high mountain areas have any significant glacial development today.

TYPES OF GLACIERS (p. 660):

Note the distinction between *continental ice sheets*, such as those that covered much of northern North America during the Pleistocene, and *mountain glaciers* (including both *highland icefields* and *alpine glaciers*).

GLACIER FORMATION AND MOVEMENT (p. 563):

This section focuses on the processes of glacier formation, movement, erosion, and deposition. These processes will be illustrated again in subsequent sections on glacial landforms.

Changing Snow to Ice (p. 563): Note that an accumulation of snow is not enough to form a glacier. Over many years, the accumulation of snow and ice must be greater than the amount of *ablation* (melting and sublimation). Also note that snow must go through a process of compaction and recrystallization to form glacial ice (Figure 19-11, p. 563).

Glacial Movement (p. 564): This is an important section. First, note that when ice is under extreme pressure (such as within a thick glacier) it is capable of flowing and conforming to the topography (although some of the movement of glaciers is also due to *basal slip*).

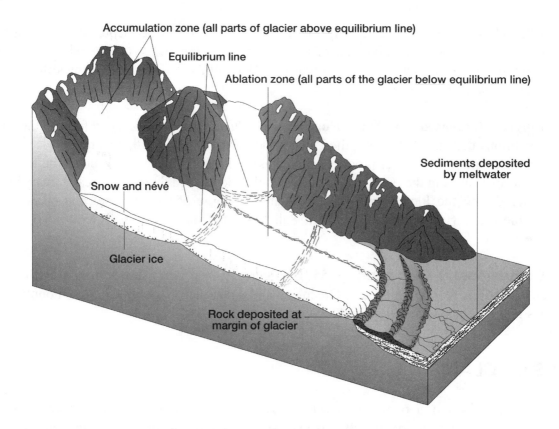

Figure 19-12: Cross section through an alpine glacier. The upper portion is an area of net ice accumulation. Below the equilibrium line there is more ablation than accumulation.

Second, glaciers are almost always in a state of continual flow, either flowing out from the center of a continental ice sheet, or flowing down-valley as a mountain glacier. **Figure 19-12** (shown above) illustrates that the upper part of an alpine glacier is an area of accumulation, where ice is added to the glacier, while the lower part of the glacier is an area of ablation, where the ice flowing down from the accumulation zone finally melts. During periods of increased accumulation of ice or slower melting, the glacier can flow farther down-valley before melting away. During periods of reduced accumulation or faster melting, the glacier continues to flow down-valley, but the ice melts away sooner—so the end of the glacier retreats up its valley.

The flow of ice within a glacier continues even if a glacier is no longer advancing. **Figure 19-13** (shown on the following page) illustrates this important concept. Notice the large rock marked with an arrow in the top diagram. This rock is being carried by the flow of the ice toward the end of the glacier. This rock will continue to be carried forward by the flow if ice even though the end of the glacier is retreating. Be sure to review the animation *Flow of Ice Within a Glacier* for an illustration of this concept.

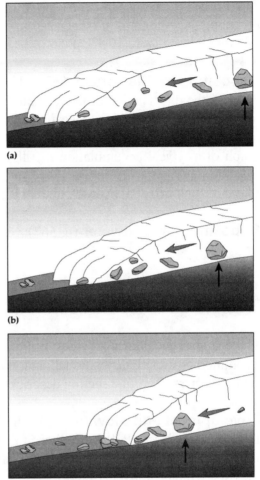

Figure 19-13: A flowing glacier is not necessarily an advancing glacier. In this sequential illustration, the front of the glacier is clearly retreating, but the ice continues to flow forward. The boulder marked by an arrow illustrates this principle.

THE EFFECTS OF GLACIERS (p. 565):

Erosion by Glaciers (p. 565): There are two important kinds of erosive action to note. *Glacial plucking* takes place when meltwater seeps down into the cracks in the rock below the glacier and refreezes. When the glacier moves on, rocks broken off through frost wedging can be pulled out of the bedrock by these "fingers" of ice extending down from the glacier.

The second type of erosive action is simple *abrasion*. The rocks carried along the bottom of a glacier act as "tools" that help the glacier erode through abrasion.

Probably the greatest amount of glacial erosion takes place through plucking, which tends to leave an irregular surface. Abrasion accomplishes less erosion, and tends to leave a smooth, polished or striated surface (see the photographs in Figure 19-14, p. 565).

Transportation by Glaciers (p. 566): Material is moved by a glacier not only in the ice (especially along the bottom of the glacier), but also by the meltwater under and on top of the glacier (see the photograph in Figure 19-15, p. 566).

Deposition by Glaciers (p. 567): The general term *drift* refers to any debris moved by a glacier (both by the direct action of the ice and by the meltwater). The term *till* specifically refers to rock deposited directly by the ice. Because till is not deposited by running water, it tends to be an accumulation of rock that is angular and unsorted (all sizes mixed together). Figure 19-16 (p. 567) is a photograph of a typical accumulation of till. One special kind of till is referred to as a *glacial erratic* (see the photograph in Figure 19-17, p. 568). Erratics are large boulders, and are often a different kind of rock from the bedrock upon which they are resting.

Deposition by Meltwater (p. 567): *Glaciofluvial deposition* refers to drift left by glacial meltwater.

CONTINENTAL ICE SHEETS (p. 568):

The chapter concludes with a description of the development and movement of glaciers, and the most common erosional, depositional, and glaciofluvial landforms produced by both continental and mountain glaciers. The first section describes the landforms left by continental glaciers.

Development and Flow (p. 568): The Pleistocene ice sheets in the Northern Hemisphere did not form over the North Pole but rather in the subarctic regions over the continents where there was a large accumulation of snow. These ice sheets flowed out in all directions and covered the entire landscape with thick layers of ice.

Erosion by Ice Sheets (p. 568): Continental ice sheets tended to gently smooth the landscape, but by no means did they produce a flat landscape.

Note the distinctive landform called a *roche moutonnée* that develops when glaciers move over a bedrock hill. Figure 19-19 (p. 569) and Figure 19-20 (p. 570) show that the side facing the advancing ice (the *stoss side*) is gently smoothed by glacial abrasion, while the back side (the lee side) is steepened and roughened through plucking as the glacier advances over the hill. A roche moutonnée can be produced by either continental or mountain glaciation.

Deposition by Ice Sheets (p. 569): A *moraine* is one of the most conspicuous glacial landforms. Moraine is a general term that refers to the mounds of till that are left by retreating glaciers. Figure 19-22 (p. 571) illustrates the development of a *terminal moraine*, the ridge of till deposited at the margin of the ice at its position of maximum advance. In this diagram, follow the motion of the boulders in the ice, and notice that a terminal moraine can grow even when a glacier is not advancing.

During the retreat of a glacier, the front of the glacier may stall for periods of time, producing another ridge of till called a *recessional moraine*. Figure 19-23 (p. 572) is a map showing the prominent terminal and recessional moraines in the United States formed during the last major glacial advance of the Pleistocene.

Figure 19-21 (shown on the following page) illustrates some of the other depositional landforms associated with continental glaciation. *Drumlins* are mounds of till that evidently have been "reworked" by a later advance of ice. A *kettle* is a depression formed when blocks of ice were left in glacial deposits. Many of these kettles remained filled with water as lakes (Figure 19-24, p. 572).

Glaciofluvial Features (p. 572): Glaciofluvial landforms are those created by the meltwater associated with glaciers, both under a glacier, and beyond the margin of the ice (Figure 19-21). Beyond the margin of the continental ice sheets, a landform called an *outwash plain* typically develops. These are relatively flat areas that have been decorated with outwash deposits brought by meltwater.

Eskers are glaciofluvial landforms seen today as sinuous ridges of sand and gravel. Eskers formed when streams under a glacier became choked with meltwater debris.

MOUNTAIN GLACIERS (p. 575):

Unlike the dominant action of continental glaciers, mountain glaciers tend to steepen and deepen the pre-glacial topography.

Development and Flow (p. 575): During the Pleistocene, most alpine glaciers formed in protected areas near the tops of preexisting stream valleys, and then flowed down-valley, often joining with other tributaries to form large valley glaciers. Review the animation *Glacial Processes* for descriptions of the development and effects of glaciers.

Erosion by Mountain Glaciers (p. 575): The most basic erosional landform of alpine glaciation is the *cirque*. These are bowl- or amphitheater-shaped depressions eroded out of bedrock just below the peak of a mountain. They form as the upper part of a glacier pulls away from the top of the valley, plucking out rock, forming a steep headwall (Figure 19-32, p. 576). Three small cirques in the mountains of Utah are shown in the photograph on page 578 (Figure 19-36).

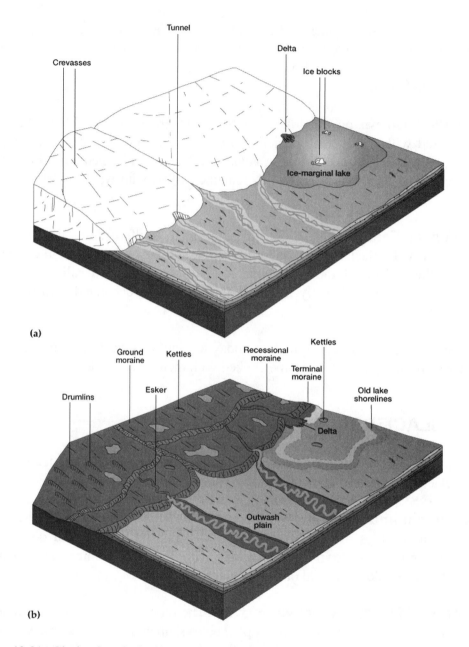

Figure 19-21: Glacier-deposited and glaciofluvial deposited features of a landscape (a) covered by a continental ice sheet and (b) after the sheet has retreated.

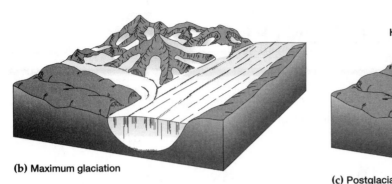

(b) Maximum glaciation

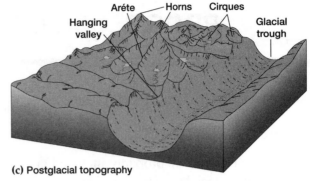

(c) Postglacial topography

Figure 19-33: The development of landforms by mountain glaciation. (b) Landscape during glaciation. (c) Landscape after glaciation.

Notice in **Figure 19-33** (Figures 19-33b and 19-33c are shown above; the complete diagram is on page 577) that when cirques are cut back into a mountain peak from three or four sides, a pyramid-shaped peak called a *horn* will develop (see the photograph in Figure 19-35, p. 578). When glaciers cut back into a ridge from both sides, a jagged ridge crest called an *arête* will form.

Alpine glaciers tend to deepen and steepen former river valleys, producing a characteristic U-shaped glacial trough. However, the profile of a glacial valley tends not to be smooth and regular, but is often characterized by a series of *glacial steps* (Figure 19-39, p. 580). Lakes that form in each of the steps are usually connected by a stream, and are called *paternoster lakes* since they resemble the beads of a rosary.

Another important erosional feature of alpine glaciation is the *hanging valley*. Tributary glaciers joining a main valley glacier rarely erode as deeply as the main glacier. When the ice melts, these tributary glaciers leave valleys "hanging" high above the level of the main glacial trough (Figure 19-40, p. 580).

Deposition by Mountain Glaciers (p. 580): Alpine glaciers produce both terminal and recessional moraines (in the same fashion as continental ice sheets). However, often the most prominent depositional features left by alpine glaciers are *lateral moraines*. These are mounds of till that build up along the sides of a valley glacier (Figure 19-41, p. 581, and Figure 19-43, p. 582).

Causes of the Pleistocene (p. 584):

Some of the climate change factors that are likely to have been associated with the Pleistocene are discussed in this section. Figure 19-47 (p. 585) shows the global temperature fluctuations connected with the onset of glacial episodes over the last 800,000 years.

PROGRESSIVE CONTENT REVIEW

1. The _____ epoch was the most recent episode of global glaciation, beginning about _____ million years ago, and ending about _____ thousand years ago. (p. 555)

   Pleistocene
   1.8
   9 to10

2. The Pleistocene probably included at least _____ episodes of major glacial advance. (p. 556)

   18

3. At its maximum extent, Pleistocene glaciers covered about _____ of Earth's land surface. (p. 556)

   one-third

4. In the _____ zone beyond the maximum extent of the ice, _____ produced many erosional and depositional features. (p. 557)

   periglacial
   meltwater

5. During the Pleistocene glacial advances, the level of the oceans _____ (rose/dropped) as water became locked up on land as ice. (p. 557)

   dropped

6. The enormous weight of glacial ice caused the crust below continental ice sheets to _____ (rise/sink). After the ice retreated, these areas began to _____ in isostatic adjustment. (p. 557)

   sink
   rise

7. Because of the greater availability of water during the Pleistocene, many _____ developed in basins in areas outside the margins of the ice. (p. 557)

   lakes

8. Today, the largest continental ice sheet is found on _____. (p. 558)

   Antarctica

9. In high mountain areas, ice can accumulate to cover all but the highest peaks, forming a _____ _____. (p. 562)

   highland icefield

10. Alpine glaciers confined to their upper-most basins are called _____ glaciers, while those flowing down valleys and spreading out broadly over the flatland below the mountains are known as _____ glaciers. (p. 562)

    cirque

    piedmont

11.	The existence of a glacier depends on the balance between the _____ of ice and the _____ of ice. (p. 563)

accumulation; ablation

12.	Over time, snow is compacted into granules of ice called _____. (p. 563)

névé

13.	The equilibrium line of a glacier represents the boundary between the upper zone of _____ and the lower zone of _____. (pp. 563–564)

accumulation
ablation

14.	Glacial ice may break at the surface of a glacier, but deep in the glacier, ice under confining _____ is capable of flowing. (p. 564)

pressure

15.	When the outer edge of a glacier is retreating, the ice inside a glacier is still flowing _____. (p. 564)

forward

16.	_____ takes place when water from a glacier extends down into _____ or _____ in the rock below and refreezes. Rock is then extracted when the glacier advances. (p. 565)

Plucking
joints or fractures

17.	The abrasion of glaciers is aided by _____ dragged along the bottom of the ice, acting as abrasive tools. (p. 565)

rocks

18.	The most typical component of a glacier's load is ground up rock known as _____ _____. (p. 566)

glacial flour

19.	Additional erosion by glaciers can be accomplished by the _____ that runs over and under a glacier. (p. 566)

meltwater

20.	_____ refers to all material moved and deposited by any kind of glacial action, while _____ is a term that refers only to material moved directly by the ice. (p. 567)

Drift
till

21.	A glacial _____ is a large boulder deposited by a glacier. (p. 567)

erratic

22.	_____ deposition refers to material moved and deposited by glacial meltwater. (p. 567)

Glaciofluvial

23.   A roche moutonnée is an erosional feature produced by glacial _____ on one side of a bedrock hill, and glacial _____ on the lee side. (p. 568)

abrasion
  plucking

24.   A _____ moraine is a mound of _____ that develops at the edge of the ice at the position of maximum glacial advance. (p. 571)

terminal; till

25.   A _____ moraine marks a location of ice stabilization during a period of glacial retreat. (p. 571)

recessional

26.   A _____ forms when a block of ice melts and leaves a depression in the post-glacial landscape. (p. 571)

kettle

27.   _____ drift refers to the glacial debris that has been sorted by glaciofluvial action. (p. 572)

Stratified

28.   The most extensive glaciofluvial feature is the _____ _____, formed beyond the margin of the ice by the meltwater of the glacier. (p. 572)

outwash plain

29.   A _____ _____ is a lengthy deposit of glaciofluvial alluvium along a valley bottom beyond the outwash plain. (p. 573)

valley train

30.   A _____ is a bedrock "amphitheater" formed at the upper end of an alpine glacial valley. (p. 575)

cirque

31.   Where alpine glaciers erode back into a mountain peak from three or four sides, a pyramid-shaped _____ is formed, while a serrated ridge known as an _____ is formed when cirques are eroded back into a ridge from opposite sides. (p. 576)

horn
arête

32.   A lake occupying an empty cirque is called a _____. (p. 577)

tarn

33.   Alpine glaciers tend to _____ and _____ preexisting river valleys, forming a _____-shaped glacial trough. (p. 578)

deepen and steepen
U

34.   _____ lakes may form in the depressions of the "steps" of a glacial valley. (p. 579)

Paternoster

35. Tributary glaciers rarely cut down as deeply as the main trunk glaciers, so after deglaciation, _____ valleys may be left high above the main glacial valley. (p. 580)

hanging

36. _____ moraines are mounds of till that form along the sides of a valley glacier, while _____ moraines form when two glaciers come together, leaving a mound of till down the middle of a valley. (pp. 580–582)

Lateral
medial

SELF-TEST

1. The last Pleistocene glaciers melted back about:
   (a) 1,000 years ago.
   (b) 10,000 years ago.
   (c) 100,000 years ago.
   (d) 1,000,000 years ago.

2. Beyond the margins of the Pleistocene glaciers, which of the following did *not* take place?
   (a) Erosion and deposition by meltwater.
   (b) Deposition of till.
   (c) Frost wedging and weathering.
   (d) Solifluction.

3. In areas covered by thick Pleistocene ice sheets:
   (a) the land was depressed by the weight of the ice, and is still rebounding.
   (b) the land was depressed by the weight of the ice, but has not yet started to rebound.
   (c) the land was depressed by the intense cold from the overlying ice.
   (d) the level of the land below the ice generally did not change.

4. Today, the largest continental ice cap in the world is found:
   (a) in Greenland.
   (b) in Antarctica.
   (c) in Siberia.
   (d) in Alaska.

5.   The ice under great pressure inside a glacier:
        (a)   will generally break as the glacier moves over irregular terrain.
        (b)   is not capable of accomplishing any erosion.
        (c)   can bend or flow as the glacier moves over irregular terrain.
        (d)   will stop flowing.

6.   When the front of a valley glacier is melting back in a retreating stage:
        (a)   the ice inside the glacier stops flowing.
        (b)   the ice inside the glacier begins to flow uphill.
        (c)   the ice inside the glacier can still flow forward.
        (d)   the ice on the top of the glacier flows uphill, while the ice along the bottom flows downhill.

7.   Glacial "plucking" occurs when:
        (a)   rocks beneath a glacier are dislodged by frozen meltwater in joints and cracks.
        (b)   rocks at the bottom of a glacier scour a resistant bedrock surface.
        (c)   the bottom of a glacier polishes soft rock with meltwater.
        (d)   when the top of a glacier fractures as it passes over an irregularity in the topography.

8.   Glacial "flour" is:
        (a)   the snow that falls on top of a glacier
        (b)   the fine sands that are produced as meltwater flows over an outwash plain.
        (c)   the rock that falls on top of a valley glacier from surrounding hills.
        (d)   finely ground rock from glacial erosion.

9.   Glacial drift is:
        (a)   any material moved by glacial ice or meltwater.
        (b)   only the debris directly carried by glacial ice.
        (c)   new snow before it has become névé.
        (d)   powdered ice that is scraped off along the sides of a glacier.

10.   Till is:
        (a)   sand moved by glacial meltwater.
        (b)   frozen water inside bedrock cracks.
        (c)   unsorted and fragmented rock moved by glacial ice.
        (d)   well-sorted and rounded cobbles moved by meltwater streams.

11.   Which of the following features is the result of deposition during alpine glaciation?
        (a)   Cirque.   (b)   Lateral moraine.
        (c)   Horn.   (d)   Hanging valley.

12. Which of the following features is the result of glaciofluvial deposition by continental glaciers?
    (a) Roche moutonnée
    (b) Glacial striations.
    (c) Terminal moraine.
    (d) Valley train.

13. Which of the following features is the result of erosion by alpine glaciers?
    (a) Cirque.
    (b) Esker.
    (c) Terminal moraine.
    (d) Kame.

14. Kettles form when:
    (a) continental glaciers scour a depression in resistant bedrock.
    (b) blocks of ice melt, leaving depressions in an outwash plain.
    (c) a cirque lake dries up.
    (d) a meltwater stream under a glacier clogs with debris.

15. A horn forms when:
    (a) alpine glaciers cut into their cirque headwalls around a peak from three or four sides.
    (b) alpine glaciers flow down a valley over resistant rock.
    (c) continental glaciers flow over low hill tops of resistant rock.
    (d) meltwater deepens a preexisting stream valley.

16. The steep, rough side of a roche moutonnée develops due to:
    (a) abrasion.
    (b) erosion by meltwater.
    (c) the deposition of till.
    (d) glacial plucking.

17. Medial moraines usually develop:
    (a) when a tributary valley glacier joins a main trunk glacier.
    (b) along the sides of a large valley glacier.
    (c) when rock carried along the bottom of a valley glacier is pushed to the top of the ice.
    (d) when a meltwater stream flows over a valley glacier.

18. Glacial erratics are the result of:
    (a) glacial erosion.
    (b) glaciofluvial erosion.
    (c) glacial deposition.

19.   Recessional moraines left by a continental ice sheet:
        (a)   indicate the maximum forward advance of the ice.
        (b)   indicate the locations where the margin of a retreating ice sheet temporarily stabilized.
        (c)   are bedrock depressions, smoothed by glacial erosion.
        (d)   are stream deposits left by meltwater.

20.   Paternoster lakes are *primarily* a consequence of:
        (a)   alpine glacial erosion.
        (b)   alpine glacial deposition.
        (c)   glaciofluvial deposition.
        (d)   continental glacial deposition.

ANSWERS TO SELF-TEST:

1.	b	6.	c	11.	b	16.	d
2.	b	7.	a	12.	d	17.	a
3.	a	8.	d	13.	a	18.	c
4.	b	9.	a	14.	b	19.	b
5.	c	10.	c	15.	a	20.	a

HINTS FOR TEXTBOOK STUDY QUESTIONS

1.   Consider the impact of the Pleistocene glaciations on the landscape, as well as when the Pleistocene ended.

2.   See Figure 19-1 (p. 556).

3.   Consider what happens to sea level if large amounts of water are locked up as ice on the continents.

4.   See Figure 13-21 in Chapter 13 (p. 402).

5.   This term is discussed on page 557.

6.   For example, see Figure 19-2 (p. 558).

7.   See Figure 19-3 (p. 558).

8.   See Figures 19-8 and 19-9 (p. 562) and the associated text material beginning on page 561.

9.   These concepts are discussed on page 563.

10.   See Figure 19-11 (p. 563) and the associated text material.

11.   Review the animation *Flow of Ice Within a Glacier*.

12.   Consider the dynamics of ice under pressure, as well as the lubricating effects of meltwater. This is discussed beginning on page 564.

13.   This is illustrated in Figure 19-13 (on page 259 of the Study Guide) and in the animation *Flow of Ice Within a Glacier*.

14.   As an example of this difference, consider the formation of a roche moutonnée (see Figure 19-19, p. 569).

15.   See the photograph in Figure 19-16 (p. 567).

16.   You may want to compare the appearance of till in Figure 19-6 (p. 567) with that of alluvium shown in Figure 16-6 (p. 484).

17.   A photograph of an erratic is shown in Figure 19-17 (p. 568).

18.   The key to this difference is the term *fluvial* in glaciofluvial.

19.   See Figure 19-19 (p. 569).

20.   Figures 19-21 and 19-22 (pp. 570–571) illustrate this process.

21.   See Figure 19-24 (p. 572).

22.   This concept is discussed on page 572.

23.   See Figure 19-21 (p. 570) and the associated text material.

24.   Consider the erosional and depositional processes of continental glaciers that would produce irregular terrain with many depressions.

25.   Consider the dominant glacial processes at work in mountainous areas. Also, describe some of the common landforms left by mountain glaciers.

26.   Figure 19-33 (p. 577) illustrates this.

27.   See Figure 19-39 (p. 580).

28.   The formation of a cirque is well illustrated in Figure 19-32 (p. 576). Also see Figure 19-33 (on page 263 of the Study Guide).

29.   See Figure 19-39 (p. 580) and consider where lakes might form after the ice is gone.

30.   "Lateral" refers to the side; see Figure 19-41 (p. 581).

31.   Look at Figure 19-33 (on page 263 of the Study Guide); imagine what happens to the lateral moraines when a tributary glacier joins a main valley glacier.

32.   See Figure 19-45 (p. 584) and the associated text beginning on page 583.

33.   This is described on page 584.

ADDITIONAL STUDY QUESTIONS

1.   Why are recessional and terminal moraines often less prominent than lateral moraines in valleys that have experienced alpine glaciation?

2.   Refer to the map showing the maximum extent of the Pleistocene ice sheet in North America (Figure 19-1b, p. 556). Why was the ice sheet centered on central Canada rather than the North Pole, where it would have been colder?

Hints for Additional Study Questions:

1.   Relate the location of terminal and recessional moraines on a valley bottom to the likely location of glaciofluvial and fluvial processes.

2.   Consider the role of precipitation in producing an ice sheet.

CHAPTER 20

Coastal Processes and Terrain

OVERVIEW

This chapter introduces the processes that are at work shaping coastal landforms. Chapter 20 begins by describing the special conditions found along the coastlines of the ocean (and to a certain extent, large lakes). Because it is difficult to generalize about coastal landforms, the chapter focuses on the variety of processes that shape coastlines: coastal erosion, transportation, and deposition. The chapter concludes with examples of common coastal landform assemblages.

In this chapter you should concentrate on the processes at work. This will make understanding the great variety of coastal landforms easier. Pay close attention to the formation and erosive power of waves, and to the various mechanisms of sediment transport that are at work along shorelines.

KEY CONCEPTS

COASTAL PROCESSES (p. 589):

The focus of this chapter is on the processes at work along ocean coastlines. However, many of the coastal processes described here may also be operating, to a certain extent, around lake shores. Keep in mind that the tectonic, weathering, mass wasting, and fluvial processes described in previous chapters may also be at work along coastlines.

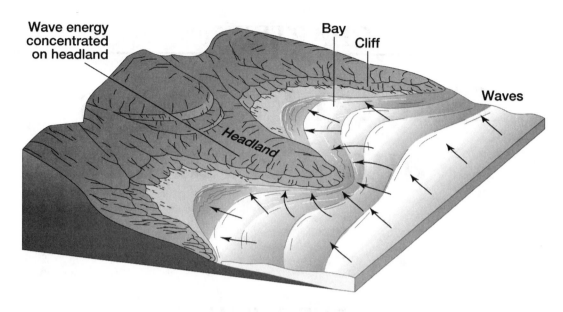

Figure 20-5: Refraction of waves on an irregular coastline. The waves approach the headlands first and then pivot toward it. Thus wave energy is concentrated on the headlands and is diminished in the bays.

Waves (p. 590): Waves are by far the most important agent of coastal erosion. Most waves are generated by wind. Especially note that in the open ocean, as a wave passes, most of the movement of the water is in a circular motion up and down (a so-called *wave of oscillation*), but as the wave approaches shore, the lower portion of the wave begins to slow as it encounters the bottom; as the wave slows, its height increases and the wave finally falls forward and "breaks" (and becomes a *wave of translation*). Great amounts of energy can be transferred across the open ocean through relatively small waves of oscillation; this energy is released when waves of translation strike the shore.

Wave Refraction (p. 591): Waves can bend around irregularities in the coastline through the process of *wave refraction* (**Figure 20-5**, shown above). As a wave approaches shore, the segment of the wave that encounters the shallow seafloor first begins to slow (near the headlands), but the segment of the wave in deeper water continues to move quickly until it encounters shallow water (in the bay). This means that waves will typically strike parallel (or nearly parallel) to the shoreline. Be sure to review the animation ***Wave Motion and Wave Refraction*** for a description of these processes.

Wave Erosion (p. 592): Wind-generated waves—especially storm waves—are the most powerful erosive force along a coastline.

Tsunami (p. 593): Seismic sea waves or *tsunami* are triggered by a sudden disruption of the ocean floor. The great power of large tsunami comes from the way in which they are generated.

Notice in Figure 20-8 (p. 595) that fault motion or other disturbance of the ocean floor displaces the entire water column. Out in the open ocean most tsunami are inconspicuous because they have a very long wavelength; but as they approach shore they slow, decreasing the wavelength but increasing wave height.

Tides (p. 594): Keep in mind that the movement of tidal waters usually is not a significant sculptor of coastlines (for an exception, see the photograph in Figure 20-9, p. 595). Tides are discussed in detail in Chapter 9 (pp. 267–268) and in the animation *Tides*.

Changes in Sea Level and Lake Level (p. 595): When we discussed glaciation (Chapter 19) we described the impact of the Pleistocene glaciations on sea level, noting that during the periods of maximum glaciation so much water was locked up as glacial ice on the continents that the level of the ocean dropped as much as 130 meters (430 feet).

Organic Secretions (p. 596): The buildup of coral is a very important process shaping tropical coastlines. This topic will be discussed in greater detail later in the chapter.

Currents and Coastal Sediment Transport (p. 597): Although there are many different kinds of currents along coastlines, coastal landforms are affected most significantly by *longshore currents* (discussed below). The major ocean currents that were described in the chapters on weather and climate do very little to shape coastlines.

Two important mechanisms of sediment transport are mentioned in this section. *Beach drifting* is illustrated in **Figure 20-12** (shown on the following page). Where waves wash onshore at an angle, sand is transported down the beach in the general direction of the waves. This zigzag pattern results in the gradual movement of sand along the shore.

The longshore current (shown with the large arrows in Figure 20-12) is the other key transportation mechanism along coastlines. Longshore currents are set up by the action of the waves and generally flow along the coastline parallel to the shore. Longshore currents often carry great quantities of sand along a shoreline. See the animation *Coastal Sediment Transport* for a review of these transportation mechanisms.

Coastal Deposition (p. 599): Just as streams deposit their load when the speed of water decreases, deposition along coastlines takes place when the power of a current diminishes. For example, a longshore current may deposit sand when it passes over a deeper spot where its energy is spread out and its velocity decreases.

The other key point of this section is to recognize that the size and shape of many coastal depositional features, such as beaches, represents a balance between material constantly being deposited and material constantly being eroded and carried away—this is known as the *sediment budget*.

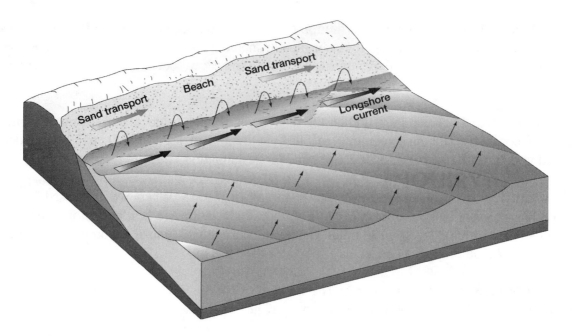

Figure 20-12: Beach drifting involves the zigzag movement of sand along a beach in a general downwind direction. Sand is brought onto the beach obliquely by a wave, and then is returned seaward by the backwash. The general direction of the longshore current offshore is shown with large arrows.

COASTAL LANDFORMS (p. 599):

Depositional Landforms (p. 599): The general structure of a *beach* is shown in Figure 20-15 (p. 600). You may also want to view the animation ***Coastal Stabilization Structures*** for a description of the consequences of building various kinds of structures—such as *groins* and *breakwaters*—along a shoreline.

Spits (p. 600): Three kinds of spits—*spits, baymouth bars*, and *tombolos*—are illustrated in Figure 20-16 (p. 600). In each case, they form where the strength of the current carrying sediments is diminished. Note that a spit typically points downcurrent (the current is shown in Figure 20-16 with an arrow), and that a tombolo forms in areas with waves or currents that converge from two directions.

Barrier Islands (p. 600): *Barrier islands* are illustrated in Figure 20-20 showing Padre Island along the coast of Texas (p. 602). Note that these depositional features have developed in fairly shallow coastal waters, where waves begin to break some distance offshore. The larger barrier islands evidently formed during periods of lower sea level during the Pleistocene. In areas with large barrier islands, water may be isolated behind the island forming a lagoon, which is destined to fill in with sediments over time (Figure 20-21, p. 602).

Shorelines of Submergence (p. 603): After the last major glacial episode, sea level rose and flooded many of the low-lying stream valleys that were cut when sea level was lower. The result is called a *shoreline of submergence*—in this case, a *ria shoreline*, where stream valleys have become inlets and the tops of hills have become islands (see Figure 20-23, p. 603). Figure 20-24 (p. 604) shows a *fjord*—a glacial valley that has been flooded by the sea; note the very steep walls of the inlet, which is typical of a fjord.

Shorelines of Emergence and Erosion (p. 604): In some regions of the world, the coastline has been tectonically rising, resulting in a *shoreline of emergence*. One common set of landforms that can result from this is the combination of a *wave-cut platform* ("bench"), a cliff, and an uplifted *marine terrace* (Figure 20-26, p. 605). The marine terrace represents a former wave-cut platform that has been uplifted (see the photograph in Figure 20-27, p. 605). The cliff tends to wear back through undercutting by waves, expanding the new wave-cut platform.

Coral Coasts (p. 605): The *coral polyp* is an animal that excretes an exoskeleton of calcium carbonate. Colonies of coral can build up to form massive reef structures. The coral polyp is actually a fragile creature that can only live within a narrow range of water temperature, clarity, and salinity. The three basic types of coral reef are largely distinguished by their relationship to land (Figure 20-31, p. 608). A *fringing reef* builds up next to the shore, a *barrier reef* builds up some distance offshore, while an *atoll* is a discontinuous ring around a lagoon without a central island above sea level.

PROGRESSIVE CONTENT REVIEW

1. _____ is the most important generator of ocean waves. (p. 590)

   Wind

2. Waves in the open ocean are waves of _____ in which most of the motion of the water is up and down as the wave passes. (p. 590)

   oscillation

3. As a wave moves into shallow water, the top of the wave begins to fall over as it is slowed by the frictional drag along the ocean _____. The top of the wave finally falls over and forward, and becomes a wave of _____. (p. 591)

   bottom
   translation

4. A breaking wave pushes water up on the beach as _____, and the water flows back down off the shore as _____. (p. 591)

   swash
   backwash

5. Waves bend around coastal irregularities through the process of wave _____. This tends to focus the action of waves on _____ projecting out from the shore. (pp. 591–592)

refraction
headlands

6. Most coastal erosion is accomplished by _____ action, but this is often assisted by the _____ effect of sand and gravel. (p. 592)

wave
abrasive

7. The chemical action of water is also a factor in coastal erosion since most rocks are _____ to some extent in seawater. (p. 592)

soluble

8. Tsunamis are caused by underwater _____ or volcanic eruptions. These waves tend to be inconspicuous in the open ocean since they have a very long _____. (p. 593)

earthquakes

wavelength

9. Tides rise and fall in a cycle that takes approximately _____ hours. (p. 594)

12

10. During the Pleistocene glacial advances the level of the oceans _____ (rose/dropped). (pp. 595–596)

dropped

11. Along the shores of bodies of water that freeze during the winter, _____ _____ can deform the shoreline topography. (p. 596)

ice push

12. Streams flowing into the ocean provide much of the _____ and other sediment that is transported and deposited along coastlines. (p. 597)

sand

13. Most movement of sediments along a coast is accomplished by _____ action and local _____. (p. 597)

wave; currents

14. _____ currents move sediments along a coastline, parallel to the shoreline. (p. 597)

Longshore

15. Waves breaking on the shore at an oblique angle can cause the zigzagging movement of sand along a coast in a process known as _____ _____. (p. 598)

beach drifting

16. The _____ _____ of a beach refers to the balance of the sediment being deposited and the sediment being removed by waves, beach drifting, and longshore currents. (p. 599)

sediment budget

17. The _____ of a beach is the zone of sediment deposition above the high-water line, whereas the _____ is the zone of the beach regularly covered by the rise and fall of the tides. (p. 599)

backshore
foreshore

18. A linear deposit of sand connected to the shore is called a _____. Such a feature may eventually extend across a bay, closing off a lagoon with a _____ bar. (p. 600)

spit
baymouth

19. A _____ _____ is a long, narrow sandbar that develops offshore in areas where the depth of the water is relatively _____. With time, these bars can close off a quiet body of water behind them, forming a _____. (pp. 600–601)

barrier island

shallow
lagoon

20. Where river valleys have been "drowned" by rising sea levels, a _____ shoreline results. (p. 603)

ria

21. A fjorded coast develops where the ocean has flooded valleys cut by _____. (p. 603)

glaciers

22. Coastal cliffs wear back as a _____ is cut at water level, and with time, the overhanging rock collapses. (pp. 604–605)

notch

23. A _____ _____ is formed when a wave-cut platform is uplifted above the water level along a tectonically rising coast. (p. 605)

marine terrace

24. Coral formations develop in warm, _____ oceans. (p. 605)

tropical

25. _____ polyps excrete an exoskeleton of _____ _____ that can eventually build up into large coastal reef structures. (p. 605)

Coral;
    calcium carbonate

26. A _____ reef is a ridge of coral that develops roughly parallel to the coast, and some distance offshore. An _____ is a circular reef structure, with no land above sea level within the enclosed _____. (pp. 606–609)

barrier
atoll

lagoon

SELF-TEST

1. Most waves are formed by:
   (a) tides.
   (b) wind.
   (c) earthquakes.
   (d) rivers.

2. Waves bend ("refract") around coastal irregularities because:
   (a) the wind will always change direction around a headland.
   (b) the portion of a wave encountering shallow water first will speed up.
   (c) the portion of a wave encountering shallow water first will slow down.

3. Longshore currents:
   (a) generally move downwind, parallel to the shore.
   (b) generally move upwind, parallel to the shore.
   (c) form in coastal areas where strong tidal variations are present.
   (d) generally move sand away from the shore and out to sea.

4. Which is *not* a major factor influencing the erosive power of waves?
   (a) The speed of the waves.
   (b) The "tools" carried by waves.
   (c) Air compressed into cracks by waves.
   (d) The temperature of the water.

5. The drowned river valleys of a ria coast indicate:
   (a) a shoreline of submergence.
   (b) a shoreline of emergence.
   (c) heavy deposition by streams.
   (d) massive coral formations offshore.

6. Steep cliffs along a shoreline often indicate:
   (a) a shoreline of submergence.
   (b) a shoreline of emergence.
   (c) substantial stream deposition.
   (d) massive coral formations offshore.

7. A sand spit generally points:
   (a) downcurrent.
   (b) upcurrent.
   (c) straight out to sea.

8. Barrier islands (barrier bars) develop:
    (a) in areas of deep offshore waters.
    (b) in areas where coastlines are rising.
    (c) in areas with shallow underwater coastal platforms.
    (d) where basaltic lava from an island arc volcano has cooled in shallow water.

9. Over time, a lagoon formed by a barrier island will generally:
    (a) fill up with sediment.
    (b) form a coral barrier reef.
    (c) form a coral atoll.
    (d) become a tombolo.

10. Coral reefs can develop:
    (a) in warm tropical oceans.
    (b) in midlatitude oceans along the west coasts of continents.
    (c) where sand deposition by a longshore current is greater than transportation.
    (d) on the bottom of deep ocean trenches in tropical oceans.

11. A tsunami is formed by:
    (a) a large tidal change in shallow coastal areas.
    (b) longshore currents.
    (c) winds from storms at sea.
    (d) earthquakes below the ocean floor.

12. The outflow from streams:
    (a) supplies all of the calcium carbonate needed for coral reef formation.
    (b) is blocked from entering the ocean by waves.
    (c) provides much of the sand that is later deposited in coastal beaches.
    (d) rarely has any influence on coastal landforms.

13. Most currents along a shoreline are due to the action of:
    (a) wind.   (b) tides.
    (c) stream outflow.   (d) storms.

14. Atolls are thought to have developed:
    (a) when sea level was higher than it is today.
    (b) around an island that has eroded or subsided into the ocean.
    (c) when the oceans were cooler.
    (d) when the oceans were less salty.

15.   Fjords:
  (a)   are large coral structures in tropical seas.
  (b)   form from the deposition of glacial sands in shallow water.
  (c)   form when stream valleys become flooded.
  (d)   form when glacial valleys become flooded.

Answers to Self-Test:

1.	b	6.	b	11.	d
2.	c	7.	a	12.	c
3.	a	8.	c	13.	a
4.	d	9.	a	14.	b
5.	a	10.	a	15.	d

HINTS FOR TEXTBOOK STUDY QUESTIONS

1.   Review Figure 20-2 (p. 590) and the animation *Wave Motion and Wave Refraction*.

2.   See Figure 20-5 (on page 274 of the Study Guide) and the animation *Wave Motion and Wave Refraction*.

3.   Consider what increases the size of waves approaching a shoreline.

4.   This is discussed on page 592 in the textbook.

5.   Figure 20-8 (p. 595) and the associated text describe this, but also view the animation *Tsunami*.

6.   This is discussed in Chapter 19 on page 557 and in Chapter 20 on page 595.

7.   It is especially important to note the role of waves in the formation of longshore currents. You may want to review the animation *Coastal Sediment Transport* and Figure 20-12 (on page 276 of the Study Guide).

8.   Consider how waves striking a shoreline initiate beach drifting (Figure 20-12, p. 276 of the Study Guide).

9.   This is an important question. A "budget" refers to the balance between something being added and something being taken away. How does this relate to the amount of sand on a beach?

10.   See question 9 above. What would alter the sediment budget of a beach? How might this change with the seasons?

11.   See Figure 20-16 (p. 600); consider the role of longshore currents in establishing and maintaining both of these features.

12.   This sequence is presented in Figure 20-21 (p. 602). Why does this happen?

13.   What will happen to the sediment "budget" of this beach?

14.   See question 1 above.

15.   Review the section "Shorelines of Submergence" beginning on page 603.

16.   Begin with Figure 20-7 (p. 593).

17.   Figure 20-26 (p. 605) illustrates this process.

18.   See Figure 20-31a (p. 608). What might happen if the island begins to subside, but the coral reef continues to build?

ADDITIONAL STUDY QUESTIONS

1.   How can a "groin field" alter the down-current beaches on a shoreline?

2.   Why would beaches in the midlatitudes tend to become smaller during certain seasons of the year?

Hints for Additional Study Questions:

1.   See Figure 20-22 (p. 603) and the associated text material.

2.   Consider the influence of storms on a beach.

ADDITIONAL NOTES

ADDITIONAL NOTES

ADDITIONAL NOTES

ADDITIONAL NOTES